SOUTHERN EUROPE

SOUTHERN EUROPE

A REGIONAL AND ECONOMIC GEOGRAPHY
OF THE MEDITERRANEAN LANDS

by

MARION I. NEWBIGIN

REVISED UNDER THE EDITORSHIP OF

R. J. HARRISON CHURCH

METHUEN & CO. LTD.
36 ESSEX STREET · STRAND · WC2

First Published . . . *June* *1932*
Second Edition . . . *February* *1944*
Third Edition, revised . . *November* *1949*
Reprinted *1952* and *1960*

3·3

CATALOGUE NO. 3810/U (METHUEN)

PRINTED IN GREAT BRITAIN

PREFACE

SINCE this book is intended in the first instance for advanced students of geography, their needs have been kept in view throughout, both in the method of treatment and in the choice of subject-matter. Thus both in the general section and in those dealing with the individual countries, most space has been devoted to topics which are either insufficiently discussed or slurred over in the majority of existing text-books. In particular the treatment of Greece is, it is believed, fuller than in any other English book, while the frontiers and lands of Italy are discussed in considerable detail. In the case of Albania, also, an attempt has been made to give the essential geographical features of an area of which comparatively little is known here. These sections, in addition to that bringing out the geographical bases of the problems which present themselves in Spain at the moment will, it is hoped, give the book a somewhat wider value than the purely educational one as indicating the physical and economic facts which lie behind current political and social movements. The references, mainly either to specific pieces of research, or to books themselves containing full bibliographies, will enable those interested to pursue particular topics further.

For the numerous sketch-maps and diagrams (as well as for the index), I am indebted to the long patience and care of my sister, Miss Florence Newbigin, who has been my companion on most of my journeys to the lands described. Of the purpose of the sketch-maps something must be said. No sketch-map can hope to compare with a good atlas map, and much less with a survey map. Their value is nevertheless considerable. In the first place, they can be used to make clear key points which tend to be obscured on professional maps by the mass of detail, while at the same time it is legitimate to indicate upon them deductions or distributions which are outside the scope of the surveyor and are thus ignored by him. To serve such ends omissions are as important as what is included, and it is necessary to bear in mind that such maps profess only to present those facts which are required for the particular purpose to serve which they were drawn. They must, in other words, be constantly supplemented by reference to good atlas or large-scale maps. A second type of sketch-map included has a different aim. From the ideal standpoint a description of an area should always be followed on a large-scale map, which alone can give it vividness and reality. But even for the advanced student in a well-equipped geographical department such an ideal is rarely attainable, though it is assumed that some personal acquaintance with such maps will form a part of his training. Somewhat full references have been given here to the maps available, but an attempt has been made, at least so far as important or typical areas are concerned, to give the essential points upon reduced and generalized sketch-maps, based on survey maps. So far as town-sites are concerned some detailed maps have been given of those of special interest, omitting capitals and similar large cities commonly represented by insets on atlas maps.

Two other points of some difficulty may be noted. One is the question of the units of measurement to be employed—a problem likely to remain unsolved so long as the English-speaking world clings to its own units. Here on the one side we have the facts that the student in his preliminary studies is necessarily accustomed to use miles, feet and so forth, and to read the Fahrenheit thermometer, and that in terms of physical exertion and comfort or discomfort, such measures have a significance which metric units and degrees Centigrade cannot have. On the other side is the equally important fact that without a fairly extensive working knowledge of the metric system foreign maps and statistics mean nothing to him. In this connexion it is of interest to note that the English mountain-climber in the Alps speedily learns to think (and feel) in metric units, without labouring to convert these; otherwise local maps would be of no use to him. Here a compromise has been attempted, even if consistency has probably not always been attained. The basal principle adopted is that an introductory discussion, which must necessarily begin from previous knowledge, should be based on the more familiar units, but that a detailed survey of a particular area, which should involve some handling of locally-produced material, should employ the units in which the observations were originally made. In critical cases—in order to bridge the gap—conversions have been practised. To do this universally would appear to defeat the main purpose.

The other point of difficulty is in connexion with place-names. Where available the decisions of the Permanent Committee on Geographical Names have been accepted. But these are meantime limited in number, and the general rule that the spelling in the case of countries using the Latin alphabet should be that officially adopted, save where a name has been anglicized by long usage, is not always of great help. Tolerant Switzerland recognizes two—or three—official spellings, and though so far as towns are concerned the form used has been, in the general case, that of the language of the majority of the local population, it yet seems absurd to change the name of, for instance, a river where it crosses a language boundary. In the former Austrian lands of Italy the official view is that the familiar German names will disappear as a new generation grows up accustomed only to the often very different Italian forms. To the foreigner at least this view has many disadvantages. It means that the older literature becomes unintelligible, while many modern German writers refuse to recognize the new names even as alternatives. In this case both old and new names have been given in the first instance, and the latter used as a rule thereafter, save that in the case of boundary features the more familiar name has been commonly used. Greece and Albania naturally present very special difficulties, and there inconsistencies are difficult to avoid.

As a whole the book is inevitably detailed and demands close reading. Yet it is hoped that the details do not wholly conceal the fascination which these sunlit lands must always possess, and that through them may be caught glimpses of that constantly repeated action and reaction between man and his environment, so deeply imprinted here on a surface itself constantly changing and thus offering new problems for man's ingenuity to solve.

M. I. NEWBIGIN

EDINBURGH
April 1932

PREFACE TO SECOND EDITION

A Second Edition of this book by the late Dr. Marion I. Newbigin having become necessary, it has been thought best to re-issue it in its original form. Any serious alteration of the text at present is obviously impossible in view of the general uncertainty prevailing in Southern Europe, for until the end of the war and the conclusion of a settled peace definite statements cannot be made on political, statistical and economic questions in that region.

A few errata which the author had noted on its first publication have been corrected.

M. E. N.

1943

EDITOR'S PREFACE TO THIRD EDITION

Commissioned by the publishers to revise this book, I immediately realized that in view of the profound changes of the last fifteen years the chapters on the individual countries needed attention by specialists in those regions. I have been fortunate in securing Dr. Hans Carol of the Geographisches Institut of the University of Zurich to revise the Swiss section; Mr. F. R. Gullick, University Lecturer on

Economic Geography in the University of Oxford for the Italian chapters; Mr. R. P. Beckinsale, Departmental Lecturer in the School of Geography of the University of Oxford for the Iberian Peninsula texts, and Mr. S. H. Beaver, Reader in Economic Geography in the University of London at the London School of Economics who made himself responsible for Greece and Albania, save for the note on the Dodecanese which I have added.

Our function has been to revise the maps, facts, and statistics. The 1947 frontiers have been included. We have not attempted to change Dr. Marion Newbigin's style (save in small instances), nor have we changed her method of treatment or appraisal of various theories relating to physical geography. Thus to these theories we do not necessarily subscribe. It is hoped that this very thorough revision will revive the wide use of this well-known book.

R. J. HARRISON CHURCH

LONDON SCHOOL OF ECONOMICS
UNIVERSITY OF LONDON
June 1947

PART V—GREECE AND ALBANIA

CONTENTS

PART IV—THE IBERIAN PENINSULA

MAPS AND DIAGRAMS

CONVERSION OF METRIC UNITS

10 mm.=1 cm.=0·4 in. approximately.

100 mm.=3·9 in.   250 mm.=9·8 in.   760 mm.=30 in. nearly.

1 metre=$3\frac{1}{4}$ ft.   10 m.=33 ft.   100 m.=328 ft.   1,000 m.=3,281 ft.

1,000 ft.=305 m.   10,000 ft.=3,048 m.

1 km.=$\frac{5}{8}$ mile, or 8 km.=5 miles.   100 km.=62 miles.   1,000 km.= 621 miles.

1 sq. mile=2·6 sq. km.   1,000 sq. miles=2,592 sq. km.

1 hectare=10,000 sq. metres=2·5 acres.

100 hectares (1 sq. km.)=247 acres=$\frac{2}{5}$ sq. mile nearly.

5°C.=9°F.; but freezing-point on the Fahrenheit scale is 32°, and 0° on the Centigrade.   Thus:

$$50°\,\text{F.}-32°=18\times\frac{5}{9}=10°\,\text{C.}$$

$$30°\,\text{C.}\times\frac{9}{5}=54+32=86°\,\text{F.}$$

INTRODUCTION

EVEN if it is accepted as an axiom that no grouping of the heterogeneous political units of post-war Europe can hope to be completely logical, nevertheless it may appear at first sight as if the collocation of the six countries discussed in this volume has singularly little justification. The arrangement involves—to name but two obvious points—the separation of Greece and Albania from the other States of the Balkan Peninsula, and of Switzerland from Austria, although both are almost purely alpine States. None the less there is something to be said on the positive side.

All the six countries, with the exception of Portugal, have a very special relation to the Mediterranean Sea and thus to Mediterranean problems. This is true even of Switzerland, which, alike in the past and in the present, owes much of its significance to the way in which routes to and from the Mediterranean converge upon it. While this is partially true of Austria also, yet it seems impossible to separate that State from those which have arisen from the dismemberment of the former Austro-Hungarian Empire, and like it are strung along the line of the Danube. Yugoslavia is in essence one of those succession States, and despite the apparent length of its Adriatic coast, and the attempts being made to develop ports there, its outlook is mainly towards Central Europe rather than towards the Mediterranean Sea.

A further measure of unity is given by the relation of all six to the mountain chains which traverse them from the Cantabrian Mountains to the north-east frontier of Italy, and from the Sierra Nevada in the south-west to the great island of Crete in the south-east, and at once determine the essential features of structure and relief and control the main lines of traffic. Here, again, Portugal is marginal; but historically no less than structurally it is but a somewhat isolated segment of the Iberian peninsula, which is yet much more of a physiographical unit than the complex Balkan one.

Finally, all six countries display in parts of their territories the typical Mediterranean climate, and in consequence the characteristic natural vegetation and cultivated crops. That this is true even of Switzerland is not always fully realized. In the two cantons of Grisons and Ticino that country not only extends over the alpine watershed but includes, particularly in the latter, tracts of country which are more typically 'Italian' than many parts of Italy. Even the canton Valais, though its extension over the crest in the region of the Simplon pass is insignificant, shows traces of Mediterranean influence in its climate and crops. Its simple but efficient irrigation methods also form an interesting introduction to the problem of artificial watering as it presents itself in the true Mediterranean countries.

These three common elements of relation to the Mediterranean Sea and to the alpine fold-lines and the presence of the characteristic climate necessarily involve some general survey before the individual States can be considered with any profit. Thus we must first look at the characteristics of the Mediterranean Sea both from the physical and economic standpoints; then discuss generally the mountain chains without too rigid a limitation to the particular countries; and finally study the Mediterranean climatic type and its effects.

The individual countries fall naturally into three groups. Switzerland and Italy have a complex and interlocking common frontier, and form a natural starting-point. The contrasts between the physical geography of the Iberian and Italian peninsulas are as striking as those between Italy and Spain considered as political units, so that that region naturally follows. Finally, Greece and Albania have not only a common frontier but, as occurs also, if less markedly, with Italy and Switzerland, that frontier is 'unnatural', in the sense that it crosses an area of considerable uniformity within which reciprocal inter-penetration has occurred. The relations of both countries to Italy and Italian problems also present many points of interest, emphasizing once again the central position of Italy in the Mediterranean world.

PART I
GENERAL

CHAPTER I

THE MEDITERRANEAN SEA

Characters and Origin—Temperature and Salinity—Currents and
Tides—Fisheries—Depth Conditions and Divisions—Trade and
Trade-routes—References

CHARACTERS AND ORIGIN

AS is suggested by its name, the Mediterranean is a typical
example of what physical geographers call a Continental Sea,
or in German a *Binnenmeer*. Such seas, lying as they do
'within the lands', and communicating with the ocean only by
narrow and shallow straits, have necessarily peculiar oceanographical
features. Thus their waters differ notably in temperature and
salinity conditions from those of the contiguous ocean, and they are
less affected by currents and tides. Such peculiarities are the direct
result of the nature of the exit and have a number of geographical
consequences. For example, the temperature conditions influence
the climate of the adjacent lands, the limited or almost non-existent
tides affect harbours and navigation. Further, from the human
standpoint the narrowness of the connecting strait is in itself of great
importance, apart altogether from its oceanographical effects, in that
it gives the possibility of control of access to the ocean by some
particular State, with a consequent potential limitation of free movement for other riparian powers.

But if such facts lead the geographer in his classification of seas
to emphasize the nature of the exit, the geologist takes a different
standpoint. For him the depth conditions are the essential feature
on account of the light which they throw on the problem of origin.
In consequence he distinguishes between what are for him the true
Continental Seas—those which cover but a slightly submerged part
of the Continental Shelf and are thus shallow—and Inter-Continental
Seas, which occupy a major downfold of the earth's crust (geosyncline) lying between two continental masses. The Mediterranean
Sea is of this second type. It may be regarded as the modified
remnant of the ancient Mid-World Sea or Tethys, the European
section of which, from late palaeozoic throughout mesozoic and
into early tertiary times, lay between the old continental masses of

Hercynian Europe and Hercynian Africa. Into that deep and ancient sea copious masses of sediment were carried from the adjacent land-masses from triassic times till the close of the lower tertiary period. Ultimately those masses of sediment were crushed as between the jaws of a vice between the hard rocks of Central Europe and Northern Africa, with the double result of the rise of the alpine fold-mountains and the formation of the Mediterranean Sea as we know it.

The whole complex story as it is being hammered out by the geologists, still with much uncertainty of detail, is outside our scope, but the two diagrams (Figs. 1 and 2) indicate its outlines in so far

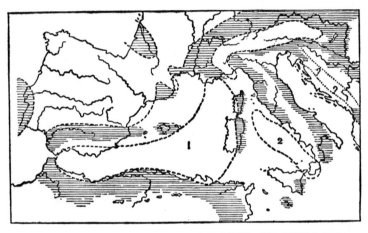

FIG. 1. SOUTH-WEST EUROPE DURING THE LOWER AND MIDDLE NEOGENE
PERIOD

The dotted lines indicate the approximate boundary between land and sea, while the shaded areas show the deposits laid down during the period. 1 and 2 mark two of the horsts or continental masses within the Neogene Sea. (*From Haug, modified.*)

as these have geographical significance. For the sake of simplicity the diagrams have been limited to the western area.

Fig. 1 shows the conditions prevailing during lower and middle neogene (miocene) times, when the Tethys here was reduced to comparatively narrow channels and straits, much of the present Western Basin of the Mediterranean Sea being occupied by the Mediterranean 'ovals', or ancient crust-blocks. Round these nuclei were moulded the geosynclinal troughs in which were deposited the sediments destined to become the future mountain chains.

Fig. 2 shows the tectonic elements of the same part of Europe, according to one view, not as we shall see later universally accepted in all its details. It will be noted that much of Spain and of the part of France included belong to Hercynian Europe, that is, to the area which was folded and uplifted in late palaeozoic times and formed the resistant Foreland against which the alpine chains were folded in their turn. A small part of the similarly resistant African Hinterland is indicated to the south-west. The remainder of the area shown constitutes a part of the 'new' Europe, which dates from the neogene or tertiary period. Its essential feature is the presence of the engirdling chains which have arisen from the sediments deposited in the earlier earth-troughs. Associated with the rise of these, though later in time, the crust-blocks which form the 'ovals' of Fig. 1 were fractured and in great part collapsed beneath the sea. A similar

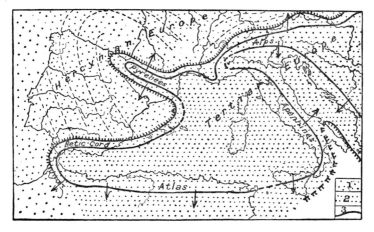

FIG. 2. TECTONIC ELEMENTS OF SOUTH-WESTERN EUROPE, ACCORDING TO STILLE

1. The areas folded in late palaeozoic time to form the Hercynian mountain chains. 2. The 'new' Europe folded in the tertiary period. 3. The main trend-lines of the tertiary fold-mountains.
The arrows indicate the direction of folding. (*From Stille.*)

negative movement affected parts of the newly-formed mountain chains, the net result being the formation of the Western Basin of the Mediterranean Sea.

In more detail it should be noted that, according to Stille, the two adjacent islands of Corsica and Sardinia, forming together what is conveniently called the land-mass of Corsardinia, represent in part at least a remnant of a crust-block, still remaining above sea-level.

The Balearic Isles, again, on the view represented here, have originated from the partial collapse of the chain which once linked the Betic Cordillera of southern Spain to the Pyrenees. Similarly, the Strait of Gibraltar is represented as due to a breaking of an earlier connexion between the Betic Cordillera and the Atlas, just as the wider strait between north-eastern Tunisia and Sicily is the result of a fracture and collapse of a former link between the Atlas and the Apennine folds. This view of the origin of the Strait of Gibraltar has been now abandoned by many geologists, while the connexion between the Pyrenees and the Betic Cordillera has been questioned.

Fig. 3 is taken from a diagram which is but a variant of Fig. 2, but has been inserted to illustrate a point of much geographical importance. It should be noted that, in contrast to Fig. 2, a distinction is made here between the Alpid and Dinarid folds of Suess, and that between them, save in the Swiss Alps, lie what are called by Kober *Zwischengebirge* (Betwixt Mountains), also known as the Median Mass. With the meaning of this conception of a median mass between the uplifted border chains we are not at present concerned; but the diagram makes clear an essential contrast between the western and the eastern Mediterranean. The former is completely encircled by mountains belonging to both the Alpid and Dinarid series; the latter lies wholly south of the Dinarides. Thus the two basins of which the Mediterranean Sea consists are as little comparable in structural relations as they are in latitude. From the structural point of view the Western Basin has a smaller mirror image in the area covered by the Balkan peninsula, the Aegean, Asia Minor, and the Black Sea. Crete, like Algeria and Tunisia, is traversed by the Dinarides, and in all essentials marks the southern limit of the Mediterranean world to the east, as the Atlas Lands mark it to the west. East of the Atlas Lands the northern coast of Africa is both literally and figuratively—that is, alike in latitude and in its characteristics—'off the map' for man in the Mediterranean area, even although, well to the south of Crete, Barka (Cyrenaica) displays along a narrow strip certain Mediterranean climatic features.

These facts have had noteworthy historical consequences, and they mean that from the standpoint of human geography the Mediterranean Sea falls rather into the two divisions of the Aegean and its annexes on the one hand and the Western Basin on the other, than into the Eastern and Western Basins of the physical geographer. But nevertheless the Sea is a physical unit, and the fact that it displays a certain rough parallelism to the mesozoic Tethys which constituted the future line of the alpine chains is of great importance. Despite their obvious breaks and their less conspicuous passes these chains form in the main a division line between Central and Southern Europe. They check and control while they do not inhibit transverse movement, and on the European shores their proximity to the Sea, no less than their complex course, makes longitudinal communication difficult and circuitous. The Sea, on the other hand, not only facilitates intercommunication, but, save where, as on the African coast in the Eastern Basin, latitude and the absence of coastal mountain chains introduce modifications, ensures a general similarity of

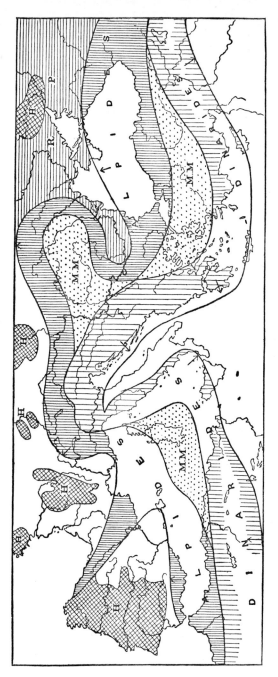

FIG. 3. THE ALPID AND DINARID FOLDS

The Hercynian horsts are indicated by the letter H, the most conspicuous being the Spanish Meseta. R.P. = the Russian Platform extending into Roumania. M.M. = the median masses or Zwischengebirge. As before, the arrows show the direction of folding. (*From Wills, after Kober, modified.*)

climate and vegetation from west to east and from north to south. Thus Southern or Mediterranean Europe has a unity which is denied to Central Europe. Climate in particular is influenced by the great mass of relatively warm water which the Mediterranean contains, and the reasons for its presence demand some consideration.

TEMPERATURE AND SALINITY

From the oceanographical standpoint the outstanding features of the waters of the Mediterranean Sea are the high salinity, showing little variation from surface to bottom, and, particularly in winter, the small vertical temperature range. In both respects there is a marked contrast with Atlantic water. Fig. 4 shows the vertical distribution of temperature and salinity in winter at a station in the Tyrrhenian Sea. The maximum temperature here is 13·9°C. at a depth of 500 m. as compared with 13·6° at the surface, and the minimum 13·2° at the bottom depth of 1,800 m. In other words, the range from surface to bottom is not much more than half a degree. Similar conditions prevail throughout, and even where the depths sink to 3,000–4,000 m. the bottom temperatures in winter are still of the order of 13°C. (56°F.). In the Atlantic, with similar winter surface temperatures, the figures at depths of 3,000–4,000 m. are from 2·5°–5° (36°–41°F.), indicating at once a much greater range and much colder deeper water.

As regards salinity, the diagram shows that at the same station it is about 38 $^0/_{00}$ at the surface, increases to a maximum of 38·7 $^0/_{00}$ at 600 m., and thereafter diminishes slightly, but is practically constant from 1,000 m. to the bottom. From these conditions it is deduced that the deeper waters of the Mediterranean originate within that sea and are not of external origin. As we shall see later, the colder, less salt waters of the deeper layers of the Atlantic are kept out by the sill at Gibraltar.

Fig. 5 shows the contrast between summer and winter temperatures in the upper waters of the Mediterranean at a station between Sardinia and the Balearic Isles. In winter the surface water is cooled slightly, but broadly speaking the temperature range in the first 200 m. is negligible. In summer, on the other hand, the surface layers are warmed notably by the sun. At this station the surface temperature reached 20·7°, but figures of over 26° (79°F.) occur to the south and east—a truly tropical heat. But the warming effect diminishes rapidly with depth. As the figure shows, while at the surface the difference between summer and winter temperatures is 8°C., at 200 m. it is slight, and at greater depths it may be said to disappear, so that the two curves if continued would coincide. In other words, the deeper waters show practically no variation in temperature throughout the year, and as compared with Atlantic water are consistently warm.

It is clear, then, that the sun's heat is stored up in this great reservoir of warm water, never chilled in its depths by cold water

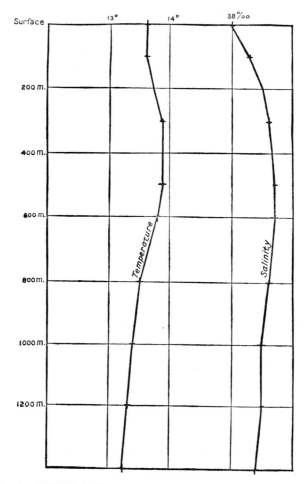

FIG. 4. VERTICAL DISTRIBUTION OF TEMPERATURE AND SALINITY IN WINTER AT A STATION IN THE TYRRHENIAN SEA IN LAT. 41°

Depths are in metres, temperatures in degrees centigrade, salinities in parts per thousand.

of extraneous origin, and having a thin layer at the surface raised in summer to temperatures characteristic of lower latitudes elsewhere. Across its surface blow the westerly winds of winter, bringing to the coastal lands everywhere those mild winters which are one of the outstanding features of the rhythm of Mediterranean life. But a price has to be paid for these benefits. The general uniformity from surface to bottom means a slowing down of the mechanism which ensures in the oceans a mixing of the different layers of water. Though there is not that absence of vertical movement which deprives the bottom waters of the Black Sea of oxygen and thus of life, yet the deeper waters of the Mediterranean are relatively poor in oxygen, and its fisheries of but moderate value. Other causes

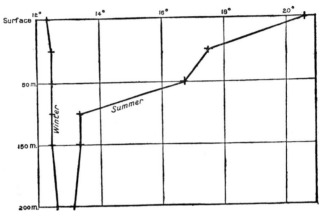

FIG. 5. VERTICAL DISTRIBUTION OF TEMPERATURE IN SUMMER AND WINTER IN THE UPPER WATERS OF THE MEDITERRANEAN AT A STATION BETWEEN SARDINIA AND THE BALEARIC ISLES

Depths in metres, temperatures in degrees centigrade.

than the relative scarcity of oxygen also influence the fisheries. The 'tropical' character of the water is reflected in the absence of such valuable temperate forms as cod and haddock, and in the presence of a great variety of small and mostly bony fish. Further, the uniformity of the conditions is in itself doubtless unfavourable to fish, since the great fishing-grounds of the world occur where current action brings masses of water of different densities, because of different salinity and temperature, into contact. In the Mediterranean not only is that valuable social fish the herring absent, but the related sardine, though present, occurs in a smaller race than in the Atlantic.

CURRENTS AND TIDES

The high salinity of the Mediterranean waters is due to the intense evaporation, especially during the summer months, and to the comparatively small amount of water brought in by rivers. It will be noted that the proximity of the fold-mountains to the shores means a general limitation of the drainage basins of the rivers. Thus the Western Basin, with its characteristic girdle of mountains, in particular, is scantily supplied with river water.

The loss of water by evaporation is compensated for in three ways: by the water brought in by the rivers; by atmospheric precipitation; by excess of inflow over outflow in the case of the currents through the Strait of Gibraltar and the Bosporus-Dardanelles channel.

Of these factors by far the most important is the Gibraltar inflow, as is indicated by the following table, taken from Schott:

Percentage Compensation of Water Evaporated

70·6 per cent by excess of Gibraltar in-current.
21·3 per cent by atmospheric precipitation.
4·9 per cent by river water.
3·2 per cent by excess of Bosporus in-current.

Some examination of the conditions at the Strait of Gibraltar is thus necessary, more especially since, as we have already seen, the character of the Atlantic inflow has an important bearing on the temperature conditions within the Mediterranean Sea.

The Strait is relatively shallow, a well-marked sill rising to less than 400 m. below the surface. Through this narrow (some 14 km. at the narrowest point) and shallow passageway a powerful surface current, extending downwards to 50–100 m. sweeps inward to the Mediterranean at a rate of two and a half geographical miles per hour. Below 100 m., but necessarily limited in depth by the presence of the sill (Fig. 6), there is an outflowing current of warm and salt Mediterranean water. Owing to its high salinity it is denser than the Atlantic water, and plunges downward like a submarine waterfall over the edge of the sill. Its presence is indicated (Fig. 7) by the increase in salinity and the slight increase in temperature of the deeper waters of the Atlantic outside the Strait. By the delicate modern methods of observation it is possible to follow this 'Mediterranean' water southwards along the shores of Morocco, northwards along those of Portugal, and westwards into the open ocean. It has even been traced so far as the west coast of Ireland. Similarly, the influence of the less saline Atlantic surface water can be traced within the Mediterranean as far east as the coast of Egypt, while the salter, outflowing deeper current takes its origin in the Levant.

As already suggested, similar though less marked currents occur in the Bosporus-Dardanelles channel, where there is again a surface current of less saline Black Sea water and a deeper outflow of more saline Mediterranean water. It has also been shown that the narrowing and shallowing of the Mediterranean Sea between the island of

Sicily and the coast of Tunisia, which marks the limit between the Eastern and Western Basins, makes it possible to recognize there quite clearly the two superimposed currents, though the rapidity of flow is less than at the Strait of Gibraltar.

Because of the double inflow of fresher water at the north-eastern and south-western extremities of the Sea, itself as we have seen a result of the high evaporation and thus of the high salinity of its waters, and because also of the effects of the winds and of the earth's rotation, there is set up in the Sea as a whole a cyclonic or counter-clockwise system of surface currents. Broadly, it may be said that the direction of these is easterly along the south coast and westerly along the north coast, becoming northerly on west-facing coasts such as those of the Levant and the Adriatic, and having a southerly component on east-facing coasts such as those of Italy and Spain (see Fig. 10). Obvious human effects of these conditions are traceable in the position of Venice to the north of the Po mouth, of Marseille to the east of the Rhone, of Barcelona to the north-east of the Ebro; that is, the port in each case is in the direction away from the drift of the river-borne alluvium.

These surface currents are compensated by lower currents, at depths of 300–500 m., moving in a generally westerly direction towards the Strait of Gibraltar, save in the Aegean, where the flow is towards the Dardanelles and thus to the Black Sea. But these currents do not involve the deeper layers of water, the whole system being controlled by the height of the sill at Gibraltar, which entirely shuts out those slow movements of abyssal water characteristic of the open oceans, and also ensures that the surface inflow is limited to waters of temperatures similar to those of Mediterranean surface water, and having in consequence no chilling effect.

Thus the importance of the Strait and of its form can scarcely be over-estimated. It is of geologically recent origin, dating only from later pliocene times, though it had probably a predecessor along the line of the present Guadalquivir valley. As a waterway also it had comparatively little significance till the construction of the Suez Canal in 1869 made the Mediterranean Sea a through route. But its influence on Mediterranean life has been great and continuous. Were it absent the Sea would dry up owing to the excessive evaporation. Had it been wide and deep the special features of the waters of the Mediterranean would have been lost owing to a more complete intermingling with ocean water, and the whole physical setting would have been greatly modified.

Though the Mediterranean is commonly described as tideless, the adjective is not strictly accurate, even if it is true that in most parts tidal movements are not conspicuous. At Gibraltar the difference between high and low water reaches 1·2 m., the figure falling to

o·3 m. in the Lipari Islands and to o·14 m. at Genoa, though it rises
to 2 m. in the Gulf of Gabès. Generally it may be said that the
movements are quite obvious at the heads of long gulfs, and where
these are shallow may, as in the lagoons of Venice, expose considerable stretches of mud-banks at low water. Further, their existence
everywhere can be detected by precise measurement, even where
the rise and fall is too slight to produce any apparent effect. Corfu,
for example, seems to have no tide, but a rise of 6 cm. (under 2½ in.)
does in point of fact occur.

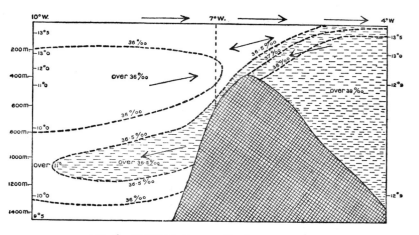

FIG. 6. CURRENTS IN THE STRAIT OF GIBRALTAR

The sill is cross-hatched; the arrows indicate the surface flow of cool, less
saline Atlantic water into the Mediterranean, and the deeper flow of warm,
more saline Mediterranean water into the Atlantic. Temperatures are
in degrees centigrade; salinities in parts per thousand; depths in metres.
(*After Schott.*)

Apart from the unfavourable effects, as in facilitating delta formation and the development of lagoon coasts with bounding sandbanks,
the insignificant tidal movements must have had a favourable influence on early navigation, as harbours can be entered or left at any
time. Just because, however, there is in the general case so little
tide and such a slight development of tidal currents, the exceptions
were noted and dreaded by the early navigators. Examples are the
tidal ebb and flow in the Gulf of Gabès, where the effects were much
exaggerated by classical writers, and the complex currents in the
narrow channel which separates the island of Euboea from the Greek
mainland, and, particularly, those of the Strait of Messina. In some
cases the effects of tidal currents are complicated by seiches, that is,
the pendulum-like swing of water under the influence of winds,
sudden changes of atmospheric pressure, and so forth. Seiches have

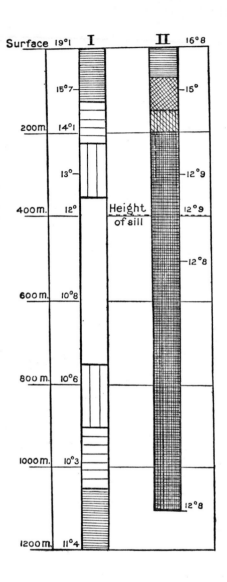

FIG. 7. SALINITY AND TEMPERATURE CONDITIONS EAST AND WEST OF THE SILL AT GIBRALTAR

I. Atlantic Station in lat. 36°, long. 7°W.
II. Mediterranean Station in lat. 36°, long. 5°W.

Observations taken in June. Depths are in metres; temperatures in degrees centigrade; salinities in parts per thousand, shown by shading: 1. Salinity of less than 35·75. 2. Under 36. 3. Under 36·25. 4. Under 36·50. 5. Under 37·75. 6. Under 38·25. 7. Over 38·25.

Note the increase of temperature and salinity in the deeper Atlantic waters as the result of the outflow of dense Mediterranean water, and cf. Fig. 6.

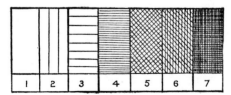

been most studied in lakes, but they tend to occur also in gulfs and bays of the sea, and have been noted in various parts of the Mediterranean, particularly in the Euboea channel mentioned above.

FISHERIES

It has been already pointed out that some of the more important fish of our own seas are absent from the Mediterranean. The absentees include especially those forms which command a considerable market when preserved, and can be captured in such numbers as to make large-scale organization profitable. Within the Mediterranean fishing is carried on extensively, but the methods are usually primitive. Except for tunny, sardines, and anchovies few kinds can be preserved satisfactorily, and few kinds can be obtained in large numbers. The 'mixed fry' which is so common a dish in Italy and elsewhere is a natural consequence of the variety of the catch. The difficulty of preserving many of the characteristic forms, combined with the great demand during the fasts of the Catholic and Orthodox churches, accounts for the considerable import of dried fish from Newfoundland and elsewhere.

Invertebrates are eaten in greater variety than is common elsewhere, so that in addition to the crustaceans and shellfish familiar in most European marine fish-markets, such forms as cuttles and sea-urchins make their appearance. The cuttles are both eaten fresh and are preserved by drying.

As well as furnishing food the Mediterranean fisheries supply such economic products as red coral and sponges, the once-famous purple dye having been replaced in the world market by artificial products. Coral is obtained especially in the Gulf of Naples, to the south-west of Sardinia, and off the coasts of Algeria, Tunisia, and Tripoli, as well as of the eastern Adriatic and of Catalonia. The working up of the coral is one of the minor industries carried on by the large population of Naples. The fact is not without interest, for it reminds us that delicacy of manipulation has always been a characteristic of Mediterranean folk, and some of their crafts have survived all the changes which the industrial period has brought. Those handicrafts, again, have a regional basis in the general narrowness of the belt between mountains and sea, where alone men can settle in any numbers. There skilled handling of material, whether of bud-grafts of fruit-trees, of silkworms and cocoons, or of limited supplies of mineral products, has always been a condition of survival.

Sponge-fishing is carried on, especially by Greeks and Arabs, from the east coast of Tunisia to the Levant, as well as among the Greek islands and off Dalmatia. The sponge-fisheries of Tunisia, e.g. of Sfax, are especially interesting, not only because they bring a considerable Greek population, but because of the primitive fashion in which they are carried on.

Finally, it may be noted that the high salinity of the water, combined with the great evaporation during the hot and dry summer, encourages the extraction of salt from sea-water, which is carried on almost everywhere where the necessary flat or lagoon coast is available. Parts of the east coasts of Sicily and Tunisia and of the Mediterranean coast of France may be named as examples, but many others will be noted in the course of the regional surveys. That sun heat can be used in place of the fuel necessary in the case of the brine pumped from the salt-mines of, e.g., the Salzkammergut is an interesting if minor illustration of the way in which the peculiar climate influences Mediterranean life.

DEPTH CONDITIONS AND DIVISIONS

It is a natural consequence of the mode of origin of the Mediterranean Sea from the progressive collapse of parts of old crust-blocks and young fold-mountains that its form should be exceedingly complex. Deep (3,000–4,000 m.) and wide basins of cauldron-like shape alternate with narrow and shallow belts, often prolonged above the surface into islands. The intervening slopes are frequently steep, and both active volcanoes and the liability to earthquake shocks bear testimony to the youth and instability of the whole area. Many of the existing features indeed, such as the formation of the Aegean and the in-filling of the area which now forms the North Italian plains, are of very recent origin.

Thus the whole has a complexity in striking contrast to the relative simplicity of conditions farther east, as in India, where the fold-mountains overlook that filled-in portion of the Tethys which constitutes the northern plains, themselves bounded southwards by the old crust-block of the Deccan, or in the analogous case of the Tigris-Euphrates plains between the fold-mountains and the Arabian crust-block. In the Mediterranean region we have not only the great continuous water surface, with a total area of nearly 3,000,000 sq. km., but the fact that alike within the Sea and on the adjacent continents relief is such as to force traffic to move along certain definite lines. More than this, the juxtaposition of mountain and sea limits sharply the characteristic climate, to which the culture of the Mediterranean folk is so closely adapted. Thus the first spread of Minoan—of which, however, little is known—and of the later Greek culture was doubly limited, first by the actual waterways and second by the restriction to climatically suitable tracts. Nowhere, perhaps, is the progressive adaptation of man to natural conditions and the progressive utilization of these more beautifully illustrated than here; but for the appreciation of such developments some detailed knowledge of the physical setting is necessary. To what has been already said about the waters of the Mediterranean Sea we must therefore add some discussion of the depth conditions and of the natural divisions.

It has been already indicated that the customary distinction between Eastern and Western Basins is not satisfactory from the purely geographical standpoint, for the two are not strictly comparable. The roughly triangular Western Basin does, however,

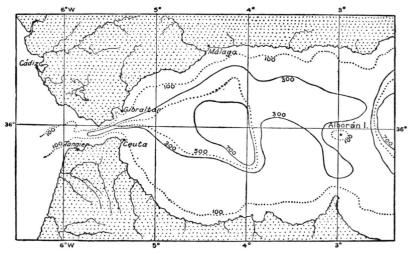

FIG. 8. THE STRAIT OF GIBRALTAR AND THE ALBORÁN BASIN

Depths are in fathoms.

(*From the Admiralty Chart.*)

constitute a unit within which minor elements can be recognized. These are three in number between the obvious western and eastern limits of the Strait of Gibraltar and the analogous though wider and more complex Sicilian Strait, and consist of the narrowed western Alborán Basin, to which Philippson has given the appropriate name of Forecourt (*Vorhof*); the large Balearic Basin; the smaller though deeper Tyrrhenian Basin.

As regards the first, we have to note that the shallowest part of the Strait of Gibraltar is not in its narrowest region, that is, off Tarifa, but farther west where it begins to widen. South of Gibraltar itself depths of over 1,000 m. (over 550 fm.) already occur, and eastward the floor slopes rapidly to 1,445 m. (790 fm.) between the almost parallel coasts of Spain and Morocco (Fig. 8). This hollow forms the Alborán Basin, bounded to the east by a ridge from whose surface rises the small (Spanish) island of Alborán. The island, which is low, barren, and waterless, has no apparent importance, but students of the history of cartography may have noticed as a curious fact that it is much in evidence on early maps and charts. The reason is obvious enough. Alborán lies some 166 km. from the Strait of Gibraltar in a due east direction. Thus, for any mariner approaching from the east it is a signpost to the Strait. Conversely, for one sailing from the west it marks the point where the hitherto narrow 'forecourt' opens out into the wide Mediterranean, and where therefore a course must be set for the particular harbour aimed for, while up to this point comparatively little divergence from an eastward course is possible.

Eastwards of the Alborán ridge the coasts of Spain and the Atlas Lands diverge rapidly and the wide Balearic Basin opens. This has a maximum depth of 3,149 m. (over 1,720 fm.) to the south-west of Sardinia, and alike off the coast of Algeria and off the French Riviera the submarine slope is exceedingly steep. Across the north-west border of the basin lie the Balearic Isles, connected to the Spanish mainland by a shelf whose greatest depth below the surface is 825 m. Eastward the basin is limited by the Corsardinian land-mass, linked to the Tuscan archipelago and mainland by a shallow sill, and less obviously to Tunisia by a slightly-developed ridge, not rising nearer the surface than 1,900 m. (1,039 fm.). North-westwards the basin has as an annex the shallow Gulf of Lions, which has an eastern counterpart in the Gulf of Genoa, though the latter, as one would expect from the mountains which skirt the coast, is much deeper.

East of the Corsardinian land-mass and its continuations in the submarine ridges to the north-east and south lies the deep Tyrrhenian Basin, sinking near the centre to 3,731 m. (2,040 fm.), while large tracts are over 3,000 m. (1,640 fm.) deep. Of particular interest is the gap between Sicily and Tunisia (Fig. 9), which forms its south-eastern exit. This has a peculiarly complex floor. From the western extremity of Sicily there extends towards Cape Bon in Tunisia, a distance of 150 km., a belt of shallow water bounded on either side by deeps. The greatest depth here is about 324 m. (177 fm.), but to the south-east the floor sinks to a minor basin with a maximum depth of 1,628 m. (892 fm.), which offers not a little analogy to the Alborán Basin in the west. On the edge of this basin lies the volcanic island of Pantellaria, which still displays signs of activity both at the surface and under the sea. The other volcanic islands (Lampedusa, etc.) lie on the coastal platform of Tunisia, while the low-lying Maltese group, composed of tertiary limestones, rise similarly from the platform, which extends south of the eastern end of Sicily.

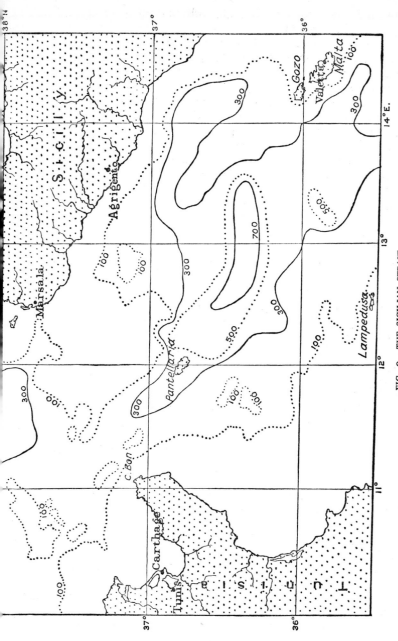

FIG. 9. THE SICILIAN STRAIT

Depths are in fathoms. (*From the Admiralty Chart.*)

3

Beyond, the sea-floor sinks abruptly to the great depths of the complex Eastern Basin.

Finally we have to note that the Strait of Messina, varying in width from 4 km. in the north to about 19 km. in the south, is relatively deep, though to the north a submarine ridge rises to within 100 m. of the surface, and plays an important part in the production of the complex currents already noted. Since these currents, though they form no obstacle to steamer traffic, made, and indeed still make, the passage dangerous for small boats, we may say that the Western Basin has only two main water-exits, both of geologically recent origin. Both lie between Europe and the Atlas Lands, and in the past have served as links between the two. As has been already suggested, indeed, in the case of the Gibraltar exit the connexion between the two opposite land-masses has for most of historical time been more important than that between the two water-bodies. In this connexion one should note that the shape of the 'forecourt' means that communication is not limited to the Strait, but is easy over a considerable stretch of both coasts. On the other hand, the direction of the Atlas folds, broadly parallel to the coast, and often close to it, no less than the correlated suddenness with which the Mediterranean climate gives way to the desert one beyond, makes penetration to the interior difficult for Mediterranean folk. Thus the direction of movement throughout historical time has been mainly from Africa to Europe rather than in the reverse direction. Indeed, the bringing of the western end of the Atlas Lands completely under European influence, though often attempted, has only recently been achieved.

Conditions are somewhat more favourable at the eastern exit, because of the way in which the fold-lines swing round into Sicily and peninsular Italy, giving the possibility of finding an entrance by the east coast of Tunisia, behind and parallel to the Atlas folds. Further, the sea-way has preserved a continuous historical importance to which the Strait of Gibraltar offers little analogy. To these facts a whole series of sites, ancient and modern, bears eloquent witness—we need only mention as examples Phoenician and Roman Carthage, Arab and French Tunis, Greek and modern Syracuse, Girgenti, Malta. The present-day juxtaposition of the three great powers of Italy, France, and Britain within the gap is in itself significant of the permanent effect of the natural conditions.

But if the eastern coast of Tunisia offers a possible line of entrance to the Atlas Lands, there is no doubt that the easiest approach to continental Europe from this Western Basin lies within that shallow north-western extension of the Balearic Basin which forms the Gulf of Lions. Only here, and particularly from Marseille and so to the Rhone valley, is there a direct and easy entrance into the interior.

But it must be noted that the gap, due to the fact that the shore of the Gulf of Lions is low and has no continuous hill backing, while it facilitates entrance into the interior means also that the climate undergoes modification. Thus not only were the Greek colonies purely coastal, but they developed especially to the right and left of the actual gap, as at Marseille and at Emporion on the Gulf of Rosas, that is, where Alps and Pyrenees respectively give some shelter from continental influences.

Thus we see that the three great breaks in the mountain girdle of the Western Basin have each played an important part in its story. Through the south-eastern gate came from very early days onwards a stream of cultural influences flowing in the direction of the Mediterranean under-current. But, in contradistinction to its physical analogue, it left the area rather by the north-western land-gate than by the Atlantic water one, and even then only after a long period of adaptation had made progress possible beyond the strict limit of the characteristic climate. Not until long after influences derived from the Mediterranian area, under Roman agency, had thoroughly interpenetrated continental Europe, and been carried far beyond its limits, was a powerful return current set up, giving at last to the Strait of Gibraltar the importance to which it seemed destined by nature. Thus it may be said that the geologically late origin of the Strait had as it were a historical reflex; for in historical time its function as a link between two land-masses long antedated its role as a connexion between the continuous outer ocean and the branched and complex inner water area.

The fact that Mediterranean cultural influences were unable to make on North Africa the same kind of impression which they did on Central Europe is readily understood. The Atlas Lands are generally difficult of access from the sea, offer but limited tracts of high productivity, and, particularly, have a hinterland so fundamentally different in character, and so forbidding, that the kind of infiltration which occurred on the opposite shore is virtually impossible.

Turning next to the Eastern Mediterranean we find that beyond the shallowing indicated by the platform on which Malta stands the sea-floor slopes abruptly down to the deeps of the Ionian Sea. This narrows steadily northwards, owing to the convergence of Italy and Greece, but instead of ending blindly there opens by the narrow Strait of Otranto into that long and narrow gulf which we call the Adriatic Sea. Southwards there is no obvious limit to the Ionian Sea, and here, indeed, between Cape Leuca in Italy and the Gulf of Sidra, we have not only the widest north–south belt of water in the Mediterranean but that which is most completely empty of islands. It is here also that the greatest—'almost oceanic'—depths occur, several areas dropping below 4,000 m. (2,187 fm.). In accordance with the usual rule, however, the deepest sounding so far obtained, 4,400 m. (2,406 fm.), does not occur in the region most remote from land, but to the south of Greece in lat. 35° 44·8′, long. 21° 45·8′. It is thus near where the Dinarid fold-lines swing round to pass through Crete; the submarine slopes in this region are exceedingly steep.

Just as the Ionian Basin has no definite southern boundary, though depths diminish in that direction, so also it has no very apparent eastern limit. Nevertheless, a narrowing between Crete and the northward bulge of the African coast in Barka, combined with a slight rise (depths over 2,000 m.) between the two, delimits it from the more easterly area. This is sometimes regarded as consisting of an Egyptian and a Syrian Basin, separated by a rise running from the western end of Cyprus towards the Nile delta. In the former the depths rarely exceed 3,000 m. and never reach 4,000 m. The deepest sounding known is one of 3,865 m. to the east of Rhodes, that is, again near the area of folding. The small Syrian Basin does not reach anything like equivalent depths.

As already indicated, it is characteristic of this whole eastern area that fold-mountains are limited to its northern shores, the southern being formed by the undisturbed rocks of Africa, so that it is not 'Mediterranean' in the limited sense in which the word is used to designate well-defined climatic and cultural conditions. Thus the area considered as a whole is less important than the northern continuations which form the Aegean, Adriatic, and Black Seas. Of the last little need be said. Not only are the lands which bound it outside the scope of this volume, but, although fold-mountains and the Mediterranean climate are represented in a limited area to the north, in the Crimea, as well as to the south, and although also at certain historical periods its relations with the Mediterranean have been fairly intimate, yet it is in essence outside its limits. It sinks in the centre to depths of over 2,000 m., this central flat-bottomed trough being connected with the shallowed area to the north by steep slopes; the relation of this central deep to the fractured fold-lines indicated by the Balkan-Crimean-Caucasus ranges (Fig. 3) should be noted. The Sea of Marmara is also relatively deep, sinking in minor hollows to well below 1,000 m. It is separated from a depression (see below) on the floor of the North Aegean only by the narrowed part of the Gallipoli peninsula and its bordering platform, and presents the appearance of being but a continuation of this. The two straits are shallow and the Bosporus so narrow as to suggest an origin from an old river-valley.

In the Aegean there is a curious correspondence between surface and submarine conditions. Strings or groups of islands alternate from south to north with open lanes of water, and soundings show that ridges and platforms similarly alternate with troughs and hollows. Thus the island girdle of which Crete is the most conspicuous member has to the north an elongated trough of corresponding shape which, in harmony with the mountain heights of the island, sinks to depths well over 2,000 m. Again, north of the Cyclades, a second minor trough with a depth of not much more than 1,200 m., emphasizes the island-free lane between Euboea and Chios. Finally, north-westwards of the interrupted island belt indicated by the Sporades, Lemnos, and Imbros, lies the North Aegean trough, with similar depth conditions. This is continued into the Gulf of Saros, so that the gap between it and the deep area of the Sea of Marmara is narrow.

The significance of these conditions is accentuated by the general tendency for the sea-basins to be prolonged into the bounding landmasses as gulfs and channels, and the island groups and chains to correspond similarly with promontories and peninsulas.

The Adriatic is notably different. The Strait of Otranto is relatively deep, and opposite that part of the eastern shore-line where a sudden change of direction occurs, the floor sinks to a broad basin. It used to be stated that this had a maximum depth of 1,645 m., but this is apparently an error, as the 'Najade' in 1911–12 took no sounding deeper than 1,132 m., which Brückner regards as probably the maximum. This deep basin is limited to the north-west by a line running from the remarkable peninsula which bears Mt. Gargano through the islands of Pelagosa and Lagosta to the eastern shore. Farther northwards the Adriatic is quite shallow, under 200 m. throughout, with one curious exception. Along a line between the mouths of the Italian Pescara and the Yugoslav Kerka rivers a narrow and gutter-like depression occurs, dropping to a depth of 243 m., and interrupting the general evenness of the floor of the North Adriatic. No explanation of this remarkable feature has apparently been offered.

The contrasts in shape and in relief between the Aegean and the Adriatic, themselves dependent upon the general transverse direction of the form-lines in the one case as compared with their lengthways run in the other, have had far-reaching consequences. One should note in particular that whereas the Aegean islands encourage cross traffic, and the shores of the gulfs which prolong the submarine troughs favour settlements of similar type on both sides, conditions in the Adriatic are very different. There transverse traffic has never been marked. On the eastern shore the submergence of the outer chains has given rise to the well-known Dalmatian type of coastline, with numerous elongated islands separated by calm channels from the mainland. But though the islands often display some fertility, and there are narrow strips or patches of fertile land on the mainland, the forbidding limestone hills rise so near the coast and limit so sharply the possible cultivated area, that the establishment of self-sufficing communities of any size has proved impossible. Where, in the past, stable communities have arisen it has been, as in the case of Ragusa, by virtue of entrepôt trade, not of local resources. The western coast in general, save to the north, rises steeply from the water's edge, and offered little opportunity for early settlement, ports being lacking.

Thus while Greek culture spread from the Aegean to both shores of the Ionian Sea it took but little hold in the Adriatic region. The main significance of that sea has always lain in its northward penetration, and in the possible outlets to the interior of Europe afforded at its head. Two difficulties, however, present themselves there. The one, associated with the northward shallowing and with the silt-laden rivers which, continuing the work of their earlier predecessors, are extending the plains ever farther and farther into the sea, is the difficulty of maintaining ports. Adria, close to the Po distributaries; Aquileia, to the west of the lower Isonzo; Ravenna to the north of the small Montone river—all represent attempts which failed. Venice and Trieste mark at least relative success, though both have disadvantages as compared with Marseille and Genoa.

The second difficulty is of course the mountain rim behind, which, despite its passes, shows as a whole remarkable continuity. The fact that from prehistoric times onward traffic of a kind has found means of overcoming the obstacle presented by the mountains is an interesting example—not without analogies elsewhere—of man's wonderful power of overcoming such physical barriers.

Summing up, then, we may say that from the human standpoint the two supremely important parts of the Mediterranean Sea are the Aegean and the Western Basin, with the Ionian Sea as an intermediate link. The main importance of the Adriatic lies in the way in which it gives a possible, if difficult, line of entrance to central continental Europe; but despite the fact that it extends more than two degrees of latitude farther north than the Gulf of Lions, and more than one degree north of the Gulf of Genoa, its broad alpine girdle makes it of less importance than either from this standpoint.

TRADE AND TRADE-ROUTES

Extending as it does from long. 6° W. in the Strait of Gibraltar to long. 36° E. on the Syrian coast, and from nearly lat. 46° at the head of the Adriatic to nearly 30° in the Gulf of Sidra, it is natural that the Mediterranean should always have been a highway of traffic, particularly as the land-routes on its margins are generally difficult. Further, the striking contrasts between the products of its borderlands and those of extra-Mediterranean Europe have always stimulated exchange, though this strictly Mediterranean trade is now overshadowed by the through traffic. On the other hand, exchange between the various Mediterranean Lands proper has always been limited by the general similarity of their products. A few general points in regard to these various aspects may be noted.

Though the common belief that the Sea is always calm has as little foundation as that its waters are always blue and the overhead sky clear, it is yet true that waves and storms are less of a menace than in the open ocean. Again, though there is not that regular seasonal reversal of winds which facilitated so greatly navigation to and from India in the days of sailing-ships, both wind change from winter to summer and the surface currents already described are yet of considerable importance. We do not possess those historical details which make it possible to correlate so closely the successive early Atlantic voyages with increasing knowledge and utilization of the physical conditions; but there are at least indications that a similar process occurred here.

For example, the counter-clockwise currents facilitate coastal navigation in one direction in the area as a whole, while the general tendency for the subsidiary seas and basins to develop minor cyclonic systems of their own gives at least the possibility of a relatively short return voyage. But there is more than this. A very early traffic-route (cf. J. L. Myres, *Who were the Greeks?* Cambridge, 1930) encircled the area east of the Crete-Barka line. The coastal current could be used to carry boats from the Nile mouths by a 'great circuit' route northward and westward to Crete (Fig. 10). But in this eastern part of the Sea the Etesian (northerly) winds of full summer (July–August) blow with great constancy. Some early and unknown Columbus, utilizing perhaps a chance experience, dared to abandon the guidance of the coast-line and launch out boldly from Crete into the open, trusting to these winds to carry him across the trackless water and so to the southern border, where the shore current would once again help him back to his starting-point. Once made, the discovery was, it would seem, regularly utilized. It should be noted that the relatively narrow sea between Crete and Barka facilitated this circuit, while the high peaks of Crete, snowclad for much of the year, no less than the plateau of Barka, breaking the generally featureless shore, must have formed useful guides.

Similar conditions facilitated early navigation in the Aegean, where again coastal currents and the Etesian winds of summer made circular journeys from Crete to the Dardanelles and back to the starting-point easy. The regular alternation of land and sea breezes, particularly during the warmer season when navigation was chiefly carried on, must also have been a factor in the growth of a sea-going population. It meant that anyone with a detailed knowledge of the local conditions could always find a favouring wind to bring him in and out of harbour, while the insignificance of the tides made it unnecessary to take these into account.

It may be thought that such facts are of historical rather than of actual importance. But they do in point of fact continue to exert much influence. The local traffic of the Mediterranean Sea is still largely in the hands of the Greeks, who employ sailing-vessels as well as being considerable purchasers of old 'tramps' from the great maritime nations. They are the sea-pedlars of the eastern Mediterranean, as the Vlachs are the land-pedlars of much of the Balkan peninsula. In other words, the physical conditions continue to exert their effect on man, not only in the persistence of a very old kind of traffic, but in its greater prevalence in the eastern area, where local traffic with its point-to-point sailing is easier. With that traffic again is associated a spread of Greeks which has considerable political importance. The Maltese, for reasons apparent enough from our previous study of the Sicilian Strait (p. 16), play a not dissimilar part, if necessarily on a smaller scale.

It is interesting to note that this type of trade, an inheritance from a period long antedating the rise of modern national States, and involving a wide distribution of those taking part in it, leads to various difficulties. Thus the major problems due to Greek penetration of Turkish territory have their reflection in the minor one resulting from Maltese infiltration of French North Africa.

Such local trade, however, particularly when the commodities carried are of purely Mediterranean origin, is necessarily strictly limited in amount—a fact which helps to explain its somewhat primitive organization. Broadly, it may be said to have two main bases. Though the region as a whole is but scantily supplied with minerals, particularly metallic ores, local deposits of rocks and minerals, or of articles obtained by the working up of these on the spot, have led to demand elsewhere. The point is too familiar to need elaboration, and from the days when the obsidian of Melos was a treasure beyond price to the present time, when Greece imports phosphates from Tunisia to increase the produce of her lands, this type of trade has always existed. At various periods the copper of Cyprus, the varied ores of Sardinia and Spain, the marbles of Greece and Italy, the sulphur of Sicily, the pottery based on local clays, the glass on special sands, and so forth, have played their part in stimulating it.

Less obvious both in itself and in its causes is the trade in the products of the specialized type of farming. It is commonly assumed,

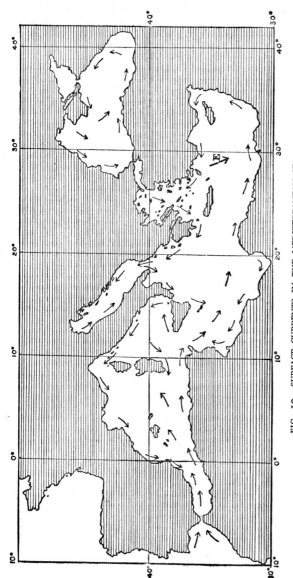

FIG. 10. SURFACE CURRENTS IN THE MEDITERRANEAN SEA

The broken arrow (E) shows the direction of the Etesian winds of July and August in the eastern area. Note that in addition to the main currents, which are easterly along the southern shore and westerly along the northern shore, all the subsidiary water bodies tend to develop minor counter-clockwise current systems of their own. (*After Schott.*)

with a measure of justification, that since these are universally produced within the area of Mediterranean climate, local trade in them
is not likely to be large. But the actual position is very complex.
For example, boats from Bari normally carry some olive oil and citrus
fruits to Dalmatian ports, which themselves have olive and some
orange trees close at hand; the most productive part of Albania is of
distinctly Mediterranean type, and may export some Mediterranean
produce to Italy, while in unfavourable years the process may be
reversed. The reasons for such trade currents are difficult to formulate briefly; but the fact that they have always been present reminds
us that a broad similarity of climate, relief, and even of tradition
need not ensure an identity of actual production. During the period
when phylloxera raged in Southern France there was a large import
of currants from Greece for wine-making, and even in more normal
times 'French' wine is not always wholly the product of grapes
grown in France. Marseille, despite the proximity of olive groves,
imports much olive oil from Tunisia, for the latter has space, labour,
and capital available for greater plantations than are possible in
France. Italy exports much silk yarn to France, and Greece has a
growing export of silkworm eggs rather than of cocoons or thread;
part of the explanation lies in the facts that in France it is less easy
than in Italy to find the labour for the rearing of the silkworms, and
in Greece mulberry-trees are not yet abundant. The list might be
lengthened greatly; but the point is rather to emphasize that local
differences in production do form the basis of an internal exchange
which is apt to be overlooked.

The causes which have stimulated exchange of products between
the Mediterranean Lands and the adjacent areas of contrasted
climate and products are much more obvious. The former have
always tended to suffer from limited supplies of prime necessities,
such as grain, timber, metallic minerals, textile fibres, and so forth,
while they are able to supply luxuries in the form either of the
products of their cultivated lands or of the specialized skill of their
inhabitants. In all such cases it is clear that the community importing
the raw materials tends to form the predominating partner in the
transaction, if only because it has the greater choice of markets.
For long the rest of Europe was constrained to buy its luxuries in
the form both of warm-temperate fruits and their products and of
highly-finished manufactured goods in Mediterranean markets, or
go without. Conditions have changed progressively. Not only are
extra-Mediterranean Europe and the U.S.A. now the main producers of elaborate manufactured goods, but the former has a wide
choice of markets in which to buy most of the luxuries which were
once a Mediterranean monopoly. With this may be associated the
progressive development of Spain, Italy, and Modern Greece into

national States, including within their territories lands not purely Mediterranean in character and yielding non-Mediterranean products. Italy's last extension increased considerably her water-power resources, and thus diminished her need for imported fuel; Greece has greatly extended her grain-producing lands and altered notably the nature of her export trade. If the whole series of changes has taken centuries to accomplish, in essentials it has been throughout the reaction of the Mediterranean folk to the condition of economic dependence to which they were gradually reduced when the Great Discoveries opened the oceans of the world to traffic. In place of the old exchange of raw materials for Mediterranean luxuries we have now mainly an exchange of machine-made goods for those high-grade commodities in the production of which the long tradition of care and skill and the perfect adaptation of environment give Mediterranean man an unquestioned advantage.

This traffic is of course far less conspicuous than the through traffic, depending largely, though far from exclusively, on the Suez Canal. In addition to that long-distance trade, already long established and itself essentially a new development—with obvious fresh elements—of a much older current based on the contrast between Mediterranean and monsoon lands, new routes have been opened up. Developments in Eastern Europe, in part checked by present-day conditions in Russia, have increased the importance of Black Sea trade, mineral oil being a notable addition to grain. Developments in Egypt have given a great cotton export. Particularly interesting also has been the development of cross-routes in the Western Basin, for the traffic carried on has its source in many cases far beyond the limits of the Mediterranean type of climate. Not only is the trade from French North Africa in such commodities as esparto grass, dates, etc., in addition to purely Mediterranean produce and minerals, already large, but there is also a curious movement of men towards France, not wholly without its analogies to the pull exerted by ancient Rome on the peoples of the European interior. If, on the one hand, Spaniards, Maltese, Greeks, and so on are drawn towards French North Africa, on the other, Africa sends its quota to France. In particular the movement of Senegalese troops towards the motherland is one fraught with tragic possibilities.

REFERENCES

For general points throughout the standard work is Alfred Philippson, *Das Mittelmeergebiet: Seine Geographische u. Kulturelle Eigenart.* (Leipzig, 1st edition, 1904; 4th edition, 1922.)
For origin and structure see the books named at the end of the next chapter.

The oceanographical details in this chapter are based mainly on the following:

Ed. Brückner, 'Das dritte Terminfahrt S.M.S. "Najade" i. d. Hochsee der Adria', in *Mitteil. d. K.K. Geog. Gesellschaft* I. (Wien, 1912.) See also articles by A. Grund in the same volume.

O. Krümmel, *Handbuch der Ozeanographie*, 2nd edition. (Stuttgart, 1907–11.)

Sir John Murray and Johan Hjort, *The Depths of the Ocean* (London, 1912). Especially for the currents at Gibraltar.

G. Schott, 'Die Gewässer des Mittelmeers', in *Ann. d. Hydrographie u. Maritimen Meteorologie*. (Berlin, 1915.)

Ibid., *Geographie d. Atlantischen Ozeans*, 2nd edition. (Hamburg, 1926.)

Alex. Supan, *Grundzüge d. Physischen Erdkunde*, Band I. 7th edition, by Erich Obst and others. (Berlin u. Leipzig, 1927.)

The Admiralty charts 2158 A and 2158 B cover respectively the eastern and western Mediterranean Sea.

A very useful map is that of the Mediterranean on the scale of 1:4,000,000 No. 31A (Europe and Asia), G.S.G.S. No. 2957 War Office.

CHAPTER II

STRUCTURE AND RELIEF OF SOUTHERN EUROPE

The Main Relief Features—Origin of the Relief—Alpides and
Dinarides—The Structure of the Western Alps—The Eastern
Alps—References

THE MAIN RELIEF FEATURES

OUR survey of the depth conditions in the Mediterranean Sea
has shown that the obvious variety of surface relief in the
surrounding lands has an under-water reflection; the whole
region, both land and sea, is one of great complexity. Further, as
has been indicated, there is much evidence tending to show that the

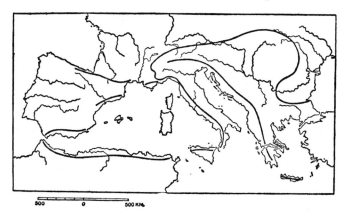

FIG. 11. THE GENERAL COURSE OF THE FOLDED MOUNTAIN CHAINS OF
SOUTHERN EUROPE

existing features are of geologically recent origin, while the active
volcanoes and the frequency of earthquakes suggest that the causes
which produced them have not ceased to act. The diversity of the
relief has exercised great and abiding influence, both direct and
indirect, upon man, and must therefore be studied in some detail.

The outstanding feature is of course the presence of the folded
mountain-chains which interpenetrate the whole area from east to
west, and from north to south, in great sweeping curves. They are
not confined to Europe but are continued into the Atlas Lands of
North Africa no less than into the peninsula of Asia Minor. In
Fig. 11 the general direction of the chains is shown in diagrammatic
form, and the figure brings out some interesting points.

We may note first that in three areas there is a pronounced curve towards the west, the inner concavity being marked by a depression. These three are (1) the Gibraltar region, where the Atlas Mountains to the south are separated from the Betic Cordillera of Spain by the Strait of Gibraltar. Within the curve lies the Alborán Basin (p. 16) of the Mediterranean Sea. (2) A marked curve occurs also in the Western Alps, which merge without notable gap into the Apennines. Here the depression behind the mountains is indicated by the North Italian plains. (3) Again, the Transylvanian Alps swing round into the Balkan Mountains, from which they are separated only by the gorge of the Danube at the Iron Gate. Within lies the depressed area of the Wallachian plain of Roumania.

The figure shows that the older hypothesis that the Betic Cordillera were once connected to the Atlas Mountains, across what is now the Strait of Gibraltar, implies that there was here a much more acute bend than in the case of the other two westward arcs. This is one of the (minor) reasons why many structural geologists have abandoned this view, though it still keeps its place in most text-books.

In three other areas there is again notable curvature, though the direction of the arc varies. Thus the great bend of the Carpathians is directed towards the north-east, and within lies the depressed area of the Hungarian plain. A second curve, with its convexity directed southwards, is indicated by the way in which the mountains of Greece are continued through Crete and Rhodes towards Asia Minor. Here the area of depression within the curve is represented by the Aegean, with its 'deeps' and island clusters (p. 20). Finally, the continuation of the Atlas folds through Sicily into peninsular Italy gives us an eastward-facing arc, bounded on either side by the deep depressions of the Tyrrhenian and Ionian Seas. In marked contrast to these great arcs we note that the Pyrenees are virtually rectilinear, and their relation to the alpine folding is doubtful.

Now these facts in regard to the direction of the chains may be correlated in quite simple fashion with the presence of the hard and resistant crust-blocks indicated in Fig. 3. Thus we may regard the Spanish Meseta as fending off, as it were, the rising fold-mountains of the Betic Cordillera. Similarly the presence of the Central Plateau of France on the one hand and of the Vosges-Black Forest block on the other must have controlled the westward bend of the Alps, which were thrust out between them. The straightness of the Pyrenees may be associated with their position between the Spanish Meseta and the Central Plateau. Again, the Bohemian crust-block, combined with that believed to lie sunk below the Hungarian plain, may be regarded as determining the curve of the Carpathians. In the centre of the Balkan peninsula lies another crust-block which may be correlated with the divergence of the Balkan Mountains and the Dinaric Alps. Finally, as already stated, beneath the Aegean and Tyrrhenian Seas lie partially-submerged blocks which help to explain the course of their marginal mountains.

But such statements do not carry us very far. They throw no light on the structure or component rocks of the different chains, nor on the reasons for the contrasts between them. Here we approach a difficult question. An enormous amount of work has been published in recent years both on the general problems of mountain-building and on the structure of the Alps, especially the Swiss Alps. These investigations have led both to great increase in our knowledge of the actual facts and also to bold speculations, as interesting as they are intricate. To what extent the geographer, as such, is concerned either with the detailed facts as now interpreted or with the hypotheses put forward to account for them, is a controversial problem, in regard to which general statements as to the scope of the subject offer comparatively little guidance. It may, however, be said at once that the attempt to formulate in full rival hypotheses—and much more to decide between them—is definitely outside his sphere. On the other hand, where modern interpretations or hypotheses throw light on obvious relief features they would appear to have definite geographical value. The following brief account represents an endeavour to select from the mass of material available such facts and views as seem to help us to form a clearer picture of the lands with which we have to deal. For fuller details reference must be made to the books mentioned on pp. 44-5 and to the bibliographies which they contain.

ORIGIN OF THE RELIEF

We may take as our starting-point the fact already noted in the last chapter that the fold-mountains of the Mediterranean area took their origin by the buckling up of great masses of sediment deposited in the ancient Tethys which lay between Hercynian Europe and Africa. Geologists distinguish between two great sets of processes or earth-movements, due to subterranean (hypogene) forces, which modify the surface. These have been described as epeirogenic and orogenic. The former are the slow vertical movements, affecting large areas, continuous over long periods of geological time, which leave the tectonic structure of the crust unaltered. The vertical movements may take place either in the upward or the downward direction, thus extending either the land or the water surfaces. Without such long-continued epeirogenic movements the accumulation of the great masses of sediments now uplifted to form the fold-mountains of Southern Europe would have been impossible.

Much more striking, however, in their immediate effects on structure and relief here are the orogenic movements of which there is such abundant evidence. Orogenic movements are 'episodic', that is, limited in geological time as well as in space, and in contrast to the epeirogenic ones produce enormous changes in the structure or tectonic build of the crust. Two main types may be recognized here. In the alpine type the rocks have been subjected to a lateral thrust which threw them into complex folds, often with overfolding and overthrusting of great masses of rocks (nappes or *Decken*). It is this alpine type which is the most conspicuous feature of the lands of Southern Europe.

In the other type of movement rocks normally harder than those which buckle up into folds respond to the tension by breaking into blocks which often show differential movement in relation to one another. The effects on relief of this type of movement are varied. Where the blocks have been thrust upward and subsequently denuded their harder rocks may present the appearance of mountain 'ranges', as in the Spanish Meseta. Where partial collapse has occurred sea 'deeps' may alternate with islands, as in the Tyrrhenian and Aegean Seas.

ALPIDES AND DINARIDES

Whether or not it is true, as is maintained by Kober, that fold-mountains are necessarily bilateral and composed of two bordering chains separated by a Median Mass, two divisions can at least be recognized in the Mediterranean area. These are indicated in Fig. 3. It will be noted that the Alpid branch, as indicated by the arrows, is the result of a northward thrust, from Africa towards Europe. As already explained, the detailed course of the mountains appears to result from the differential resistance offered by the harder rocks of the Foreland, round which the earth-waves have, as it were, curled. As a whole, however, the mighty northward thrust appears to have had relatively free play between the obstacles represented by the Spanish Meseta, or south-westward extension of Hercynian Europe, and the prolongation of the Russian Platform along the line of the lower Danube. The result is to bring the Alps and the Carpathians into the heart of Central Europe, giving it its complicated relief. At the two ends of the complex and irregular arc, on the other hand, the Alpides are marginal so far as the mainland of Europe is concerned.

As compared with the Alpides, the southern or Dinarid branch as a whole is arcuate towards the south, and, as is shown by the arrows, the thrust at the surface appears to be towards Africa, that is, always to have a southerly component. But the older and simpler conception of divergent thrusts, towards Europe and Africa respectively, has now been generally abandoned. It is believed, by many geologists at least, that all the primary movements were towards the north, deposits laid down on the African continental shelf being thrust over European ones, but that owing to the resistance offered in the central alpine area there was a process of overturning which led to a superficial counter-thrusting to the south. On this view the Dinarides represent 'a grand earth-backwash' (Wills), the overturning being most noticeable in the central area, where the pressure was greatest. As suggested by Fig. 3, this makes north-eastern Italy and the north-western Balkan peninsula represent a part of 'Africa' thrust far into Europe, while to the east (southern Greece and Crete) and west (southern Italy and Sicily) of this central area the Dinarid folds are at best but on the margin of Europe.

One other point shown in Fig. 3 may be noticed. As already explained, Kober's conception of mountain-folding involves the presence of two border chains separated by a Median Mass or Betwixt Mountains (*Zwischengebirge*). This intermontane region is absent in the Alps proper, where the two chains are not only crushed against each other but the Alpides are actually overridden by the Dinarides. Elsewhere, as is shown, the Median Mass is either partially sunk below the Sea, as in the Western Basin and in the Aegean, or concealed by the masses of superficial deposits laid down on its sunken surface, as in the Hungarian plain; or forms a rugged upland lying between the folded chains, as in the Balkan peninsula and Asia Minor.

Have such conclusions any real geographical importance? They do at least emphasize, by rendering intelligible, that essential feature of the Mediterranean Lands which we have already noticed. This is the way in which the Western Basin of the Sea is as it were balanced round the central land-mass of the Italian peninsula, not by the great Eastern Basin as a whole, but by the Aegean area. Generally they may be said to give us a clearer and more vivid picture of the actual conditions that even the best orographical map alone can afford.

There is more even than this. The individual chains are notably complex and varied, not only as regards their structure but in their component rocks. Their composition again affects scenery and often also soils, vegetation, and the use which can be made of the land—all points of geographical importance. This is especially true as regards the massive limestones which are frequently present in the Dinarides and have an enormous effect on the surface. Modern views as to the origin of the different elements and the source of their component rocks do help us to understand both why the rocks should be so varied and why particular types occur in particular places.

It may of course be objected that this is putting the cart before the horse, the conclusions before the facts on which they are based.

4

The whole grandiose conception which we have lightly sketched in is based both on facts of observation and on assumptions.

Let us sum up generally what has happened. In the first place, the geologists long since surveyed and mapped the actual rocks. Then what is called *facies* was recognized. This is defined as the sum-total of the lithological and palaeontological characteristics displayed by a deposit at a certain point or locality. In other words, it is maintained that groups of rocks, because of their contained fossils and because of their composition, can be assigned to a particular area of origin, as deep sea, shallow water, and so forth. From the facies of the sedimentary rocks involved in the alpine folding it is believed that they can be assigned to different parts of the Tethys within which they were laid down. That sea, lying as it did between Hercynian Europe and Hercynian Africa, must necessarily have been bordered by two continental shelves, African and European, with intervening central deeps, broken apparently by island festoons. There would therefore be presumably two main sets of shallow-water deposits separated by bathyal ones.

Next we come to the big assumption, not, as has been pointed out by some geologists, without a suspicion of reasoning in a circle. If rocks of certain facies can be assigned to a particular part of the Tethys, and can also be recognized within the mountains at a great distance from their supposed area of origin, their distribution and relations within the mountains can be used to unravel the tectonic structure, and particularly to trace the origin and movements of the nappes presumed to have arisen during the processes of buckling-up and overthrusting.

Thus the geologists begin with the distribution of rock types within the Alps as known, and on this basis proceed to build their theories of the tectonics of mountain-building. We are proposing to reverse the process, and accept the theories as a means of illustrating the facts of distribution. Is this justifiable? In answering the question we may note that for the geologist the structure and composition of the crust is the raw material of his subject—his starting-point. But the geographer, if he begins with relief, is concerned primarily with its relation to other phenomena, not with its causation. Even though some acquaintance with the chief rock-types of Southern Europe is essential for the grasping of the relation of the relief features to the distribution of those other phenomena, a mere catalogue would be an unwarranted strain on the memory. By looking broadly at some recent deductions and speculations we may gain our end by an indirect method.

THE STRUCTURE OF THE WESTERN ALPS

The most cursory glance at an orographical map of Switzerland (cf. Fig. 21, p. 75) shows three main relief elements, all of great importance in its geography. These are the Jura Mountains, the Plateau, and what for the geographer constitute the High Alps. The last are highly complex while the other two are relatively simple.

The Jura fall into two divisions, the Plateau Jura to the north and the Folded Jura, which form a minor arc in front of the greater one of the Alps. But except for a narrow strip near Basel the Plateau Jura do not come into the area we have to consider. It need therefore only be noted that they were virtually unaffected by the forces which produced the fold-mountains, save that in places the tension has given rise to the faulting and differential movement of blocks already described on p. 32. The Folded Jura originate near Chambéry, where they are narrow and pressed against the Alps, and die out to the east of Basel. In the intervening area, that is, opposite the gap between the Central Plateau of France and the Vosges-Black Forest block, they widen out, their arcuate outer surface being directed towards the north-west (Fig. 12). Thus their whole appearance suggests that they arose as the result of a push coming from the direction of the Alps. The crumpling—that is, the intensity of the folding—is greatest in the area immediately to the south of the Black Forest, where the folds are bunched together, and least in the central region, where they had more room to develop.

Sedimentary rocks of all ages from permian to tertiary are present, and borings indicate that they rest upon a crystalline foundation. But the specially interesting feature is that the folding affects only the surface-beds down to the Middle Trias (*Muschelkalk*), the older strata being unaffected. Thus it appears that we are here in the region which once formed the European margin of the Tethys, in which sedimentaries of varying facies were laid down during a long period of time. The dwindling orogenic forces were able to crumple up the upper layers, and thrust them over the lower and thus over the unaltered platform beneath, but produced only a relatively simple type of folding in which in the main the upfolds form ridges and the downfolds valleys.

Within Switzerland the Plateau extends from the southern shore of the Lake of Constance to the northern one of that of Geneva; but south-westwards it has a narrowed and interrupted continuation across the international frontier till it is obliterated where the Jura abut on the Alps near Chambéry. It is floored by soft sandstones and conglomerates of tertiary (upper oligocene and miocene) age called by Swiss geologists *Molasse*. The deposits are in part of marine and in part of fresh-water origin, and contain pebbles derived both from the northern border (Jura limestones and Black Forest rocks) and from the southern, from the higher tectonic elements of the Alps. The interruption just noted as breaking the continuity of the molasse deposit south of the Lake of Geneva is the Salève (Fig. 12), the conspicuous viewpoint which rises to the south of the town of Geneva. Here an upfold exposes cretaceous and jurassic rocks of the Jura type.

As a whole the Plateau represents a great downfold between the Alps and Jura. It was once a foredeep in front of the rising Alps, at times occupied by lakes and at times by the sea, and receiving the waste of the mountains as they rose and were exposed to denuding forces. But this foredeep was much more extensive than the present Plateau, for the molasse in places lies below much older rocks, showing that the Alps have advanced over the area covered by their own debris.

To the Alps we must next turn, and here we have to distinguish between the Eastern and Western Sections. The limit between the two is taken as a line from the Lake of Constance along the valley of the Upper Rhine to Chur and then nearly south to the River Maira and the Lake of Como. East and west of this line there is a notable contrast both in the rocks represented and in structure.

Within the Western Alps as thus defined the following six belts can be recognized, beginning near Lake Geneva and working towards the south-east, that is, towards Lake Como:

(1) The Prealps, a belt of moderate elevation standing out in front of the Alps, and extending from the River Arve south of the Lake of Geneva to the Lake of Thun and its effluent the River Aar.

(2) The High Calcareous Alps, which include the giants of the Bernese Oberland (Mönch, Eiger, Jungfrau, etc.), characterized by their permanent snow-cap and glaciers.

(3) A discontinuous belt of Crystalline Hercynian Massifs, including in Mont Blanc the highest of the alpine peaks.

(4) The Axial Belt of crystalline schists and gneisses forming the Cottian (Monte Viso), Graian (Gran Paradiso), Pennine (Monte Rosa), and Lepontine Alps.

(5) The Root Belt extending from Canavese near Turin to the head of the Lake of Como.

(6) The Southern Calcareous Alps, or Dinarides, which appear only in a belt round Lake Maggiore, but widen eastwards, extending into the Eastern Alps.

These six belts are indicated in a highly generalized fashion in Fig. 12. In particular it should be noted that the area shown as Belt 2 is not homogeneous throughout; it is to be regarded as including the High Calcareous Alps rather than as indicating their range. One other point is important. Of the six belts some, e.g. the

Prealps, the High Calcareous Alps, the Hercynian Massifs, are recognized on the basis of facts of observation, that is, the characters of their component rocks, their obvious structural features, and so on. But, as its name indicates, the Root Belt, which consists of highly metamorphosed rocks, steeply inclined, owes its recognition as an entity to the nappe theory. It marks the supposed area of origin of

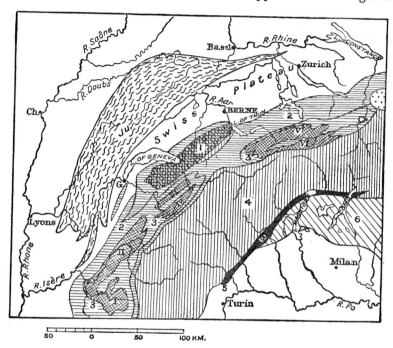

FIG. 12. TECTONIC UNITS OF THE WESTERN ALPS

Ju.=Jura Mountains. Ch.=Châlon-sur-Saône. G.=the town of Geneva. C.=the town of Chur.

1. The Prealps. 2. The High Calcareous Alps of France and Switzerland. 3. Zone of the Crystalline Hercynian Massifs (I. Mt. Pelvoux; II. Belledonne; III. the Aiguilles Rouges; IV. Mt. Blanc; V. Aar Massif; VI. St. Gothard Massif). 4. The Axial Belt or Zone of Pennine nappes. 5. The Root Belt. 6. The Southern Calcareous Alps (Dinarides).

The Swiss Plateau is left blank; the position of the Salève (p. 36) is indicated by the stippled area south of the town of Geneva.

some of the great nappes, or translated rock sheets, present in the other units.

In attempting to outline the nappe theory, and to show how it has been used to explain both the existence of the various belts of the Western Alps and the contrasts with the Eastern Alps, we may first of all return to what has been already said in regard to the Jura.

We saw there (1) that the underlying crystalline platform was unaffected; (2) that folding did not affect the deeper sedimentaries; (3) that the upper sedimentaries were folded and thrust over the lower. But the last have not travelled far from their area of origin, so that they can be followed throughout their course without difficulty. With these limited and simple orogenic phenomena we associated the dying out of the great northward thrust. In the Alps we come to the area where the push was at its maximum, so that all the resultant phenomena were accentuated. In particular, as we shall see, the underlying platform, despite its presumably original thick cover of sedimentaries, may be involved in the folding, and may appear at the surface. The folding also takes place on a gigantic scale, with great horizontal displacement of rock-sheets, and a complete separation of these from their 'roots' or bases.

A convenient starting-point for a study of the six belts is (3) the Crystalline Hercynian Massifs. These consist of a series of high mountains beginning with Argentera (Mercantour) on the Franco-Italian boundary (see Fig. 14, p. 43), and passing through Mount Pelvoux (I on Fig. 12), Belledonne, east of Grenoble (II), the Aiguilles Rouges (III), Mont Blanc (IV) to the Aar (V) and St. Gothard (VI) Massifs. By hypothesis these are uplifted portions of the Hercynian Platform, which, as we saw, underlies, in an un-altered condition, the Jura Mountains. The belt, once continuous, formed as it were a great dam against which broke mighty earth-waves coming from the south. The greatest waves were those which originated in the trough of the geosyncline, where the deposits apparently yielded most easily to the folding forces. If the analogy be continued, we may think of these waves both as breaching the Hercynian sea-wall, thus giving it its present interrupted appearance, and as flinging their earth-spray over and through it. Further, since the movements took place not in mobile water but in plastic rock, they initiated other subsidiary waves both above and below.

The Axial Belt (4), built up by the great Pennine nappes, is the visible evidence of the enormous thrust which expressed itself in series of major earth-waves. Its complex rocks are regarded as con-sisting of the greatly altered sedimentaries laid down in the central and deep part of the geosyncline (Tethys) plus a crystalline core derived from the sea-floor. The place of origin is given as the Root Belt (5). The force of the thrust brought the nappes not only in places into the gaps between the Hercynian Massifs, but, as what we have just called earth-spray, over their tops to appear in the Prealps (Belt 1).

If we turn next to Belt 2, the High Calcareous Alps, we find that they have two main components. In the first place there are elements which are analogous to those of the folded Jura, though the facies of the rocks is different; that is, the original sedimentary cover is folded without being greatly displaced from the position in which it was laid down. The difference in facies is explained by the hypothesis that the present Swiss plateau represents an old downfold which separated the true border of the old continent which lies beneath the Jura from an outer 'rise' indicated by the Hercynian Massifs, the dam or sea-wall of our analogy. Round this rise deposits were laid down differing in character from those of the area which now forms the Jura—hence the difference in facies. Some of these sediments, as just stated, were folded without much horizontal displacement. Others, originating within or to the south of the existing Massifs, were thrust as nappes over and between the latter. These form the Helvetian nappes, which constitute the second element of the High Calcareous Alps, and occur also in the Prealps. They are believed to have originated as a kind of repercussion effect from the greater movement of the Pennine nappes, beneath which they lie.

Again, in the Prealps, and represented also in small areas in the High Calcareous Alps where they have escaped denudation, occurs still a third type of nappes. These, like the Pennine nappes, originated in the Canavese Root Zone, but farther to the south, and are believed to have been carried forward on the backs of the Pennine nappes, in contradistinction to the Helvetian nappes, which underlie the latter. These, the Grisonid nappes, are composed of rocks originally laid down on the continental shore of Africa.

Finally, Belt 5, which occupies but a small area in the Western Alps, consists of rocks also laid down on the continental shelf of Africa, but brought forward by the presumed advance of the continent, not by their own movement, and thus lying more or less, so far as their relation to the underlying platform is concerned, in the position in which they were originally laid down.

Summing up, then, and taking the six belts in the order of our original list, their nature and origin may be indicated as follows:

(1) The Prealps, relatively insignificant though their relief is, are yet extraordinarily complex. Based on the original mesozoic sedimentaries and on the molasse, they are built up of Helvetian, Pennine, and Grisonid nappes, in this order. The last are hypothetically African deposits carried forward into Europe, and form also, as we shall see, an outlier of the Eastern Alps.

(2) The High Calcareous Alps are built partly of deposits laid down on the continental shelf of Europe and folded more or less *in situ*, and partly of Helvetian nappes carried over and through the Hercynian Massifs. The presence in certain localities of small outliers of Grisonid nappes suggests that these, i.e. parts of the Eastern Alps, once formed a cover over the whole western area, a cover which has been mainly removed by denudation.

(3) The Hercynian Massifs are the broken uplifted remnants of a part of the ancient Hercynian Platform which here apparently formed a slight rise in the Tethys.

(4) The Axial Belt consists of a number of nappes (Pennine nappes) which originated in the Root Belt and had their course greatly influenced by the presence of the Hercynian Massifs in front. The rocks forming the nappes are derived from the deposits of the central part of the geosyncline.

(5) The Root Belt is the presumed area of origin of the Pennine and Grisonid nappes; in the south-west it disappears under the alluvial deposits of the North Italian plains. It should be noted that no direct connexion between nappes and roots now exists, and a former connexion between particular nappes and a particular part of the Root Zone is a matter of deduction only.

(6) The Southern Calcareous Alps (Dinarides) belong to the African Hinterland. They are overfolded to the south and have reached their present position as a result of the drive of the (African) Hinterland over the contracted and buckled-up geosyncline towards the (European) Foreland.

This account, even though, as reference to the geological literature will show, it is highly generalized, may yet seem needlessly elaborate for the geographer's purpose. But, before passing to the Eastern Alps, it must be made clear by a detailed description that the Western Alps have been so dissected that the 'bones' of earth structure are as it were laid bare. The interpretation of the Eastern Alps was worked out later just because the deep-seated structures are concealed there by great rock-sheets, some of which are not represented at all in the west.

THE EASTERN ALPS

As Fig. 13 shows, the greater part of the Eastern Alps is built up of two sets of elements. The one is formed by the Southern Calcareous Alps or Dinarides. These, as we have seen, form only a narrow belt in the eastern area of the Western Alps, but expand here, forming a broad belt which includes the Alps of Bergamo, the Dolomites, and the Carso behind Trieste (Fig. 14). The other and more northerly belt (T and T′ on the figure) includes in T a belt of crystalline rocks which build up such mountains as the Silvretta group on the Swiss-Vorarlberg frontier, the splendid Oetztaler Mountains, and the Mur Alps still farther east. In front of them, stretching from the Rhine nearly to Vienna, is the Northern Limestone Zone, built of mesozoic sedimentaries which include thick beds of limestones. The Dachstein, with the other mountains of the Salzkammergut, lies in this belt (T′), the limestones of which are of quite different facies from those of the High Calcareous Alps of France and Switzerland (Fig. 12, 2).

The two belts, T' and T, represent respectively the sedimentary

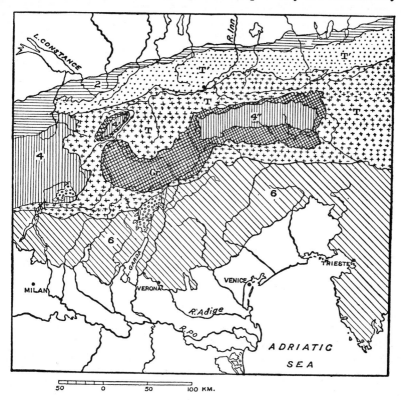

FIG. 13. TECTONIC UNITS OF THE EASTERN ALPS

As in Fig. 12, the figure 4 denotes the Pennine nappes. It will be noted that in the eastern area proper these only appear in the 'windows' of the Lower Engadine (4') and the Hohe Tauern (4''), in both cases surrounded by Grisonid nappes (Gr.). As in Fig. 12, the figure 6 denotes the Southern Calcareous Alps, or Dinarides; 2, the narrow continuation of the belt which includes the High Calcareous Alps of the western area.

T and T' are the Tirolides, T' being the northern limestone belt and T the crystallines. Two areas of intrusive eruptives are shown, one (the Adamello group) to the north-west of Lake Garda, and the other north-east of Lake Como.

The Tirolid and Grisonid nappes together constitute the Austrid or East Alpine nappes.

cover and the crystalline core of great rock-sheets, the Tirolides, which are not represented at all in the Western Alps. They overlie the Grisonid nappes, and, like them, are believed to have arisen from rocks laid down over the African shore of the Tethys, but farther to the south.

The next feature is of great importance. At two areas, in the Lower Engadine, and where the Hohe Tauern (Gross Glockner) rise like a gigantic wall between the valleys of the Pustertal and the Pinzgau, Pennine nappes (Fig. 12, 4) are exposed. Each is encircled by an area in which Grisonid nappes comes to the surface. Those nappes, as already seen, appear in the Prealps of France and Switzerland (p. 39). Nowhere, however, do Hercynian Massifs emerge at the surface in the Eastern Alps as they do in the Western (Fig. 12, 3).

The interpretation of these facts is extraordinarily interesting. It is suggested that the structures which we have described in the Western Alps are concealed in the Eastern ones by the Tirolid rock-sheets, but that in the Lower Engadine and the Hohe Tauern holes in the cover—'windows' as they are called, though 'skylights' would seem a better term—enable us to see the Western structures below. The Western Alps 'with lowered heads pass out of sight beneath their Austrian neighbours', but re-emerge in the windows. The presence of these windows again has been regarded as probably associated with a deep-seated uplift of Hercynian Massifs which has exposed the surface to sufficient denudation to reveal Pennine nappes but nothing deeper; that is, the hole in the roof (Tirolids) enables us to see the upper (Grisonid) and lower (Pennine) stories; but the basement of Hercynian rocks is beyond our ken. But it is assumed that it is there, and that it is because the whole edifice is situated on a submerged Hercynian hill that it has been exposed to the denuding forces which have swept away a part of the roof.

If the magnificent hypothesis outlined is well founded, and if it is true that the Grisonids of the Prealps are the equivalent of the Grisonids exposed in the Eastern Alps, then a further conclusion seems to follow. The whole of the Swiss Alps from the eastern edge of the Prealps to the Rhine-Como line would appear to be a fragment of a gigantic window (skylight) whose broken western frame is represented by the Prealps.

In Fig. 14 an attempt is made to correlate the obvious surface features with the facts we have been discussing. On the western edge of the area shown we note the Crystalline Massifs of the Foreland, which include the Esterel and Maures Mountains of the French Riviera.[1] Between the Black Forest and the Central Plateau lies the bow of the Jura. Behind and separated into a Swiss and a French section by the eastern end of the Lake of Geneva are the Prealps. They protrude as great outliers from a far more extensive belt of sedimentaries and Helvetian nappes, which includes the Maritime Alps, extends through the Alps of Provence to the High

[1] See Dr. Hilda Ormsby's *France* in this series.

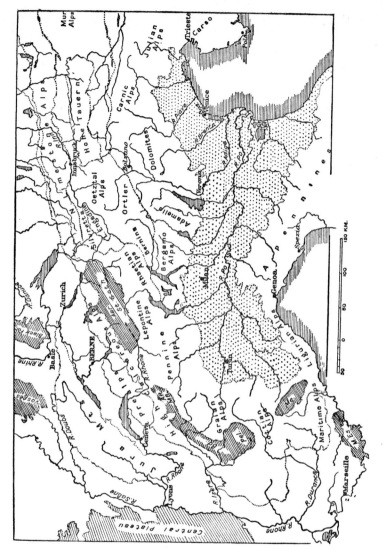

FIG. 14. REFERENCE SKETCH-MAP OF THE ALPS

The Hercynian Massifs are shaded. M. Es. = the Maures and Esterel Mountains of southern France; Me. = Mercantour; Pel. = Mt. Pelvoux; Bd. = Belledonne Massif; M.B., A.R. = Mt. Blanc and Aiguilles Rouges; Aar, St. Goth. = Aar and St. Gothard Massifs. The North Italian Plains are dotted.

Calcareous Alps of Savoy and Switzerland and narrows as it sweeps away to the east. Rising like islets from it are the Crystalline Hercynian Massifs with Mont Blanc as the monarch not of them only but of the whole Alps.

Next come the Pennine nappes, continued into the Apennines and giving rise to the semicircle of high peaks which swings round the upper basin of the Po. Eastwards they disappear but rise again to the surface in the Lower Engadine and more conspicuously in the snowclad Hohe Tauern, with glaciers recalling those of the Pennine Alps. As a general rule, however, the Eastern Alps (Tirolides and Dinarides) are lower and less extensively glaciated than the Western Alps. This is particularly true of the Southern Calcareous Alps (Dinarides) where conspicuous mountains are sometimes associated with the intrusion of young eruptive rocks (e.g. in the Adamello group).

The Tirolides, it should be noted, are regarded as a northern extension of the Dinarides, without that backward folding which characterizes the latter in the restricted sense. Both, but particularly the latter, show as compared with the Pennine nappes a tendency for the same type of element to prevail over considerable areas, and a lower degree of plasticity. The latter feature, which has been associated with their origin from deposits laid down on the African continental shelf, as compared with the Pennine nappes, which originated in the deepest part of the geosyncline, has notable structural effects. What has been called the 'elegant' folding of the Pennine nappes is absent, and the rock-sheets tend to form blocks moving as blocks rather than as long-drawn-out and reversed folds. This feature is particularly noticeable in the newer lands of Italy and is continued down the eastern side of the Adriatic. The presence of great masses of limestone right down into Greece, and their association with a very characteristic type of scenery and drainage, is of great geographical importance.

On the other hand, the facts that the Iberian peninsula is mainly a part of Hercynian Europe, even though the crystalline basis is to a considerable extent concealed under other deposits, and that the Alpine folding is marginal, make it strikingly different from the Italian peninsula and from Greece. This contrast has much influence on its geography, even though in places the Mediterranean mode of life is practised in its typical form.

REFERENCES

Three books include accounts of modern views on fold-mountains and their origin:

L. J. Wills, *The Physiographical Evolution of Britain* (London, 1929).

L. W. Collet, *The Structure of the Alps* (London, 1927).

F. Heritsch, *The Nappe Theory in the Alps*, translated by P. G. H. Boswell (London, 1929).

The first gives an exceedingly clear, brief account, mainly of the Western Alps. Collet's book (see also his article 'The Alps and Wegener's Theory', with discussion, in the *Geographical Journal* (Vol. LXVII, 4 [April], 1926) is much more detailed, while that by Heritsch (cf. the critical review by E. B. Bailey in the *Scottish Geographical Magazine*, XLVI, 1 [January], 1930), is valuable for its presentation of conflicting views, its references, and its glossary. Collet's book contains numerous references.

Mention may be made of the brief accounts of the more general aspects of the subject in Vols. I and II of Supan's *Grundzüge d. Physischen Erdkunde* (Berlin, 1927, 1930) and of L. Kober, *Der Bau der Erde*, 2nd edition (Berlin, 1928), and H. Stille, *Grundfragen d. vergleichenden Tektonik* (Berlin, 1924). See also L. Kober, *Das Alpine Europa u. seine Rahmen* (Berlin, 1931), and J. Walther, 'Mediterranis' in *Petermann's Mitteilungen* (*Ergänzungsheft*), No. 225, 1936.

CHAPTER III

CLIMATE, VEGETATION, AND LAND UTILIZATION

Mediterranean Climate, its Origin, Characters, and Distribution—
Local Winds—Distribution of Rainfall—Temperature Conditions
—Natural Vegetation and its Replacement—Land Utilization—
References

MEDITERRANEAN CLIMATE, ITS ORIGIN, CHARACTERS, AND DISTRIBUTION

THE outstanding feature of the area with which we are concerned is of course the wide prevalence within it of the Mediterranean climate (Etesian of Hettner). Both because of the presence of the Sea, and of the associated complex form of the lands, this type has here an extension in space to which there is no parallel elsewhere. In the other parts of the world in which it occurs the area affected is of limited extent, this being especially true of the south-western extremity of Africa, and simpler in form, the typical climate tending to be restricted to a short coastal strip and a few river-valleys. With the spatial extension of the climatic type in the Mediterranean Lands may be associated the fact that here only has man evolved a method of utilizing the natural resources which is so beautifully adjusted to climate and relief as to have permitted of the rise of independent and self-sufficing cultures of high standard. Elsewhere developments have been mainly or wholly secondary and derivative, often, as in California and Chile, initiated by immigrants from the Mediterranean Lands.

It has, however, to be noted that the climatic type does not prevail throughout the whole of our area, even if Switzerland be excluded. The fact already noted that the Iberian peninsula differs notably from the Italian one and the Greek sub-peninsula in its considerable area of ancient plateau and in the peripheral position of its folded mountain chains, gives to much of its surface temperature and rainfall conditions which are far from being typically Mediterranean. Apart also from its region of plateau climate, the north-western area owes to its position a rainfall which differs from the type both in total amount and in distribution throughout the year. Again, the North Italian plains, ringed round by mountains and relatively distant from the Sea, approximate alike in rainfall and temperature conditions to the modified 'continental' climate of Central Europe. Finally, though the fact is often forgotten, the figures commonly used in characterizing the Mediterranean climate tend to be those obtained from stations on the lower grounds, and, since Mediterranean man has tended to settle within reach of the great waterway, near the Sea. Changes occur with great rapidity both with elevation and with distance from the Sea. This is notably the case on Riviera coasts, where the two factors occur in combination. On the Franco-Italian, the Dalmatian, and the Albanian Rivieras a short journey may bring the traveller from the typical Mediterranean shore, with its vines, olives, and citrus fruits, to the deciduous or coniferous forest-belt, or even to the zone of mountain climate with its Alpine pastures and migratory stock animals.

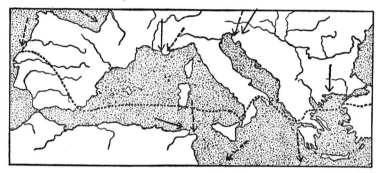

FIG. 15. PREVAILING WINDS (JANUARY AND JULY) IN THE MEDITERRANEAN REGION

The continuous arrows show January winds, the broken ones July winds. The dotted line separates the more northerly area with the maximum rainfall in autumn from the southern one, in which there is a winter maximum.

Before we study the varieties of climatic types a word or two must be said in regard to the causation of the special features of the typical Mediterranean one. Its main distinctions from those of other parts of Europe are not only the marked periodicity of the rainfall, in which it differs from the north-western area, but the partial or complete drought of some of the summer months, a marked contrast with the centre and east. The usual explanation, given in all elementary text-books, is so simple as to arouse some suspicion of its complete adequacy; it is so generalized, so oblivious of the effects of the climatic divide of the Alps that it can scarcely be the whole story.

In its usual form the explanation is as follows. It is stated that owing to the swing of the wind-belts with the sun the area in summer lies within the trade wind-belt, but in winter in that of the prevailing westerlies. From this it is deduced that the eastward-moving cyclones so characteristic of the belt of the westerlies penetrate into it from the Atlantic in winter, bringing with them their rains; while in summer, owing to their more northerly paths, they fail to reach it, and the prevailing northerly winds, which have traversed land surfaces, are dry and bring little rain.

Such statements do not, however, correspond strictly with observed facts. As Fig. 15 shows, in the northern part of the area the prevailing winds tend to have a northerly component throughout the year. In the area round the head of the Adriatic they are north-easterly both in winter and in summer, while farther west the prevailing direction is northerly in winter, becoming north-easterly in summer. Only to the south, in the region of southern Spain and the Atlas Lands, is there the seasonal change which the explanation demands, the winds here being westerly in winter and northerly in summer. Further, while it is true that the winter winds show much variability as compared with the constant and often strong (p. 23) Etesian winds of summer, which blow steadily during the day and drop at night, there appears to be little evidence that during the winter months fully-formed cyclones enter from the west. In other words, the Mediterranean in winter appears to be an independent meteorological area rather than the mere extension of the zone of the westerlies (Kendrew) which the current explanation suggests.

It is believed (cf. the paper by A. Stevens, named on p. 71) that the Polar Front theory as elaborated by Bjerknes and the Norwegian school affords a more satisfactory explanation of the actual conditions. But as this is not the place for a full statement of this theory we may content ourselves with a few general observations.

In summer the Mediterranean is a region of high pressure with prevailing northerly winds, often masked locally by land and sea breezes (p. 23). In winter there is much variability, but pressures are generally low as compared with those over Central Europe and North Africa, owing to the warmth of the Sea. The southward-extending peninsulas, however, give rise to irregularities owing to pressures tending to be higher over them, particularly as their elevation causes local chilling. In consequence they behave like miniature continents, showing a contrast between a milder, wetter western and a cooler, drier eastern shore. Everywhere, however, on the low grounds the mildness of the winter in relation to latitude is well marked and is an actual and not merely a mean condition. 'Cold waves' in the sense in which they occur in the North American continent are unknown, even though there may be spells of cold weather, particularly at places like Marseille, Trieste, and Salonika, where protection from influences from the interior of the Continent is incomplete. Elevation, as on the Spanish Plateau, or relative 'remoteness' from sea-influences as in the North Italian plains or even, if to a less extent, in the similarly mountain-ringed ones of Thessaly, at once introduce modifications, and the characteristically high winter temperatures disappear.

Another general feature, associated with the slow cooling of the surface waters of the Mediterranean, is the very gradual onset of winter conditions, the autumns being long and warm. Thus the month of October at places like Palermo and Murcia has a mean temperature considerably higher than that of a Paris July, while in November temperature conditions at both the Mediterranean stations approximate towards those of an Edinburgh July. On the other hand, the rise of temperature in spring, owing to the winter cooling of the surface waters of the Sea, is relatively slow. Thus at Palermo April is cooler than November and May than October. Such facts have a considerable bearing on agricultural production, for they mean that temperatures suitable for the cool season crops, especially cereals and vegetables, are prolonged into the late spring, while those suitable for the ripening (or sun-drying, e.g. of raisins) of the characteristic fruits continue into the late autumn. The long maturation period is particularly important for the olive, which ripens slowly.

At all seasons of the year, also, there is a high percentage of sunshine, a point of great importance. The cool season rains come with local disturbances, that is, are of the storm type, and are usually heavy but do not last long. From one point of view this is a disadvantage, increasing erosion on steep deforested slopes, and leading to flooding, with all the associated risks of malaria. But the limited amount of cloud and the rapid clearing of the sky after rain have both direct and indirect effects on man. The sunshine promotes plant growth and the ripening of seeds and fruits, and has also a stimulating effect. It makes open-air life possible throughout much of the year, a very important factor where dense populations are aggregated together on the limited tracts of fertile lands, as, for example, at Naples. As modern research has shown, exposure to sunshine is particularly valuable for children and young animals, helping to ensure healthy development even when the supply of essential foodstuffs is limited. Without the clear skies and the life in the open it seems certain that both the diet and the housing conditions in many parts of the Mediterranean area would make the rearing of healthy stocks difficult.

As to actual figures, it may be noted that throughout most of the Iberian peninsula, peninsular Italy, and peninsular Greece the number of hours of sunshine per annum exceeds 2,500. This figure drops to over 2,250 hours in northern Italy and Greece, and to over 2,000 in that north-western part of the Iberian peninsula which we have already noted as being not typically Mediterranean. As a comparison we find that in the British Isles the maximum figure is about 1,500 hours, dropping to under 750 hours in parts of the Highlands of Scotland. The association of much sunshine with drought and drying winds during the summer season is a factor in maintaining public health in lands where sanitation is as a rule defective. It has also of course economic importance in making the open-air drying of fruits and of tobacco-leaves possible.

LOCAL WINDS

Since our area is either mountainous (Switzerland) or combines accentuated relief with proximity to a sea which shows, especially in winter, highly variable pressure conditions, local winds are very marked. These may, as in the case of the bora of the Adriatic, blow with a force which has much effect both on navigation and on harbour sites, apart from the destruction which they may cause on land. Since also they may produce notable temperature variations, which, particularly in the case of the foehn of the Alps, exert influence on the distribution alike of natural vegetation and of cultivated crops, and elsewhere, as in parts of Sicily and of Spain, and in Thessaly, may determine the harvest yield of a particular year, their geographical importance is great. Further, much as with the question of the characteristic seasonal distribution of rainfall in Mediterranean Lands, the accounts given in elementary text-books tend to over-simplify the problem.

We may conveniently begin with the foehn winds of the Alps— the warm, dry winds which in many cases raise the mean temperatures of the valleys through which they blow, serve as potent agents in the melting of snow, and increase greatly the risk of fire in the huddled villages of wooden houses common in the area. Their direction is normally southerly, south-east or south or more rarely south-west, and they prevail especially in certain valleys of the Northern Alps from Besançon in France to the Vorarlberg in Austria, though even the Salzkammergut may be affected. In a less-marked form, both as to force and frequency, they also occur elsewhere. Within their chief area of distribution it is the direction of the valleys which determines the prevalence of the foehn, east-to-west valleys, such as the Rhone valley in canton Valais, or the Aar valley between Brienz and Thun, being normally exempt, while south-to-north valleys are particularly affected. Of the latter, mention may be made of the Rhine valley from Chur to the Lake of Constance, the Reuss from Andermatt to its entrance into the Lake of Lucerne, the Rhone below the bend at Martigny to the Lake of Geneva, the Upper Aar (Haslital) above Meiringen. In such valleys the force of the wind is greatest at places nearest the high and steep mountain wall which forms the southern limit.

The usual explanation given is that when pressure is low to the north of the Alps and high to the south, air is sucked over, and being warmed and dried by compression appears as a warm, dry, down-valley wind in the northern valleys. The fact that temperatures at northern stations during a foehn may be much higher than those at southern stations at a lower level, despite the cooling as the air passes over the crest, is often slurred over. Further, when the mistral of southern France is dealt with its coldness as compared with foehn winds is explained as due to the fact that the air in its region of origin is so cold that even the compression does not raise it to the level of the temperatures normally prevailing in Provence. Thus the impression is apt to be left that the Swiss valleys are warmed by the

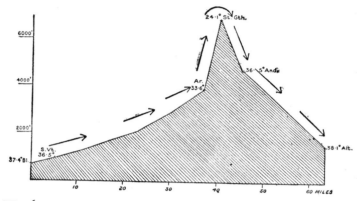

FIG. 16. TEMPERATURE CONDITIONS DURING A FOEHN PERIOD IN THE UPPER REUSS VALLEY (CANTON URI, SWITZERLAND)

For detailed explanation see text. Temperatures are in degrees Fahrenheit, heights in feet, distances in miles.

passage into them of warm southern air. Such a suggestion has no real foundation and does not explain the curious anomalies, as that in the Val Bregaglia, on the southerly side of the Maloja pass, a *north* wind sometimes blows which at times is of a mild bora type, i.e. cold and dry, and at others of a foehn type, that is, warm and dry.

The diagram (Fig. 16) shows the conditions which actually prevailed on the two sides of the Alps in the St. Gothard region during a winter (January 31–February 1) foehn period. Bellinzona (Bl.), S. Vittore (S. Vt.), and Airolo (Ar.) are in the Ticino valley to the south of the St. Gothard (St. Gth.) Massif, Andermatt (And.) and Altdorf (Alt.) in the Reuss valley to the north. At Bellinzona the wind was northerly and the weather wet, while at all the other stations it was southerly; Altdorf, near the entrance of the Reuss into the Lake of Lucerne, showed a very strong foehn. At S. Vittore the relative humidity was 85 per cent, but at Altdorf only 28 per cent, while the temperature at the latter station was exceedingly high for the station and the altitude (1,489 ft.). It will be noticed that temperatures were the same at S. Vittore and Andermatt, though the latter lies at an altitude nearly 4,000 ft. higher, while Bellinzona was much colder than Altdorf. At the St. Gothard station temperatures were only slightly higher than those normal for the season. Assuming that air was ascending from near Bellinzona to the St. Gothard, a distance of about 6,000 ft., it must have cooled by some 13° F., that is, approximately two degrees for every 1,000 ft. of ascent. But on descending through a distance of 5,400 ft. to Altdorf it was warmed by 34°, over six degrees per 1,000 ft.; that is, there was three times as much warming on the descent as cooling during the ascent. This was of course due to the liberation of heat from the nearly saturated air during its rise, and the magnitude of the difference produced the violence of the wind in the Reuss valley.

It is thus clear that the strength and warm, dry character of the foehn at Altdorf was due to the following combination of conditions. The air at the place of origin was cool and nearly saturated. Since temperatures at the St. Gothard were slightly above normal, precipitation with liberation of heat had been presumably going on during the whole ascent, so that cooling was slight. Compression on the downward path raised temperatures out of all proportion to the loss on the ascent.

It follows that if the air at the place of origin had been relatively dry, and if also its temperature had been relatively high in relation to that on the slopes, the difference between the cooling and warming processes would have been less, and the wind would have lost much of its force; for if it had been relatively dry the liberation of heat due to precipitation would have been less and cooling consequently greater. If, also, the slopes had been much colder than the area of origin, then precipitation would have been completed early in the journey with the first chilling, and no heat would have been liberated in the later upward movement. Thus the ascending air would be greatly chilled, and the difference between the loss on the ascent and the gain on the descent would be much reduced, with a resultant loss in the force of the current. In summer the air at the region of origin tends to be both warmer and drier than in winter, and in consequence powerful foehns are limited to the cooler parts of the year.

Conditions during a typical bora at Trieste illustrate further the points already made. Thus during a very severe November bora at Trieste the temperature on the edge of the Carso plateau above was 31·7° at a height of 1,135 ft., the relative humidity 82 per cent, the north-east wind exceedingly strong. Near Trieste (height of station 49 ft.) the temperature was 38·8°, the wind again north-east and of gale force, the humidity 55 per cent. It will be noted that the air had been both warmed and dried during its descent, the actual warming, about 6·5° per 1,000 ft., being somewhat greater than in the case of the foehn wind already described. *Physically*—that is to say, the wind was of 'foehn' type—it was a warmed and dried descending current. But since the normal mean temperature of November near Trieste is 50°, its cooling effect was very marked and the air contained much of its original moisture.

Of the mistral it is scarcely necessary to speak, since in its fully-developed form it is virtually confined to the Mediterranean coast of France, even though it may extend to the mouth of the Ebro on the one side and to the head of the Gulf of Genoa on the other. It is of the bora type, but generally north-westerly or north in direction.

In the more southerly parts of the Mediterranean, particularly in south-eastern Spain, Sicily, southern peninsular Italy, and Greece, with the islands, southerly local winds occur of varied type. To such winds the name scirocco is given in lands of Italian speech, but there are various types of scirocco. By derivation the word should be applied to dry winds, but in southern Italy and on the Dalmatian coast the name is given to warm, wet winds of very oppressive type. These occur especially in the cooler season, and seem to be due to the indraft of air in front of a moving depression.

But on the northern coast of Sicily, as at Palermo, and on the south-eastern coast of Spain, particularly near Almería but extending north-east to Cape Nao, the wind being called *leveche* here, there is another type which is particularly hot, dry, dust-laden, and blighting in its effects on vegetation. Though not limited to one season, this kind of scirocco blows especially in spring. The wind seems to be of the foehn type and to originate in North Africa. In the Spanish area the air is little modified during its passage over the narrow Mediterranean 'forecourt' (p. 15), so that it shows the same kind of features at Oran in Algeria as at Almería in Spain. In the latter country its penetration is very limited, so that it is chiefly the coastal area which suffers; but this, of course, particularly near Murcia, is the area of densest settlement. In the case of Sicily the passage over the interior highlands of the island accentuates the hot, dry character of the wind as it descends to the northern shore.

Such winds have often much importance in Mediterranean life. They may cause serious damage to fruit-trees, especially the delicate citrus types, and this is the more disastrous as it may affect not one season's crop only but damage the trees permanently, while replacement is necessarily a slow process. Delicate operations like bud-grafting or the rooting of cuttings may also fail.

DISTRIBUTION OF RAINFALL

In place of studying separately the various types of climate represented in our area, we shall take a general survey first of rainfall and then of temperature conditions.

In Fig. 17, Basel (1), Lugano (2), and Milan (3) illustrate the transition from the Central European seasonal distribution of rainfall to the sub-Mediterranean type which prevails in the north Italian plains. Basel and Lugano both lie at a height of about 800 ft.; Milan at 476 ft. It will be noted that at Basel summer (June–August) is definitely the wettest season, and winter (a) the driest (15 per cent of total of 32 in.). But autumn has over and spring only slightly less than 25 per cent. Lugano has twice the total fall of Basel, and autumn ranks as the wettest season, though summer falls very little behind. Winter, with but 11 per cent of the total, is proportionately even drier than at Basel. Milan retains the 'continental' feature of a relatively dry winter (19 per cent), though the dryness is much less marked than at the other two stations; but it shows an approach, though only an approach, to the Mediterranean feature of a dry summer (c). Some 23 per cent of the total precipitation of 40 in. falls during this season as compared with 31 per cent at Lugano. The two driest months at Milan are February and July; the two wettest October and May. With minor variants this condition is widespread in the plains, extending from Turin to Venice and from the lake stations and the middle Adige valley to Bologna.

Santiago (4) in north-western Spain has the high total fall of 65 in., and winter is definitely the wettest period (33 per cent), while summer (10 per cent) is the driest. But July, the driest month, has 2 in., and 7 in. fall during the three summer months. Thus it can scarcely be said that even partial summer drought occurs. In other words, the climate is western rather than Mediterranean, and this part of Spain lies in a southern prolongation of the Atlantic belt of Europe.

Madrid (5) shows strongly contrasted conditions. Here the total is low, under 17 in.; most of the rain (33 per cent) falls in spring (b) and autumn (d, 30 per cent), summer (12 per cent) being the driest season, though winter is also dry. A closely similar *régime* prevails at Valladolid, where, however, the total is little over 12 in. Both stations stand at a height of over 2,000 ft., on the plateau, and the peculiar conditions are a direct consequence of its height and extent. In spring the surface warms up rapidly after the winter chilling, and, owing to the topography, temperature contrasts between adjacent areas develop, giving rise to rains of the thunderstorm type. Similar conditions, somewhat less marked, occur in autumn as temperatures drop, but summer and winter are periods of relative stability; low or high pressures develop respectively and little rain falls.

Leaving for a moment the consideration of the *régimes* in the Ebro and Guadalquivir valleys we may turn to Lisbon (6), Palermo (7),

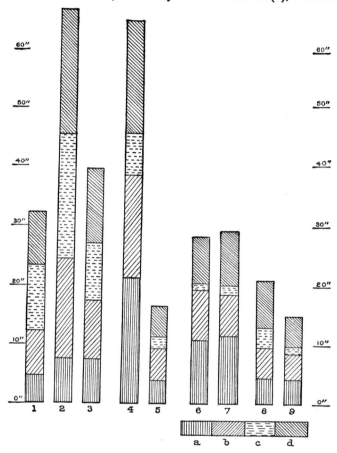

FIG. 17. SEASONAL RAINFALL DISTRIBUTION AT NON-MEDITERRANEAN AND MEDITERRANEAN STATIONS

In each column a=winter, b=spring, c=summer, d=autumn, while the height of the column shows total rainfall in inches.
1. Basel. 2. Lugano. 3. Milan. 4. Santiago. 5. Madrid. 6. Lisbon. 7. Palermo. 8. Barcelona. 9. Murcia.

Barcelona (8), and Murcia (9), all of which illustrate typical Mediterranean rainfall. The first point to notice is that (cf. Fig. 15) the first two lie to the south and the other two to the north of the line dividing the southern area, in which the maximum rainfall is in winter, from the more northerly one in which it is in autumn, with a secondary maximum in spring. All the stations are on or near (Murcia) the coast, and Lisbon, the highest, is little over 300 ft. above sea-level. Table I supplements the diagrams and brings out the essential facts.

TABLE I

Seasonal Distribution (Percentages of Total) of Rainfall at Mediterranean Lowland Stations

Station	Lat.	Total Rainfall. Inches	Per cent Winter	Per cent Spring	Per cent Summer	Per cent Autumn
Lisbon . . .	38° 42′	28·7	38	30	3	28
Palermo . . .	38° 6′	29·8	39	24	5	31
Barcelona . .	41° 22′	21·1	21	23	17	39
Murcia . . .	37° 59′	15·1	27	30	8	35

Note.—Percentages are calculated only to nearest whole number, fractions being neglected.

Looking at the three Iberian stations we note that Lisbon and Murcia illustrate the point already made that westerly stations tend to have a higher rainfall than easterly ones. But the comparison of Murcia and Palermo emphasizes the fact that this must be taken as referring to the individual land-masses and not to the Mediterranean area as a whole. Similarly, while a comparison of Barcelona and Murcia (as indeed of Santiago and Lisbon) shows that there is a general tendency for rainfall to diminish towards the south, the figure for Palermo reminds us that latitude is not in itself the determining factor. The relation between latitude and intensity of summer drought is somewhat closer; but it is more accurate to say that a winter maximum is associated with a marked summer minimum (Lisbon and Palermo), while summer drought tends to be less accentuated where an autumn maximum occurs.

The second table (II) combined with Fig. 18, illustrates some further points. Saragossa (1) is in the Ebro valley, Jaén (2) and Granada (3) in the Guadalquivir one, Potenza (4) on the high ground of southern peninsular Italy, and Caltanisetta (5) on the inner highland of Sicily. All the stations are inland and all at some height above sea-level.

Considering the Italian stations first we find that Caltanisetta, despite its elevation, has a *régime* which resembles closely that of Palermo. The total fall is notably less, but the characteristic features, accentuated summer drought, winter maximum, are present as before. Potenza again shows the usual features of stations lying to

TABLE II

Seasonal Distribution (Percentages of Total) of Rainfall at Mediterranean Upland Stations

Station	Height above sea-level. Feet	Lat.	Total Rainfall. Inches	Per cent Winter	Per cent Spring	Per cent Summer	Per cent Autumn
Saragossa	673	41° 38′	12·4	19	34	19	28
Jaén	1,887	37° 47′	28·4	33	36	6	24
Granada	2,198	37° 11′	19·7	31	34	6	29
Potenza	2,707	40° 39′	25·1	28	26	14	32
Caltanisetta	1,807	37° 27′	23·1	42	23	5	30

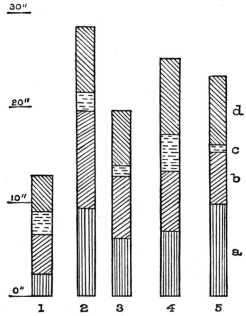

FIG. 18. SEASONAL RAINFALL DISTRIBUTION AT FIVE UPLAND MEDITERRANEAN STATIONS

1. Saragossa. 2. Jaén. 3. Granada. 4. Potenza.
5. Caltanisetta. (Cf. Table II and Fig. 17.)

the north of the dividing line already mentioned, that is, the summer drought is less accentuated, the maximum fall is in autumn; but again the total fall is diminished as compared with the western coastal station of Naples (32·8 in.) in a similar latitude. As contrasted with these we find that the three Spanish stations deviate notably from type and show the influence of the proximity of the plateau. Saragossa has a remarkably low rainfall, which is a result of its position in a valley cut off from the sea on all sides by higher ground. As at the two other stations, the maximum fall is in spring, a condition which, as we have seen, is characteristic of the plateau, while summer and winter have identical percentages. At both Jaén (2) and Granada (3) summer drought is accentuated, but spring is again the wettest season instead of winter, as would be expected from the position. Thus the three stations, together with Madrid and Valladolid, illustrate the fact that in its climatology as in its structure the peninsula is highly anomalous as compared with the Italian one. The typical Mediterranean climate is confined to parts of its coast, the north-western area deviating from the type. Much of the interior is arid and shows the peculiar feature of a spring maximum of rainfall.

In this survey nothing has been said of Greece or Albania. In both cases, particularly in the latter, reliable long-period figures for series of stations are not available on the same scale as in Spain and Italy. Generally, however, the conditions resemble those prevailing in southern peninsular Italy and Sicily, though Greece is often regarded as much more arid. The reason is interesting. Rainfall figures for many of the better-known Greek stations, such as Athens, Nauplia, some of the Aegean Islands, and so on, are of the order of 15 in.–20 in. (roughly 380–500 mm.), which seems low as compared with Italian stations like Naples or Palermo (30 in.–33 in. or 762–838 mm.). But we have to remember that the Greek stations mentioned lie to the east of the peninsular land-mass, and often in distinctly lower latitudes than the Italian ones with which they are compared. In the Italian area an easterly position causes a comparable drop in the total amount, e.g. Catania and Agrigento in Sicily have totals of the order of 20 in., Foggia in peninsular Italy has not much more than 18 in. Arta in western Greece in a latitude slightly higher than Palermo has a total of over 43 in., much higher than either Naples or Palermo.

TEMPERATURE CONDITIONS

The accompanying table (III) gives the mean temperature of the hottest and coldest months at the stations whose rainfall *régime* we have already considered, with one or two additions to illustrate particular points. It shows also the number of months in which the mean drops below 50°F. (10°C.), which may be taken as that of early May over much of the British Isles, and of those in which it exceeds 60°F. (15.6°C.) which represents roughly the mean of the summer months here (cf. also Fig. 19).

TABLE III

Mean Temperature Conditions (Degrees F.)

Station	Mean Temp. Hottest Month Degrees	Mean Temp. Coldest Month Degrees	No. of Months with Mean below 50° F.	No. of Months with Mean above 60° F.
Basel . . .	66·4	31·8	7	3
Lugano . . .	70·7	34·4	5	4
Cadenabbia . .	70·7	37·5	5	4
Milan . . .	74·8	32·4	5	5
Santiago . . .	66·0	45·1	4	4
Madrid . . .	75·7	39·7	5	4
Lisbon . . .	70·2	49·3	1	6
Palermo . . .	76·6	50·5	0	6
Barcelona . .	73·9	46·4	3	6
Murcia . . .	78·8	50·2	0	7
Saragossa . .	75·5	40·6	5	5
Valladolid . .	69·9	35·7	6	4
Seville . . .	85	52·1	0	7
Granada . . .	77·4	42·9	3	5
Potenza . . .	68·9	37·1	6	4
Caltanisetta . .	76·1	43·6	4	4
Catania . . .	79·5	51·5	0	7
Foggia . . .	78·9	43·4	3	6

It will be noted that at Basel, taken as representing the lower stations of Switzerland, winters are decidedly colder, summers rather warmer than in our own country, while the number of months in which the monthly mean exceeds 50° is quite comparable. At Lugano the effect of position at the southern base of the Alps and of the presence of the lake is very obvious both in summer and winter. The winters are milder though still remarkably cold judged by our standards, the summers much warmer, the period during which active growth of plants may be expected to occur much longer. These conditions are accentuated to the east, as on the shores of Como Lake and on those of Garda Lake, which lies somewhat farther south. Thus Cadenabbia (Villa Carlotta) on Como Lake, at an elevation some 250 ft. less than that of Lugano but in almost precisely the same latitude, has considerably warmer winters, though the mean July temperatures are identical. As compared with these lake stations Milan is characterized by its much colder winters and hotter summers, that is, 'continental' features reappear.

The actual figures at these stations should be carefully noted, for a good deal of misconception exists in regard to the 'oases' of luxuriant vegetation on the lake shores. The flowering trees and shrubs which form their glory in spring and early summer are frequently of the Chinese type—that is, tolerant of somewhat cold winters—and the change in the economic plants from west to east reflects the gradual increase in winter temperatures and the lengthening of the growing season. Thus the vine and the hardier fruit-trees (peach, almond, walnut) without the olive are characteristic of the extreme west, as round Lake Maggiore. The olive appears in the central area, as around Como Lake, while in the extreme east it is accompanied by citrus fruits as economic crops; for citrons and even the delicate lemon will grow on the Riviera coast (Gardone) of Garda Lake, though winter protection is necessary, and the trees are obviously at the extreme climatic limit.

Olives and citrus fruits alike are necessarily excluded from the plains, though vines and mulberries thrive. The intensity and duration of the summer heat also make it possible to grow crops, like rice, which demand high temperatures but have not a prolonged vegetative period.

The figures for Santiago, showing the mild winters and moderate summers, emphasize what has been already said as to the Atlantic character of the north-western region of Spain. Again, those for Madrid indicate its continental character, the long, cold winters and the short but hot summers forming a remarkable contrast with the conditions at Barcelona.

The four following lowland stations illustrate very typical Mediterranean conditions. It should be noted that at Palermo and Murcia the temperatures of the coldest months are comparable to those of an English October, when our gardens are still flowery and productive, while at all stations the summers are long and warm. Not only therefore do the temperatures permit of a large range of crop plants, but there need not be any completely 'dead' season; something of direct use to the grower can be obtained from the land at all periods of the year. This, though it is the 'type' condition, is of very limited distribution in the Mediterranean Lands we have to consider here.

In the next group of stations Seville (height 66 ft.) has been substituted for the station of Jaén, included in the rainfall table on p. 57, in order to emphasize the effect of elevation at Granada in lowering both summer and winter temperatures and shortening the length of the warm season. The latitudes are virtually identical, Seville being slightly farther north; in addition to being lower, however, it is exposed to sea influences, while Granada, as we have already seen, is affected by the high plateau area to the north. The influence both of elevation and of increasing distance from the sea is also illustrated by the series (cf. Fig. 19) Barcelona (4), Saragossa (5), Valladolid (6) (2,345 ft.). It will be noted that at Saragossa, where the elevation is moderate (673 ft.), the interior position

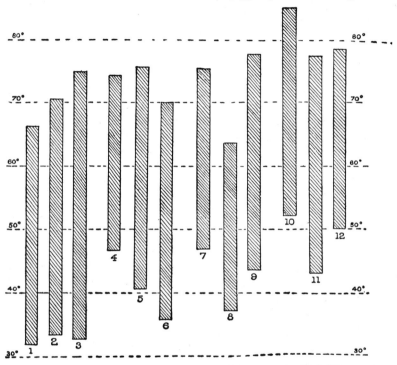

FIG. 19. TEMPERATURE RANGES AT NON-MEDITERRANEAN AND MEDITERRANEAN STATIONS

The top of each column shows the mean temperature (in degrees Fahrenheit) of the hottest month, and the base that of the coldest month, so that the height of the column indicates the range in degrees Fahrenheit. The first group illustrates the conditions prevailing north and south of the Alps. In the other three groups, latitudes are similar within the group, the differences in temperatures and ranges being due to the position (see text and Table III).

1. Basel. 2. Lugano. 3. Milan. 4. Barcelona. 5. Saragossa. 6. Valladolid. 7. Naples. 8. Potenza. 9. Foggia. 10. Seville. 11. Granada. 12. Murcia.

lowers winter and raises summer temperatures as compared with the coastal station of Barcelona. Valladolid, however, like Granada, has both its summer and winter temperatures lowered.

To the two high-level Italian stations included in the rainfall table Catania and Foggia have been added. The former is coastal (height 82 ft.), the latter is some twenty miles distant from the sea and placed at an elevation of 295 ft., four degrees farther north than Catania and one degree north of Potenza. Again, the effect of great elevation in lowering both winter and summer temperatures should be noted in the case of both the insular and peninsular pairs. Potenza is particularly interesting, for the mean January temperature is nearly 10° lower than that at Naples in almost the same latitude. It lies nearly fifty miles from the nearest sea at an elevation of nearly 3,000 ft., but the effect of such conditions in a latitude of nearly $40\frac{1}{2}°$ is not always realized.

This summary account, brief though it is, gives a general idea of the conditions which influence the natural vegetation and cultivated crops in the countries we have to consider. It may be emphasized once again that generalizations about the Mediterranean climate are peculiarly dangerous, even when applied to the peninsulas, because of the effect of local conditions. This is especially true as regards winter temperatures. Certain areas, such as those illustrated by the stations of Seville, Murcia, Palermo, Catania, have no winter in the northern sense, for the temperatures are such that no definite growth check occurs. But Foggia has shown us that even at quite moderate elevations in low latitudes mean January temperatures may be lower than those found in the favoured south-western parts of the British Isles. Further, the statement that the Mediterranean climate reappears in the belt along the lakes at the southern base of the Alps requires to be taken with qualifications, both as regards rainfall and temperatures. January, on the shores of the Lake of Como, is colder than it is at low-level stations in the eastern British Isles, and summers are far from showing even partial drought.

NATURAL VEGETATION AND ITS REPLACEMENT

Any discussion of the plants and plant associations can only be cursory in view of the mass of material available. Further, the fact that their broader features, so far as the Mediterranean countries are concerned, are summarized in the elementary text-books makes it possible to assume that these are already more or less familiar, while any detailed study demands more knowledge of systematic botany than can be assumed on the part of the ordinary geographical student. We shall therefore limit our survey to general principles.

Most of the area with which we have to do, whether alpine or Mediterranean or sub-Mediterranean, falls within the tract which from the ecological standpoint is woodland; that is, the climatic conditions generally permit of the growth of woody plants provided other factors, such as soil, exposure, and elevation, are suitable. The chief exceptions are the more arid areas of Spain, which form steppe lands (Fig. 20), often reminiscent of those of North Africa, and the high pastures of the mountain regions, which are snow-clad for much of the year, but show a short, seasonal growth of dwarfed herbaceous plants forming highly nutritious food for stock. The woodland associations fall into various divisions, but before considering these some general points may be noted.

There is much evidence to suggest that prior to the Glacial Period a luxuriant forest, including many evergreen forms, had a wide distribution in the northern hemisphere. This persists to some

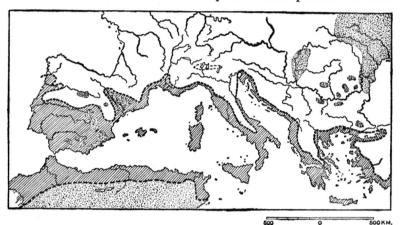

FIG. 20. DISTRIBUTION OF AREAS OF TYPICAL MEDITERRANEAN VEGETATION AND OF STEPPE

The dotted line indicates the northern limit of the olive, the isolated area at the base of the Alps round the North Italian lakes being shown quite diagrammatically. Areas within which the climatic conditions on the low grounds favour Mediterranean Evergreen Woodland are shaded, while the dotted areas (note especially the Ebro valley and parts of the Spanish Meseta) are the steppes (cf. Fig. 73). (*After Philippson.*)

extent, particularly so far as its angiospermous elements are concerned, in the lower latitudes of eastern North America and eastern non-tropical Asia, while western North America shows a great wealth of coniferous species, some of which had a much wider distribution in tertiary times. But in Europe, and especially western Europe, numbers of the tertiary forms, whose presence at one time is proved by fossils, are now absent as native species. That this is not due to the existing climatic conditions is shown by the fact that when introduced from eastern Asia or North America many species not only thrive as individuals, but establish themselves readily, that is, are capable of reproducing themselves without man's aid. It is therefore believed that their disappearance as native species is best explained as due not to the Ice Age itself—for this prevailed equally in North America—but to the presence of the transverse mountain chains and the Mediterranean Sea. These in combination checked what in rather loose phraseology is called their southern retreat, whereas in eastern North America sanctuary was found to the south (note that the peninsula of Florida all but reaches the tropic), and a northward spread became possible as the climate improved. Similar conditions exist in eastern Asia, but there of course land surfaces are continuous to and beyond the tropic.

Because of the process of extermination, in western Europe generally the woodlands, in all their types, are relatively poor in species. This condition reaches its maximum in Highland Scotland, where but one forest-forming conifer—the Scots pine—is native, and afforestation has to be carried on mainly with introduced species. As one would expect, also, if the explanation offered is correct, it is least marked in the Balkan region. There high and continuous transverse mountain chains are absent, the water boundary towards Asia is narrow, and the narrowness and dissection of the secondary Greek peninsula, no less than its southern extension, must have kept the climate moderate, even during the height of the northern glaciation. The effects of the glaciation indeed are believed (Turrill) to have reached their extreme southern limit, so far as temperatures were concerned, in the latitude of Central Albania. Minor sanctuaries must therefore have been present in the area which would serve as centres for future re-colonization. An interesting example of the process is, according to Turrill, furnished by the Judas-tree, with its showy pinkish flowers. This leguminous tree reaches as a native its western limit in southern France, but the genus (Cercis) is one of the typical widespread tertiary genera with living representatives alike in North America and eastern Asia. The suggestion is that it was once distributed throughout much of Europe, but except in the Balkan region was exterminated during the Ice Age, and from that area spread, in post-glacial times and to a limited extent, to the west. Cypress, native in the east but 'sub-spontaneous' only in the west, is another example of the same re-colonizing process.

The Swiss Alps occupy as it were an intermediate position between the conditions in the extreme west of Europe and those in the southeast. Thus they have more forest-forming conifers than the Highlands of Scotland, e.g. common spruce, silver fir, larch, and Arolla pine are added to the Scots pine, but some of the forms present in the Eastern and Dinaric Alps are absent.

The first point, then, about the woodlands in our area is that their relative poverty of species has been in all probability a factor in diminishing their density and extent, even apart from man's influence. The basis of this assertion is that every species of plant has a certain limit of range, thriving best under a particular set of conditions, while the size of the individuals and the capacity for effective reproduction alike diminish as these conditions alter. Within a given area, therefore, the smaller the number of species the more likelihood there is that certain sites will be unoccupied or contain only scattered and stunted specimens, reproducing themselves with difficulty. The Arolla pine in the Swiss Alps is an interesting example of a form which has not only a limited distribution there, but seems barely able to maintain its hold. One of the factors is the edibility of the large, plump seeds, relished by man as well as by bird and beast. Not only is there likely to be a greater loss of seed than in the case of conifers which have small, wind-borne seeds, but the latter appear to have a greater chance of distribution to suitable sites in a mountain area where these are limited and discontinuous. Widely distributed in northern Asia, the Arolla pine appears to be an example of a form which extended its range in the post-glacial period but is imperfectly adapted to present conditions in western Europe. Thus, though in this case spread was from the east and north-east instead of from the south-east, it appears, like the Judas-tree, to suggest that when man within the area acquired the power of purposefully modifying his environment he found himself confronted with a plant cover already in a state of flux, of disturbed equilibrium.

Of that disturbed equilibrium he took full advantage, and throughout the period of which we have any detailed knowledge of his activities he has been engaged in modifying, and mainly destroying, the woodlands, both directly and indirectly. The result is that the statement with which we began that the lands we are discussing are mainly ecologically woodland has to be modified by saying that at the present time the areas which by any extension of the term can be called forested are limited, while productive forests in the forester's sense are more limited still.

In a broad and general sense the woodlands fall into three groups —the evergreen woods of the Mediterranean lowlands; the deciduous forests (including oaks, beech in parts of the area, sweet chestnut, etc.) of the cooler and damper areas; the mountain forests, mainly coniferous. Mediterranean man's attack upon the first has been continuous and direct; or, it would be more accurate to say, he has sought continuously to replace the varied species present by a few of direct use to him. The olive groves, whether or not it be true that their trees are derived directly from the wild olivaster, indicate the nature of the replacing process. 'Grove', it may be noted, is a somewhat inadequate term, for where the olive really thrives it forms literally forests, extending over wide extents of ground. Again, the fact that dense scrub or maquis rather than high forest covers much of the unoccupied parts of the low grounds is due in part to such causes as that man has striven to extend his groves to their utmost limit, so that some of the maquis areas represent lands which have fallen out of cultivation; that his demands for wood for fuel and constructional purposes, especially boat-building, have been continuous; that while soil formation processes are slow, denudation, owing to the nature of the rainfall, is rapid, and the strong local winds also help to carry away soils laid bare artificially.

To such causes must be added the fact that the goat, the stock animal best fitted to Mediterranean conditions, is the great forest-destroyer. It nibbles bushes and the lower branches of trees as well as tree seedlings, and, being more sensitive to cold and damp and less intolerant of heat than the domesticated sheep, which has had its coat thickened by artificial selection, it is well adapted to the Mediterranean type of climate. Further, since it is not purely a grass-eater, it makes no demands on lands capable of yielding food for man, a very important point where these are so limited as they are in the Mediterranean area generally. Owing to its agility also, much greater than that of sheep or cattle, it can browse on steep slopes, and find food of a sort on those limestone crags where the dense maquis thins out to the garigue, characterized by scattered, often spiny and aromatic, stunted shrubs and under-shrubs. But, where numerous, goats may prevent completely any natural re-generation of forest, and their effect is cumulative. Where high forest is destroyed by natural decay, storms, landslips, fire or felling, and goats are allowed to pasture on the cleared area, natural re-growth is rendered impossible and the forest soil may be subjected to such wastage that artificial reconstruction becomes impossible.

The deciduous forests have not fared much better than the ever-green ones. Where they occurred on the lower and more level grounds the tendency, as in Europe generally, has been to clear the land for the cultivation of cereal and similar crops. The slopes, where the conditions exclude the olive, will carry the less tender fruit-bearing trees and shrubs, such as vines, figs, peaches, almonds, walnuts, cherries, and so on, with the mulberry for silkworm-rearing. The fact that the Spanish or sweet chestnut yields an important article of food has helped to preserve natural woods of that tree.

Conditions are somewhat different in the zone of mountain forests, for their constituent conifers, which ascend to the tree limit, cannot be replaced by trees yielding food-products. But particularly in the Swiss Alps the cultivation of herbaceous crops, mainly cereals, has been pushed to its extreme limit, which is often astonishingly high. Thus above Zermatt, in lat. 46°, cereals are grown up to a height of 6,800 ft. Generally in the mountain areas there is a great tempta-tion to clear the sunnier slopes, especially where these are moderate and not exposed to excessive erosion, in order to grow food for man. It is thus common to find forests limited to the steep and shady sides of the valleys. But within even wider limits clearing has been practised to extend pasturages. True mountain pastures or alps lie in theory above the tree limit, and are available for only a short period of the year. But grass and other fodder plants grow freely at lower levels if not killed out by the shading and competition of trees, and there their growing period is longer; the dwarfing so characteristic of the plants of the true alps is absent. In many areas, therefore, forests have been deliberately cleared to extend these lower pastures, which will yield a hay crop in addition to an early and late growth which can be consumed on the spot by the stock animals on their way up to and down from the high alps. In parts of the mountain chains, notably in the French Alps and the Pyrenees, this clearing has been carried to a disastrous extent. Even where, as in Switzerland, the dangers of reckless deforestation have been realized and conservation and afforestation practised, much wastage has taken place.

Summing up, then, we find that in the Mediterranean lowlands high forest, if it formerly existed on an extensive scale, has been largely destroyed, and the characteristic associations are the dense scrubs of the maquis type, with evergreen shrubs and under-shrubs, often thorny, with reduced and well-protected leaves. On unfavourable sites, especially where limestones are exposed, the formation becomes open, bare rock being exposed between the stunted shrubs. Locally patches of high forest occur, as of the Aleppo, the stone and the maritime pines, or of evergreen oaks, and plantations of exotic trees, notably Australian eucalyptus, have been made. Many of the ornamental trees are also exotic, introduced from North America, eastern Asia, and elsewhere. Fruit-trees of many types, including olives, citrus, carobs, and many others are widespread.

Where winters are cool or cold and summer drought is not marked, deciduous or mixed forests may persist, but there also clearing has been widespread. The coniferous mountain forests have been on the whole less modified than the other types, and form the main timber reserve, though the supply of timber is generally insufficient for even local needs.

One other point may be noted. It is characteristic generally of the lower grounds within the area of Mediterranean climate that certain introduced species, particularly prickly pear (cactus) and agave from North America, and South African forms, such as the fleshy mesembryanthemums, are abundant and tend to occupy waste ground. In the more frequented parts such aliens may appear more conspicuous than the native maquis plants, and they are almost always represented in illustrations of Mediterranean scenery. Their presence is interesting on many counts, not least because the phenomenon is comparatively rare north of the Alps, where alien cannot as a rule compete with native 'weeds'. In the European Mediterranean countries, again, it is as a rule less marked than in the trans-Mediterranean Lands, and much less so than for example in Australia and New Zealand, where introduced species are often veritable pests.

From one point of view this spread of exotics may be regarded as a consequence of the relative isolation of the areas of Mediterranean climate, owing to the mountain girdle which acts as a barrier to migration, while the limited size of the tracts with the typical climate must act as a check to the evolution of adapted endemic forms. From another standpoint it emphasizes once again the great contrasts between the Mediterranean climate and those of most other parts of Europe. In all the extra-Mediterranean western part, at least, the rainfall alike in distribution and amount is equally favourable to trees and herbs, so that forest destruction extends grassland or ploughland. Within the area of accentuated Mediterranean climate the activity of water-demanding herbaceous plants is limited to the cooler and damper seasons of the year, and they must necessarily rest as seeds or underground parts during the dry, hot period. Thus destruction of forest does not extend grassland, but rather brush or scrub, and also leaves spaces which can be occupied by aliens adapted to dry and warm climates. The absence of low-level natural meadow-land, and the limitation of herbaceous crops to a part of the year or to irrigated tracts, are the essential features of the area from the human standpoint.

LAND UTILIZATION

It is an inevitable consequence of these facts that the agriculture of the Mediterranean countries is strikingly different from that of the rest of Europe, while the presence of mountains and plateaux within them or on their margins introduces a contrasting note.

With the characteristic prolongation of the productive period till it may cover nearly the whole year is associated a concentration in space, the same area yielding both short- and long-season crops. Because of the relative flatness of the temperature curve and the height at which it starts, the corresponding curve of human activity shows minor undulations rather than peaks of activity. In consequence of this spread of activity in time neither labour-saving methods nor the seasonal importation of labourers are essential; Mediterranean man still depends mainly on his own muscles. This in its turn means that with the absence of numerous large stock animals and of complicated modern machines little land need be sterilized for farm-buildings, and the typical settlement is the large village rather than the isolated homestead. But the limited amount of live stock (apart from the goat), itself conditioned by the small amount of low-level pasture, means that natural fertilizers in the form of farmyard manure are difficult to obtain. Fallowing therefore is often resorted to, and the fallowed lands, like the undrained and infertile tracts incapable of cultivation, yield some pasture during the cooler season, though heat, drought, and insect pests make them generally unsuited to stock in summer. Then, however, the mountain pastures are green and fresh. Here, then, we come to those vertical migratory movements of stock, the transhumance of the French geographers, characteristic generally of areas of accentuated relief, but occurring within the Mediterranean zone and on its margins in varied and peculiar forms.

Most interesting because most primitive are the conditions in the Balkan peninsula, though the frontiers and the denser settlement of, e.g., Greek Macedonia, have produced great changes. Here the migratory herdsmen are often Vlachs, differing in racial breed from the cultivators; the movements are on a great scale, from coastal low grounds to interior mountains; and involve whole communities, not herdsmen alone. Necessarily at least two sets of settlements, the summer and winter villages, must be present. Such movements are possible only where the area concerned is not densely settled, for the animals must feed on the march; where international frontiers are absent; and where also local administration is not highly developed and the animals themselves belong to unspecialized breeds. The two last conditions are very important, for the more specialized the breed the more sensitive it is as a rule to disease, and the more essential it is that local authorities should have the power and the will to control movement and enforce sanitary regulations. The persistence down to our own day of these large-scale movements in the Balkan peninsula is one of the results of the Turkish invasion, and with the virtual disappearance of the Turk from Europe it must undergo great modifications. Sheep constitute a large proportion of the stock animals.

It is not then to be expected that in Mediterranean Europe outside that peninsula this type of movement should exist, but the problem of making the best use of the upland pastures is one that is far from easy to solve. It is particularly difficult in Spain, where, for the climatic reasons already described, much of the plateau yields spring and autumn but not summer or winter pasturage, while summer grazing may be found on the higher mountains, as in the Pyrenees, and winter pastures on the low grounds. In Spain also the antagonism between the migratory shepherd and the settled cultivator has been till recently acute. The problem is difficult also in southern France, though there the railway is now often used to carry the flocks from the winter pastures on the deltaic lowlands of the Rhone to the summer pastures in the mountains. This use of railways for stock movements is also now increasing in Spain. In the North Italian plains, where climate and relief give large tracts of meadow-land, and where also irrigation can be carried on, the problem hardly presents itself. There several crops of hay can be harvested on the low ground for winter fodder while the animals are absent in the mountains. The abundance of rich fodder means also a predominance of dairy cattle as against sheep.

In the Swiss Alps generally the movements are of the simple type common to mountain regions, and equally developed in Norway; that is, the richer grass of the valleys and lower grounds is largely made into hay to be used for stall-feeding in winter, while the herbage of the high pastures is consumed on the spot in summer. Cattle predominate over sheep. But in the canton Valais, where the main (Rhone) valley has a peculiarly warm and dry climate for the latitude and elevation, a highly complex type of movement, very delicately adjusted to local conditions, has been evolved. This has been studied especially in the Val d'Anniviers (cf. references on p. 71). Its most interesting features are that the herdsmen combine a somewhat elaborate agriculture with stock-rearing, especially of cattle, though a vertical distance of over 3,700 ft. may separate the lowest cultivated lands from the highest alps.

Since the Rhone valley at Sierre (about 1,900 ft. at the opening of the Val d'Anniviers) is warm enough for the vine and autumn-sown wheat and rye, while spring-sown crops of rye and barley will ripen generally up to 5,400 ft., the conditions in the Zermatt area farther east (p. 66) being quite exceptional, and beans, potatoes, and other hardy crops mature some thousand feet farther up, we have the Mediterranean feature of a prolonged harvesting period. The low-level cereals may ripen at the end of June; July–September are the harvest months at the upper levels, and the vintage in the Rhone valley occurs in October. There is also a certain resemblance to Balkan conditions in that more than one true village (as compared with mere shelters used for cheese-making) is necessary, and that the movements involve the whole community with the most important possessions of its members. But settlements here are multiple, not merely dual. In the Val d'Anniviers the chief village of each group stands on a sunny slope at a height of from 4,000 ft. upwards; there are others, or another, in the spring pasture region, one in the main valley in the region of vineyards, in addition to the high huts, often at two or three levels, used only by the herdsmen for a few weeks in summer. Further the movements are very complex, not merely the upward movement in summer and the downward one in autumn common elsewhere. Thus after the autumn vintage the whole community travels upwards to the *mayens*, or spring pastures, where the hay which was stored in summer while the cows were up on the high alps is consumed; a downward movement occurs in early spring back to the Rhone valley to tend the vines, followed by a return to the chief village to sow crops there, and so on.

The whole system may be compared roughly to a Mediterranean farm pulled out vertically, as it were, so that thousands of feet may separate the three constituent elements of fruit-tree, short-season crops and live stock, for goats and pigs accompany the herds of cattle to the high alps in summer. The essential difference is that here it is the live stock that are counted on to yield a surplus for sale after the needs of the cultivator are satisfied, while in Mediterranean farming, with infrequent exceptions, it is some form of woody plant which gives the marketable product (olives, olive oil, wine, fruit of many kinds, cork, silk dependent on the mulberry-tree, and so on). It is important also to bear in mind that within the area of typical Mediterranean climate, cattle, and especially dairy cattle of specialized breeds, are relatively infrequent, since they demand abundant water, rich fodder, and are very susceptible to insect attack. Sheep and goats, asses and mules rather than highly-bred horses, with some buffaloes (especially in parts of Italy) constitute the chief forms of live stock.

REFERENCES

CLIMATE

See Supan and Philippson, op. cit., and such general works as De Martonne, *Traité de Géographie Physique* (Paris, 1924); also the following:
J. Hann, *Handbuch d. Klimatologie* (Stuttgart, 3rd edition, 1908); 4th edition by R. Süring (Leipzig, 1926).
A. Hettner, *Die Klimate d. Erde* (Leipzig, 1930).
W. G. Kendrew, *The Climates of the Continents* (Oxford, 1922), and *Climate* (Oxford, 1938).
A. Austin Miller, *Climatology* (London, 1931, 1938, and 1944).
A. Stevens, 'The New Outlook in Meteorology and its Geographical Bearings', in *Scottish Geographical Magazine*, XLIII, 1927, p. 218.

NATURAL VEGETATION AND CULTIVATED CROPS

Most of the larger works on physical geography (Supan, De Martonne, etc.) give some account of plant associations. See also Philippson, op. cit., and the author's *Frequented Ways* (London, 1922) and *The Mediterranean Lands* (London, 1924); also E. C. Semple, *The Geography of the Mediterranean Region* (New York, 1931).
Apart from general discussions of cultivated crops, etc., J. Brunhes, *La Géographie Humaine* (Paris, 1910, available also in a not wholly satisfactory English translation), gives a detailed account of the conditions in the Val d'Anniviers; these are also described in a pamphlet by J. Jegerlehner, *Das Val d'Anniviers* (Berne, 1904).

The olive has been the subject of various detailed studies: cf. Fischer, 'Der Oelbaum', in *Petermann's Ergänzungsheft*, 147 (Gotha, 1904); but a more recent article by A. R. Toniolo, 'La Distribuzione dell' olivo e l'estensione d. provincia climatica mediterranea n. Veneto Occidentale', in *Rivista Geografica Italiana*, January–April, 1914, may be mentioned, especially for its detailed study of conditions on the Lake of Garda.

For the natural vegetation of the Swiss Alps, H. Christ's *Das Pflanzen-leben d. Schweiz* (Zurich, 1882), is valuable, especially for its maps, but of course long antedates modern developments of ecological botany; see also the present author's article on 'The Swiss Valais' in the *Scottish Geographical Magazine*, XXIV, 1907. W. B. Turrill's *The Plant Life of the Balkan Peninsula* (Oxford, 1929) is invaluable, but not easy reading.

The great series of monographs published by Engler u. Drude under the general title of *Die Vegetation d. Erde* contains volumes dealing with parts of the area; note especially M. Willkomm, *Grundzüge d. Pflanzenver-breitung a. d. Iberischen Halbinsel* (Leipzig, 1896). A pamphlet entitled *Excursions Botaniques en Espagne et au Portugal* by R. Chodat (Geneva, 1909) gives a number of details in regard to Iberian plants.

MEDITERRANEAN LIFE AND PROBLEMS

Life of peoples in the Mediterranean is well described in Charles Parrain, *La Méditerranée—Les Hommes et leurs travaux*, 8ᵉ édition, 1936. Excellent general studies are W. G. East, 'The Mediterranean Problem', in *Geographical Review*, 1938, p. 83, and his concise study, *Mediterranean Problems*, 1940. A classic is A. Siegfried, *Vue Générale de la Méditerranée*, 15ᵉ édition, 1943, and others are the two parts of Vol. 7 of the *Géographie Universelle* series, 'Méditerranée—Peninsules Méditerranéennes'. The historical side is treated by J. Holland Rose in *The Mediterranean in the Ancient World*, 1933.

PART II
SWITZERLAND AND THE SWISS ALPS

CHAPTER IV

COMPOSITION, BOUNDARIES, AND RELIEF OF SWITZERLAND

The Swiss Confederation—Relation of Boundaries to Relief Elements—Divisions of Swiss Alps—Route Lines of the Western High Alps—The Eastern Alps in Grisons

THE SWISS CONFEDERATION

FROM various points of view Switzerland is a land of anomalies. Parts of its surface are probably personally familiar to more English-speaking people than almost any other area in continental Europe, and Englishmen have played an important part alike in exploring its mountains and in investigating some of their problems. Of the innumerable English books and papers dealing with the country, also, not a few are of high and permanent value, and there are many English mountaineers, geologists, and botanists who have a singularly detailed knowledge of those aspects of the country which appeal to them particularly. Yet few European countries are so sketchily treated in the average English geographical text-book, and ignorance of it as a whole is widespread both among students of geography and the educated public. Even the post-war tendency to idealize it on the ground that its inhabitants have solved some of those nationality problems which seem so insoluble elsewhere has not as a rule led to a serious study of the actual conditions.

Part of the reason why the country is known to many in certain aspects but arouses little interest as a whole, and has been studied rather by the devotees of particular sciences than by the geographer, is clear enough. Switzerland undoubtedly has lost something by its very success in bringing together in a loose confederation peoples diverse in speech, in religion, in sympathies, in modes of life, in economic relations. For the foreigner at least it is difficult to perceive any distinctively Swiss attitude towards life, and he gets an impression of an admirably-run piece of mechanism rather than of an organic whole. Again, small as is the country, the total area (15,940 sq. miles) approximating to twice that of Wales, it is extremely complex; has not, despite the common belief to the contrary, easily grasped and purely 'natural' boundaries; cannot, except

73

in the roughest fashion, be divided into satisfactory natural regions, and generally tends to escape from any simple framework on which a brief description might be based. It is not unnatural, then, that geographers should tend to evade a task at once arduous and not apparently rewarding, and seek an escape in generalization, combined with an excursion along one of those side-avenues which present themselves so abundantly in a land still undergoing severe glaciation, and having but recently emerged from a period of greater glaciation.

The absence of unity which represents part of the price Switzerland has paid for its success in establishing what is in essence a non-national though eminently stable state, may be illustrated by some notes on the constituent parts. The territory is divided into twenty-five virtually independent cantons, of which Grisons (Graubünden), the largest, has a smaller area than the West Riding of Yorkshire; while the least, formed by the town of Basel, extends over only 14 sq. miles. How little basis has the common belief that the country is almost entirely peopled by scattered mountain folk is indicated by the fact that in the year 1941 over 18 per cent of the total population of over 4,300,000 lived within the four large towns. Of these the three largest—Zurich, Basel, and Geneva—are peripheral, the last two practically on the frontier, while only Berne, the fourth, is well within the country. In the same year over 28 per cent of the total population lived in the fourteen towns of over 20,000 inhabitants, and of these towns all, save Basel and Chaux-de-Fonds, are placed on, or on the borders of, the Plateau, which extends from the Lake of Constance to that of Geneva (Fig. 21). The most densely peopled cantons, also, apart from that formed by the town of Basel, are Geneva and Zurich, which are separated from one another by the whole breadth of the country, no less than by a difference of speech and outlook. If in theory and to a large extent in practice all educated people speak at least two of the four officially recognized languages, yet the mother-tongue must necessarily serve as the main instrument of culture, and tend to turn intellectual life towards the adjacent great power which shares the language.

Nor is unity any more obvious in the case of the thinly-peopled and mountainous cantons. The three with the lowest density are Grisons, Uri, and Valais, and they do form a continuous strip of territory from the Austro-Italian frontier in the north-east to the Franco-Italian one in the south-west. This belt includes but 7 per cent of the total population in an area forming 32 per cent of the total surface, and is characterized by a general absence of large towns, Chur, with 17,000, being the largest. But within this tract the areas chiefly settled are the river-valleys, the Upper Rhine, and to a less extent the Upper Inn in Grisons, the Upper Reuss in Uri,

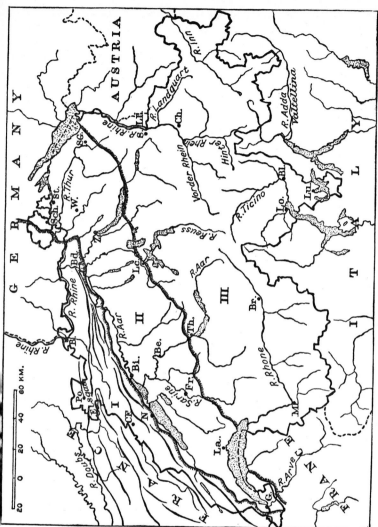

I. The Jura. II. The Plateau. III. The Alps. Po. = Porrentruy; B. = Basel; Bd. = Baden; Sch. = Schaffhausen; St. = Stein; W. = Winterthur; SG. = St. Gallen; S. = Sargans; Ch. = Chur; Bl. = Bellinzona; Bi. = Biel; Fr. = Fribourg; N. = Neuchâtel; Lu. = Lugano; Lo. = Locarno; Br. = Brig; M. = Martigny; La. = Lausanne; G. = Geneva; CF. = Chaux-de-Fonds; Be. = Berne; Th. = Thun; Lc. = Lucerne; Z. = Zurich.

LI. is the principality of Liechtenstein.

The stippled line shows the boundary between the regions; the black line the Swiss frontier; the broken lines the frontiers of adjacent countries.

FIG. 21. THE FRONTIERS AND NATURAL DIVISIONS OF SWITZERLAND

and the Alpine Rhone and its tributaries in Valais, and intercommunication between them is not easy. Valais shows the peculiar
feature of a change of language midway, French, roughly speaking
(Fig. 22), being spoken to the west of the town of Sierre and German
to the east. Within Grisons, German, Romansch, and Italian are
all spoken, the Romansch area being extensive. Further, there are
villages in southern Grisons which in winter can only communicate
with difficulty with the rest of the country, the easiest route lying
through Italian territory. This is likewise at least partially true of
some villages in Valais on the south side of the Simplon pass.

Under such conditions, and especially when we add that the
accretion of elements went on from 1291 to 1815, a Swiss atmo-
sphere and a common tradition can scarcely be expected. Yet it
would be unjust to regard the country as merely the great *carrefour*
of Europe, for love of the mountains and of liberty, closely linked in
the consciousness of the people, does serve as a unifying influence.
If it is untrue to say that the Swiss are mainly hardy mountain
peasants, wringing a spare livelihood from the reluctant soil, it is
yet true that the mountains, with their pure air, their glistening
snows, and their brilliant flowers, are never far below the horizon
even of the townsfolk.

RELATION OF BOUNDARIES TO THE RELIEF ELEMENTS

Our study of the Alps has already made clear that three great
elements—the Jura, the Plateau, and the Alps in the limited sense
—are represented within Switzerland (Fig. 21). But it remains to
emphasize the fact that all three transcend the national frontiers.
This is least true of the Plateau, though even it must be regarded as
beginning well within France, in the vicinity of Chambéry or
Aix-les-Bains, where the syncline dies out with the approach of the
Jura to the Alps, and as extending beyond the national frontier in
the north-east. The frontier crosses the lakes both of Constance and
Geneva, which thus form the north-east and south-west borders of
the Swiss Plateau; yet in detail its course is complex. Thus the town
of Constance, though on the south side of its lake, is German, while
that of Geneva, with the surrounding cantonal territory, extends
round the south-western end of its lake. The lake frontiers of
Switzerland, which include those crossing Maggiore and Lugano,
are indeed particularly interesting. It should be noted that the
waters of the Lake of Geneva form part of the frontier with France
(Savoy), those of Constance with Germany and Austria.

The frontier shows no simple relation to the Folded Jura, the
second main tectonic element. In the south-west it runs for a short
distance along the inner base of the mountains, leaving them wholly

within France. But to the north, from Basel eastwards, the Folded Jura lie wholly within Switzerland, the Lägern, which forms the terminal point, lying immediately to the east of the town of Baden, on the River Limmat (the effluent of the Lake of Zurich) before it joins the Aar. In the intervening area the frontier, though not a crest one, runs lengthways to the chain, so that here the Folded Jura

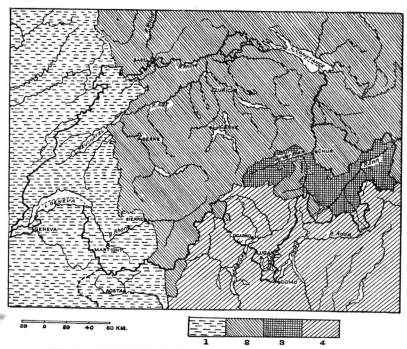

FIG. 22. DISTRIBUTION OF LANGUAGES IN SWITZERLAND AND THE NEIGHBOURING COUNTRIES

1. French. 2. German. 3. Romansch. 4. Italian.

The frontier of Switzerland is shown by a thick black line, those of the adjacent countries by broken lines. Note the extension of German and French over the Italian frontier, the limited extension of Italian in Switzerland (canton Ticino), and the change from French to German near the small town of Sierre in the canton Valais.

are partly French and partly Swiss, and no marked differences in occupations, relief, or scenery distinguishes the two sides.

In the north conditions are complicated by the presence of the Table or Plateau Jura, and the relation of the frontier to this belt of unfolded jurassic limestones. The latter is wide in Germany (Swabia) and in France (Franche Comté), but is narrowed in the intervening area by the crystalline massif of the Black Forest. As will be shown later the Rhine, from its exit from the Lake of Constance to Basel, has a somewhat complicated course in relation to the underlying rocks, but the immediate point is that the frontier here is not, as one is apt to assume, purely a riverine one. It is in point of fact highly complicated, and in four areas there is a northern bend of the line which brings both banks, with a varying amount of land to the north of the river, within Swiss territory. These four are the region north of the little town of Stein, that which almost encircles Schaffhausen, the Rafzerfeld north of Eglisau, and that round Basel. Further, in the whole belt from the Lake of Constance to Basel, the railway network is dense, especially on the Swiss side, and the river can be bridged without difficulty, so that intercommunication is easy between northern Switzerland and Germany. Downstream from Basel the Rhine is navigable, while at the eastern end the Lake of Constance is available for steamer traffic between Swiss and German ports, the Austrian part of the shore being relatively unimportant. The whole belt is traversed by important international railway routes, of which the most important are those leading to the St. Gothard and Arlberg tunnels. The former enables south-western Germany and western Europe generally to communicate with Milan, Genoa, and thus with the Mediterranean shore; the latter leads to Vienna and the east.

West of Basel conditions are different. Here again the frontier extends into the Table Jura, particularly in the curious 'enclave' of Ajoie (Elsgau) with the town of Porrentruy (Ger., Pruntrut), separated from the Folded Jura by the ridge of Mont Terrible, and traversed by an important line of rail connecting to Paris via Belfort. Other causes which seem to facilitate international relations here are that, considerably to the west of Basel (Fig. 22), the German language gives way to French, while the Catholic element in the population increases. But this region is separated from the densely-peopled parts of Switzerland by the whole width of the Folded Jura, at once offering great obstacles to communication on account of the nature of the valleys, and unfavourable to close settlement. The French side of the frontier is also somewhat thinly peopled and relatively remote from the industrialized areas of that country.

Most complicated of all is the frontier in the region of the High Alps. The details are best studied in connexion with the tectonic elements of which these are made up, but meantime it may be noted that it bears no simple relation to the relief. Far from being always a crest frontier, it includes lacustrine, riverine (Rhine from the Lake of Constance to Sargans) and valley sections. It leaves many of the more important passes, such as the St. Gothard, the Simplon, the Bernina, the Maloja, and the San Bernadino, wholly within Swiss territory, which extends also a greater or less distance down the hither side of the range crossed by the pass. The Great St. Bernard and the Splügen are among the few major passes where the boundary posts stand where one would theoretically expect them, that is, at the summit level.

Further, within the country the great stretch of high land known as the Bernese Oberland constitutes a barrier between the two cantons of Berne and Valais in some ways more formidable than that which separates Valais from (Italian) Piedmont. Within canton Grisons, again, the sections which drain to the River Adda have difficult connexion with the two main drainage systems of the canton, that is with the Upper Inn and the Hinter Rhein. The run of the frontier also is such that in addition to the long Italian portion there are shorter French and Austrian ones, apart from that which abuts on the small principality of Liechtenstein.

It is thus clear that Switzerland has frontier problems enough. Even when the frontier is a crest one, however, it presents little difficulty to the Swiss peasant, to whom mountain climbing is part of his daily work, and is thus not a barrier.

DIVISIONS OF THE SWISS ALPS

Any general survey of the alpine area of Switzerland must be based upon a recognition of the tectonic elements represented, as they have been broadly described in Chapter II. The first point is to note that the national territory transgresses the division line between the Eastern and the Western Alps, so that a part of the former are Swiss. So far the limit between the two has been taken generally as the Rhine–Chur–Lake-of-Como line, which has the advantage that it can be followed readily on an atlas map. But it is obvious that if the Rhine valley affords a guide from the Lake of Constance to Chur, no similar, single topographical feature exists in the more southerly section. Geologically, the limit there can be traced from the head of Como Lake to the Piz Tremoggia in the Bernina group, and then by the Maloja and Septimer passes (Fig. 23) to the valley of the Oberhalbstein, down this to Tiefencastel, and then directly by the Lenzerheide to Chur. But though the Septimer was used by the Romans as a direct alpine crossing, it has been functionally replaced by the Splügen. It is therefore more convenient for the geographer to take the limit between the Western and Eastern Alps as following the route over this pass. That is, from Chur the Rhine is ascended to the confluence of the Vorder and Hinter Rhein at the village of Reichenau; the road there turns south along the latter past Thusis; leaves the valley at the village of Splügen; crosses the pass and descends by the Liro valley till this unites with the Maira at Chiavenna, past which the latter river flows direct to the Lake of Como. According to this definition the Alpine area of Switzerland falls mainly within the Western Alps, that is, within the area where the surface rocks have been largely stripped off to expose the deeper layers beneath. Only the mountains of the eastern part of canton Grisons are included in the Eastern Alps, where the tectonic elements exposed in the Western Alps can but be dimly perceived through the 'windows' in the mainly intact surface cover.

We have next to turn to the subdivisions of the Western Alps as already described (p. 36). Of these the Prealps are partly in Switzerland and partly in Savoy. As Fig. 12 shows, they are divided into two unequal parts by the Rhone and the eastern end of the Lake of Geneva, the two being called respectively the Romandes Prealps (Fribourg Alps) and the Chablais. Since the frontier runs broadly parallel to the Rhone from the elbow at Martigny to the lake, though at some distance to the south-west (Fig. 21), the Chablais Prealps lie almost wholly within Savoy, while the Romandes Prealps form the zone of hill pastures (note Gruyères, in the Sarine valley, which gives its name to the cheese) between the Swiss Plateau and the High Calcareous Alps.

Leaving for a moment the High Calcareous Alps, we may go on to speak of the Crystalline Massifs (Fig. 12), of which two, the Mont Blanc—Aiguilles Rouges and the Aar—St. Gothard blocks, are included within Switzerland, the latter wholly, the former but in part. That the Aar—St. Gothard Massif is entirely within Switzerland is very important in view of the part which the St. Gothard section plays alike as a nodal point of routes and as a section of the main watershed of Europe, the Rhine, Rhone, Ticino (Po) divide. Conditions in regard to the Mont Blanc—Aiguilles Rouges Massif are more complex. The two are separated by the Chamonix valley (vale of Chamonix), which, as will be seen later, is continued as a structural element over the Swiss frontier at the Col de Balme towards the Rhone near Martigny. The run of the frontier is such that the peak of Mont Blanc is wholly outside Switzerland, but a part of the massif, as well as a small portion of the Aiguilles Rouges one, lies within the country. The latter has no great effect on relief, but the prolongation of the Mont Blanc crystalline block into Switzerland is responsible for the presence there of a small area of glaciers (including the Orny and Saleinaz glaciers) and snow-fields, continuous with the Aiguilles of Argentière. The area is accessible from the Swiss side from the little resort of Champex, placed on a small lake (Fig. 26) above the road to the Great St. Bernard pass.

More important, however, than these frontier details is the tectonic effect of the Mont Blanc—Aiguilles Rouges and Aar—St. Gothard Massifs as expressed in the characters and direction of the High Calcareous Alps. Both massifs represent parts of the

Hercynian basement platform brought to the surface and broken into slices and wedges as the result of the tremendous pressure of the thrust from the south. Both had formerly a cover of younger, sedimentary rocks, small parts of which, as we shall see later, remain in narrow strips. But while the Hercynian basement rocks offered enormous resistance to the folding forces, snapping rather than crumpling, the greater part of their more pliable sedimentary cover yielded to the push, and was overthrust to form the great nappes of

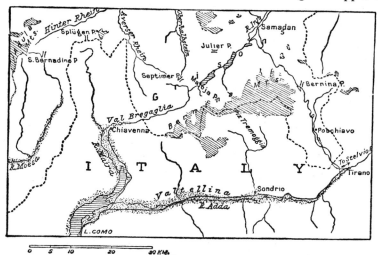

FIG. 23. THE FRONTIER BETWEEN ITALY AND CANTON GRISONS

The dotted areas are below 600 ft., and within the area shown bear vegetation of southern type. The shaded areas are the parts of the mountains covered with permanent snow or ice. Note that while to the east Swiss territory extends over the Bernina pass and down the Poschiavo valley to within a short distance of the R. Adda at Tirano, farther west it crosses the Maira valley (Val Bregaglia), and then rises to the water-parting in the region of the Splügen pass.

the High Calcareous Alps, which build up the great chain in front of the massifs.

The resistance or damming effect was greatest in the region of the Aar—St. Gothard Massif, where the great peak of the Finsteraarhorn (4,275 m.) has been carved out of the Hercynian granites of the Aar Massif. It was least in the gap between that massif and the Mont Blanc—Aiguilles Rouges one. Bearing in mind this conception of the High Calcareous Alps as originating by the pushing of the softer rocks over the top of the uplifted Hercynian wall, we arrive at an intelligible explanation of their arrangement.

They extend from Savoy in a north-easterly direction, dying away

7

in the triangle between the Lake of Constance and the south–north section of the Rhine. But in Savoy they are relatively insignificant, Mont Buet, the highest peak (3,109 m.), being as it were the equivalent of the Swiss outpost of the Säntis (2,500 m.) in the north-east. The Swiss series begins with the Tour Sallières and the Dents du Midi, separated from the Dents de Morcles by the Rhone gorge (gorge of St. Maurice). The highest of this group, the Dents du Midi, does not attain 3,300 m. Then comes a widely-spaced group, in the gap between the two massifs, consisting of the Diablerets, the Wildhorn, and the Wildstrubel, all again below 3,300 m. We are now approaching the region where the influence of the Aar—St. Gothard Massif is felt alike in the height of the individual peaks, and in the continuity of the high ground. The Balmhorn (3,712 m.) is separated from the snowclad giants of the Oberland only by the narrow Gasterntal. The Oberland peaks rise in the Jungfrau and Mönch to well over 4,000 m., and, till the narrow Haslital (River Aar) is reached, offer a continuous obstacle to cross-traffic, for all the passes are glacier ones; that is, do not permit the construction of a permanent track. This difficulty of crossing is accentuated by the fact that the peaks carved out of the Aar Massif, such as the Finsteraarhorn and the Aletschhorn, are not separated by any definite valley furrow from the High Calcareous Alps, the two being, as it were, plastered against each other.

Beyond the Haslital the peaks of the High Calcareous Alps again stand well apart from each other, and the height diminishes. Thus of the sequence Titlis, Tödi, Glärnisch, Kurfirsten, Säntis, only the Tödi reaches 3,600 m.

The next tectonic element represented in the Western Alps of Switzerland forms a part of the Axial Crystalline Belt (p. 36), here constituted by the Pennine nappes, which build up the Pennine Alps of canton Valais, no less than their lower continuations in Ticino and western Grisons. The Pennine Alps extend from the Great St. Bernard pass to the Simplon, and reach their greatest development, alike in the height of the peaks (Monte Rosa, Matterhorn, Mischabel, Weisshorn, all over 4,500 m., or 14,760 ft.), the continuity of the elevated area, and the extent of the snow-fields and glaciers, in the gap between the two great Hercynian massifs. That is, slightly to the south-west of that other great elevated area formed by the giants of the High Calcareous Alps and the peaks of the Aar Massif, lies the most important part of the Pennine Alps, with a similar magnificence of Alpine scenery and a corresponding multiplicity of high resorts (Saas, Zermatt, Zinal, Arolla, etc.).

Westwards, the chain diminishes in height and breadth as the Mont Blanc Massif is approached. North-eastwards it tails off similarly where the St. Gothard Massif seems to have blocked the advancing nappes. The Adula group (Rheinwaldhorn, 3,400 m.), and the still lower peaks (Tambo and Surettahorn) in the neighbourhood of the Splügen pass, may be said to mark its eastern limits.

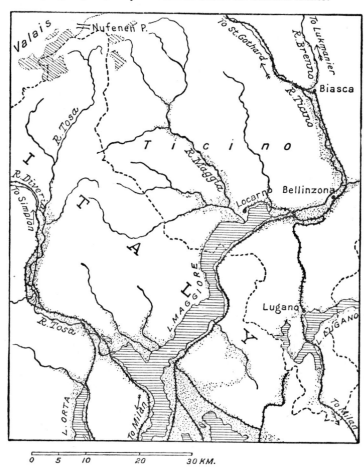

FIG. 24. THE FRONTIER BETWEEN ITALY AND CANTON TICINO

The stippling has the same significance as in Fig. 23. Note that while to the north-west (where a small part of canton Valais is shown) the frontier is a crest one, thereafter it bends far to the south, so that parts of Lakes Maggiore and Lugano, with considerable tracts of lowland in the river valleys, are included in Switzerland. The whole of the power resources of the Ticino, till its entrance into Lake Maggiore, are also Swiss.

From the Great St. Bernard to the neighbourhood of the Simplon the frontier is a crest one, leaving the largest snow-fields and glaciers on the more gently sloping Swiss side. To the east of Monte Rosa

the frontier turns northward, but is still a crest frontier till it
approaches the Simplon region, where it bends eastward, leaving
the Weissmies and a considerable part of the Diveria tributary of
the Tosa (Toce) within Switzerland (Fig. 24). Thereafter, in
harmony with the north-easterly trend of the chain, it swings far to
the north, so that the head-waters of the Tosa are Italian and the
frontier lies on the crest of the Lepontine Alps. The Tosa rises in
the vicinity of the Nufenen pass, thus reducing the common frontier
of cantons Valais and Ticino to an insignificant strip.

Canton Ticino, as 'Italian' in appearance as in speech, is thus the
result of a gigantic southern bend of the frontier, which brings into
Switzerland a section of the Southern Limestone Alps (p. 36) near
Lugano. The line then turns again to the north along the minor
crest between the Ticino-Moësa and the Lake of Como (Fig. 23),
and so we come to the complex frontier of Grisons, which will be
considered later.

ROUTE LINES OF THE WESTERN ALPS

This summary account of the Western Alps of Switzerland pre-
pares the way for some description of the main routes across them,
which form their most interesting feature. A guiding line of much
importance is the longitudinal furrow which may be traced from
Chur, near the confluence of the Vorder and Hinter Rhein, to the
Rhone elbow at Martigny (Fig. 21). It is occupied successively by
the Rhine and the Vorder Rhein, separated by the Oberalp pass
from a feeder of the Reuss; the Reuss, separated by the Furka pass
from the Rhone headstreams; and then by the Alpine Rhone throughout the greater part of its length. It is traversed by a main road and,
in appearance, by a railway; but has never served as a continuous
through route, for the obvious reason that it runs between the two
great Alpine chains just described. The 'railway' is deceptive, for
the sections Brig to Gletsch (Rhone glacier); Gletsch to Andermatt
by tunnel below the Furka; Andermatt over the Oberalp to Disentis;
are all narrow-gauge alpine lines, not continuous with the main
network of the country, and in use for but a short part of the year,
chiefly for tourist traffic. If, however, as a whole the furrow has
little importance as a route line, certain sections have much significance because of the way in which they afford access to the great
transalpine routes.

The most remarkable section is that which includes the Oberalp
and Furka passes and the Upper Reuss valley (Fig. 25). It will be
noted that the Reuss has two headstreams, the one originating near
the St. Gothard pass and the other near the Furka. After their
junction at Hospental the river flows through part of the Urserental,

The Reuss rises near the pass, and, after uniting with the Realper Reuss at Hospental, flows to Andermatt through the lower part of the Urserental, and then penetrates the Schöllenen gorge to reach Göschenen. To the south of the pass a tributary of the Ticino flows south to enter the main stream, flowing west to east in the Val Bedretto.

No attempt has been made to indicate the geology (cf. Fig. 26), but the valley furrow extending from the Vorder Rhein in the north-east to beyond the Furka pass on the western border of the map is developed on a strip of sedimentaries, the surrounding area, including the Schöllenen gorge, being floored with crystalline rocks.

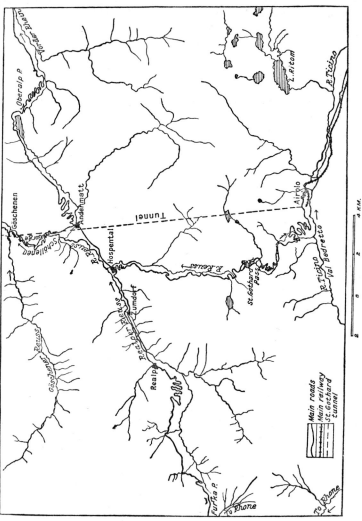

FIG. 25. DRAINAGE CONDITIONS IN THE ST. GOTHARD MASSIF

as the furrow is called in this wide and open portion. The Reuss then turns sharply and cuts through the granites of the Aar Massif the wild and gloomy Schöllenen gorge, through which it flows on its way to the Lake of Lucerne. The St. Gothard tunnel (9½ miles) avoids this gorge, being pierced direct from Göschenen to Airolo. The St. Gothard carriage road, however, finds its way by the side of the brawling Reuss, goes by Andermatt and Hospental to the pass, and descends to Airolo in the Ticino valley, whence road and railway have a clear run down to Bellinzona.

It is impossible to describe such conditions without attempting to give some explanation of them, even if this can only be partial. In itself, of course, the alternation in the Reuss valley of an open longitudinal (subsequent) and a narrow transverse (consequent) section is not an unfamiliar phenomenon, such a state of affairs being discussed in all text-books which deal with the development of river systems. But the general run of the furrow and the way in which it seems to cut through the hard rocks of the Aar—St. Gothard Massif are peculiar features here.

This massif appears to represent the culmination of the upthrust of the basement rocks, and to have had an initial steep slope to the north. This is assumed to have determined an original flow of water in the same general direction, giving rise to valleys transverse to the chain (consequent). Three of these valleys may be noted. One is the Reuss, already mentioned; the second is the Haslital, with the Grimsel pass at its head; while the third and least important as a route is the Linth valley, which has the town of Glarus in its lower section. The Linth rises in the Tödi region, and the high Kisten pass at its head, like the Grimsel, leads to the furrow, in this case to the Vorder Rhein section near Ilanz; it has, however, no great value. An interesting feature of the lower Linth, on the other hand, is the way in which it opens into a wide valley, containing the smaller Walensee and the larger Lake of Zurich, which represents, as it were, the chord of the arc Rhine-Constance-Rhine, that is, a potential Rhine short-cut (cf. p. 100 and Fig. 29).

The characters of these three consequents, the Linth, the Reuss, and the Haslital Aar, suggest that the original culmination of the massif was in the region of the present St. Gothard pass. Here rises the Reuss, the only one of the three which takes its origin in the very heart of the massif, and has been able to maintain this course. The Aar presents the appearance of being truncated near the Grimsel pass, which overlooks the part of the furrow in which the Rhone rises from its glacier. The Linth, rising in the region where the massif is dying out towards the north-east, scarcely penetrates it at all, for the Tödi, as we have seen, belongs to the High Calcareous Alps, and the peaks of the massif are here inconspicuous.

The next point to be noted is that the Aar—St. Gothard Massif, which we have hitherto regarded as a unit, is in point of fact, like the Mont Blanc—Aiguilles Rouges one, broken into wedges, the St. Gothard region being one of these. Between it and the Aar block, from a point above Brig in the Rhone valley to Disentis in the Vorder Rhein valley, part of the original sedimentary cover of the massif has been preserved in the form of a long strip. On this strip of sedimentaries the furrow has been developed in this part of its course. That is to say, the Reuss, because of its initial steep slope, has not only preserved its original direction, but by developing the subsequent Realper Reuss along the softer sedimentaries has stolen water from the Rhone. The latter, again, originally a consequent on the south-western slope of the massif, has stolen water from the Aar, because the presence of the sedimentary belt gives it greater excavating power. At the other end of the furrow, the Vorder Rhein similarly represents a greatly modified original consequent of the north-eastern slope of the massif.

The significance of such belts of sedimentaries between crystalline rocks is illustrated by Fig. 26, which shows the conditions in the Swiss continuation of the Chamonix valley, a region which offers some curious analogies to the Reuss area. It will be noted that the Trient torrent crosses the valley transversely much in the same fashion as the Reuss crosses the furrow near Andermatt. Further, the Arve, favoured by the strip of sedimentaries in the Chamonix valley, has been able to push back and effect various captures at the expense of the more northerly streams, much as the Realper Reuss has decapitated the Rhone headstreams. The Col de Balme (2,204 m.) is thus a lower equivalent of the Furka pass (2,436 m.).

Another point has to be considered before the causes which give its special value to the St. Gothard route become clear. To the south of the massif there is a second belt of sedimentaries, indicated by the course of the Ticino in the Val Bedretto. This belt is continuous, across the Nufenen pass (Fig. 24) area, with a strip which, margining the edge of the Pennine nappes, explains the origin of the part of the furrow occupied by the Rhone from near Brig to Martigny. The immediate point, however, is that the presence of the Val Bedretto, roughly parallel to the Urserental, shortens greatly the Reuss-Ticino crossing—a fact of great importance.

The further course of the Ticino is interesting. In the section from Biasca to Bellinzona (Fig. 24) it is running in a transverse valley, the upper continuation of which is formed by the Brenno tributary, which joins the main stream at Biasca. The Brenno rises in the low north-eastern continuation of the St. Gothard massif, so that the Brenno-Ticino appears to represent an original consequent, the equivalent of the Reuss on the north side of the massif. This

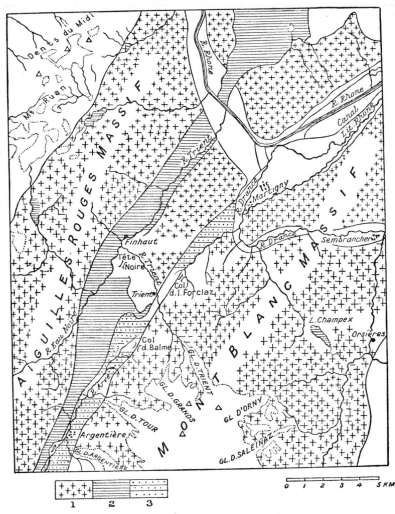

FIG. 26. THE CONTINUATION OF THE CHAMONIX VALLEY IN SWISS
TERRITORY

1. Crystalline rocks of the Aiguilles Rouges and Mont Blanc Massifs.
2. Carboniferous, and 3. Triassic sedimentaries.

The valley is developed on sedimentary rocks lying between the two
massifs. Between the frontier at the Col de Balme and the wide Rhone valley
it is divided into two parts, one occupied by the Eau Noire—Trient torrent
and the other by a tributary of the Drance. This is due to the way in which
the two strips of sedimentaries are separated in Swiss territory by a prolongation of the Mont Blanc Massif. (*From Collet, modified.*)

makes the Lukmanier pass (Fig. 29, p. 99) the equivalent of the St. Gothard one, without the special advantages of the latter. It is the connexion between the Brenno-Ticino and the longitudinal Val Bedretto on the one hand, and on the other the peculiar course of the Upper Reuss, which give the St. Gothard its supreme importance as the one short and direct crossing of the whole Alpine Belt within Switzerland. But these features again are associated both with the thinning out of the Pennine nappes in this area and with the presence of the two sedimentary belts on the flanks of the Aar and St. Gothard crystallines respectively.

We must turn next to the Simplon route, the great rival, under modern conditions, of the St. Gothard. From Martigny the railway follows the longitudinal furrow to Brig, where it enters the tunnel (12 miles) to Iselle, and thus reaches the transverse Tosa valley at Domodossola. Below Martigny the line from Lausanne traverses the High Calcareous Alps by means of the St. Maurice gorge, and, again with the help of the river-valley, makes its way through the north-eastern end of the Mont Blanc—Aiguilles Rouges Massif at the elbow bend.

The causation of the present predominance of the Simplon as a means of crossing the Pennine Alps is interesting. Between the Great St. Bernard (2,472 m.) and the Simplon (2,009 m.) passes— compare the St. Gothard (2,112 m.) and the Splügen (2,117 m.)— there is no other easy pass. The Théodule leads over a glacier, and the Monte Moro and the Col de Fenêtre both rise above 2,800 m. The Great St. Bernard (Martigny to Aosta) leads to the upper Dora Baltea, another example of those intermontane valleys developed on belts of sedimentaries. It lies between the western Pennines and the Gran Paradiso group, the latter also originating from Pennine nappes. For long the Great St. Bernard was preferred to the lower Simplon, because of the more circuitous nature of the latter, and the fact that it enters the Rhone valley at a point where there is no easy exit to the north. That long and formerly very swampy valley (cf. Fig. 36) had to be followed down to Martigny, to which, however, the Great St. Bernard afforded a direct passage. Neither the Great St. Bernard nor the Simplon, however, has the same directness as the St. Gothard, though the Schöllenen gorge there presented an obstacle not over-come till the thirteenth century.

THE EASTERN ALPS IN GRISONS

The area east of the Reichenau-Splügen line, that is, eastern Grisons, is highly complex, and presents three main points of interest. Tectonically it is important because within it is found much of the evidence upon which is based the statement that the

Western Alps disappear beneath the Eastern Alps, or, conversely, that the latter override the former. From the purely geographical standpoint we have to note that a series of historical accidents has led to the drawing of an international frontier which is unrelated to the outstanding topographical features, and in several cases crosses valley lines devoid of any break of continuity save the artificial one of customs stations. Finally, the complicated relief, the nature of the frontier, and the presence of valley sections and valleys permitting a certain density of settlement, give to the lines of communication a very special interest.

The topographical essentials may be briefly put. The Upper Inn valley (Upper Engadine), virtually continuous, despite the steep southern wall of the Maloja pass (Fig. 23), with the Val Bregaglia (Ger. Bergell), separates two mountain belts. The one has as its chief elements the splendid Bernina group (over 4,000 m.) with the Disgrazia (the 'unlucky' mountain) across the Italian frontier. The other, and north-westerly belt, consists of a series of peaks (Err, Kesch, Vadret groups, all below 3,500 m.) tending to be separated by important passes draining north-westwards to the feeders of the Hinter Rhein, and having a shorter and steeper slope to the Engadine—Val Bregaglia furrow. The two belts together form the Rhaetian Alps of geographers.

Along the north-eastern crest frontier of Grisons, and thus of Switzerland, is another belt of high ground, forming the Silvretta group (3,200 m.) near the Inn and extending as the Rhätikon (Scesaplana, under 3,000 m.) to Sargans on the Rhine. At the base of the latter lies the valley of the Prätigau (Landquart valley with Klosters), draining direct to the Rhine. This valley is floored by what are called the 'schists lustrés' ('Bündner Schiefer' of German-speaking geologists), which represent the altered sedimentary cover of the Pennine nappes. Their presence here, where they disappear beneath nappes belonging to the Eastern Alps, is regarded as part of the evidence that the Eastern Alps override the Western.

As proof it does not stand alone. Apart from the Lower Engadine window already noted (p. 42), there are other evidences that the Pennine nappes are continued beneath the overriding Austrid ones (Grisonides and Tirolides). With the details we are not concerned. But it is worth note that the Rhätikon range represents the sedimentary cover of these Eastern nappes, and is therefore the analogue, though not the tectonic homologue, of the High Calcareous Alps of the West, and that the Silvretta group and the ranges bounding the Upper Engadine—Val Bregaglia furrow are developed mainly from the crystallines of the Eastern nappes, and are thus similarly the eastern analogues of the Pennine Alps. Geographically more important is the fact that the softer schists lustrés are not confined to the floor of the Prätigau, but extend along the more southerly valleys, e.g. that of the Oberhalbstein. Their presence there may be associated with the great dissection of the region between the North Rhaetian Alps and the Rhine, and thus with the multiplicity of passes between the Engadine and that river.

The chief passes, in order from north-east to south-west, are the following (Fig. 27): (1) The Flüela, from Davos on the Landwasser

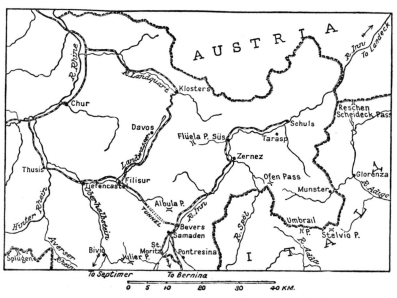

FIG. 27. PASSES AND ROUTES IN NORTH-EASTERN GRISONS

The roads are omitted for the sake of clearness, but the railways are included. The frontier is shown by a stippled line. Note that the Splügen is a frontier pass, a small area of Italian territory being shown to the south of it. In the central area a tongue of Swiss territory extends towards the Adda valley. (Cf. Fig. 23, but note the difference in the scale.)

tributary of the Hinter Rhein to Süs in the Lower Engadine. This is crossed by a carriage road and is not greatly inferior in height to the Great St. Bernard. (2) The Albula, from Filisur (Tiefencastel, Thusis) to Bevers in the Upper Engadine. Apart from the carriage road over the pass, the Albula railway (tunnel) makes this the main connexion between western Switzerland and the Engadine. (3) and (4) The Julier and Septimer passes follow the Oberhalbstein southwards from Tiefencastel. From Bivio the Julier (carriage road) leads to Silvaplana in the Upper Engadine, while the Septimer track, with its remnants of Roman paving, enters the uppermost part of the Val Bregaglia (Fig. 28).

It should be noted that the superiority of the present means of communication between the Rhine feeders and the Upper Engadine over those between the former and the Val Bregaglia is an economic rather than a topographical response. The Swiss part of the Val Bregaglia has little importance for the tourist, while the Upper Engadine is enormously frequented both in summer and winter (St. Moritz, etc.), and the costly Albula railway no less than the carriage roads reflect the fact. There is perhaps no part of Switzerland where the value of the *Fremdenindustrie* has printed itself more clearly on the surface of the land.

As contrasted with the numerous passes to the Rhine tributaries there are only two exits of any importance in Grisons from the Upper Engadine—Val Bregaglia furrow to the east and south-east. One is by the Ofen pass to the Adige (Val Venosta) and the other to the Adda (Valtellina) by the Bernina.

The Ofen pass route (carriage road) leads from Zernez in the Inn valley, through the Swiss National Park or Nature Reserve to the pass, and descends by the Rombach valley to Münster. Less than a mile below the village the road is crossed by the Italo-Swiss frontier, while the stream joins the Adige at Glorenza (Glurns). A mile or two above Münster a side valley gives access to the unimportant Umbrail pass, whence the Stelvio pass road is joined. The point to be noted is that while the Umbrail is a frontier pass, the Ofen is well within Swiss territory, which also includes in the Rombach valley a portion of the Adige system, that river otherwise having become wholly Italian in 1919.

The Bernina route (railway and road) leads from Samaden (close to Bevers, see above) past Pontresina and over the pass to Tirano in the Valtellina (Fig. 23). Here, again, the Swiss frontier, which crosses the railway within less than two miles of Tirano, is pushed far over the crest, giving the very important water-power resources of the southern slope (power station at Brusio, a few miles downstream from Poschiavo) to Switzerland. The railway is mainly a tourist line, very difficult to keep open during a large part of the year, but the connexion with the main railway system of Italy through Tirano makes it the most convenient exit to the south from the Upper Engadine.

We have still to consider the exits from the furrow given by the Inn and Maira valleys. The Inn valley changes in character between the Upper and Lower Engadine. The former is open, occupied by its string of lakes, formerly one continuous valley lake, but divided into four by the alluvial fans laid down by lateral torrents (cf. the fan laid down by the Lütschine between the Lakes of Brienz and Thun, Fig. 30). That the dividing process is still going on in the Engadine is indicated in Fig. 28, where the constriction of the lake

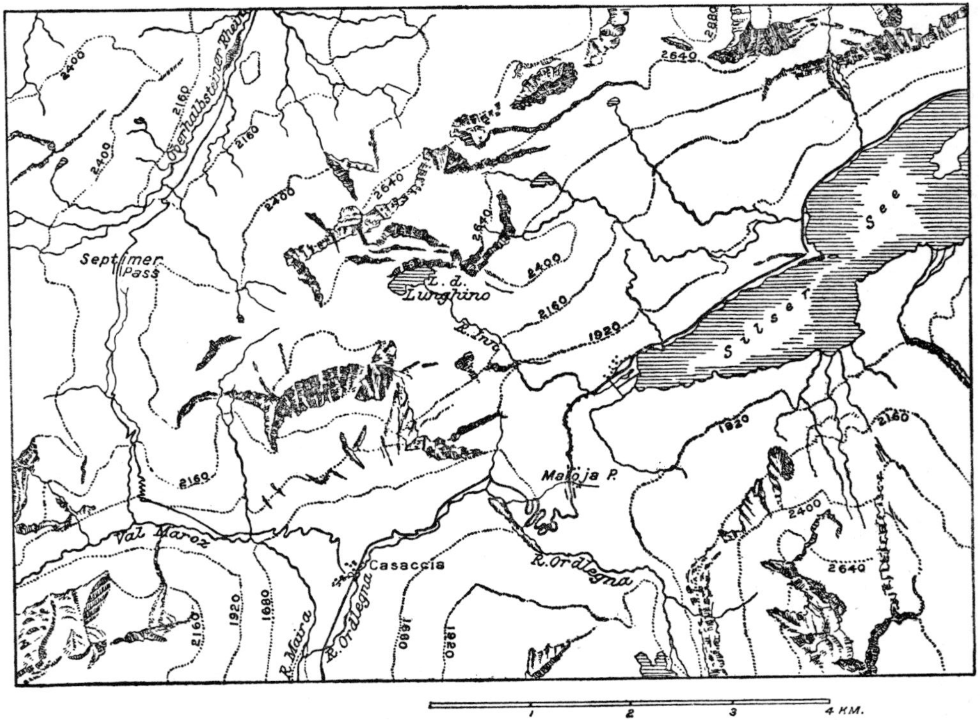

FIG. 28. THE MALOJA PASS AND THE SOURCE OF THE INN

The Inn rises in the small Lunghino lake and flows into the Silsersee, the highest of the chain of lakes which occupies the Upper Engadine. But the Maira, owing to the rapid slope of the Val Bregaglia, seems to have beheaded the original Inn. The Maira is formed near Casaccia by the union of the Val Maroz and Ordlegna torrents, both with 'elbows of capture', indicating that they, once drained to the Silsersee. The track to the Septimer pass rises from Casaccia high above the Val Maroz.

Contours are in metres, at intervals of 240 m. Rocky surfaces are shown by shading. (*From the Swiss 1/50000 map.*)

of Sils by a delta laid down by a right-bank torrent is shown. As contrasted with the sunny, gently sloping and extremely picturesque upper area, the lower valley is narrow, gloomy, and deeply incised, so that settlements are restricted to terraces often high above the valley. The famous baths of Tarasp, near which begins the 'window' of the Lower Engadine (p. 42), have led to the building of a railway from Bevers, thus connecting with the Albula line. The Austro-Swiss frontier crosses the river at the defile of Finstermünz, and the downstream motor-post route from Tarasp to Landeck on the Arlberg railway is almost as important a traffic line as the railway from Bevers.

The curious beheading of the Inn by the Maira is illustrated in Fig. 28, and the Swiss Val Bregaglia shows many other points of interest. The Italo-Swiss frontier crosses the valley, not at the gateway (La Porta) above Promontogno, which marks the transition to the 'Italian' type of vegetation, but in an open area near Casta-segna, a few miles above Chiavenna, the 'key' town. It will be noted that the Swiss villages can only communicate with the rest of the motherland direct upstream over the Maloja, though downstream they can connect with the Italian railway system at Chiavenna, and then by steamer and rail reach Lugano and the Swiss railway system. Chiavenna is also the natural market town for the Swiss villages at least of the lower Val Bregaglia. But the difficulties and delays of the frontier crossing form an artificial check to natural trends, and help to explain why the Swiss Val Bregaglia has so little importance as a tourist area, relatively to the crowded Upper Engadine.

CHAPTER V

HUMAN GEOGRAPHY OF SWITZERLAND

Origin and Relief of the Swiss Plateau—Human Geography of the
Plateau—The Jura—The Alpine Valleys

ORIGIN AND RELIEF OF THE SWISS PLATEAU

OF the three broad divisions of Switzerland—the Jura, the Plateau, and the Alps—we have so far been mainly concerned with the last. The Alps cover 60 per cent of the total surface of the country, and have a population of the order of three-quarters of a million. Not only their magnificent scenery, but the light which detailed research into their structure has thrown upon mountain-building processes in general, makes them of surpassing interest from the standpoint of physical geography. But from the human standpoint they are, save for their route-lines, of much less importance than the Plateau. This, though it covers only 30 per cent of the country, carries about 75 per cent of the total population, and it is mainly to its varied resources and relatively dense settlement that the Confederation owes its economic stability.

A note may be added here on the difficult question of nomenclature. The term Swiss Plateau (mean height, 580 m.) is commonly used by French-Swiss geologists, despite the objections to which it is open. The German-Swiss *Mittelland*—Midland Belt—has the advantage of begging no question as to origin or present characters. Other terms used by various authors are Swiss High Plain, Swiss Hill Country, and so on, and it is notable that even those who emphasize most strongly the need of avoiding descriptive names like plain and plateau, yet find themselves constrained to employ one or the other in the course of a detailed description. It seems therefore convenient to retain Swiss Plateau as a general name, while freely admitting that from the purely physiographical standpoint the area is neither plateau nor plain.

In origin, as already suggested, the Plateau represents a syncline or basin which was filled up with the waste derived from the bordering Alps and Jura. Its surface was subsequently profoundly modified by the action of running water and moving ice. Thus while the bordering mountains owe their birth to orogenic forces (p. 31), the Plateau, alike in its first origin and in its present form, is, in essentials, the result of the action of surface agents.

The tertiary (oligocene and miocene) rocks which are exposed over much of its surface afford evidence of varying conditions of deposition. They show that the basin was first occupied by a lake or lakes, apparently forming a basin of inland drainage. A period of subsidence followed, during which the sea extended in front of the rising Alps from the basin of Vienna to the (French) Rhone valley. This was followed by a new uplift, most marked in the Swiss or central section, which led to the formation of a body of fresh water, furnished with a direct sea outlet. Thus we find that the rocks consist of the molasse beds, chiefly sandstones, representing the sediments laid down in the deeper water, whether fresh or salt, and the nagelfluh conglomerates, regarded as deltaic deposits formed where the entering torrents flung down their load. The molasse beds can be divided into the lower freshwater series, where beds of clay, marls, limestones, gypsums, with some lignites derived from transported vegetation, are intercalated between the sandstones; the marine sandstones, grey in colour, and because of their relative hardness employed as building-stone; and the upper freshwater sandstones.

The nagelfluh beds are similarly either of freshwater or marine origin. Though represented on both margins they are naturally much better developed on the alpine side, where the streams had a larger catchment area and a much greater fall, and for both reasons had much more transporting power. The implications of their deltaic origin should also be borne in mind. Such deposits tend necessarily to change rapidly in thickness and in character with increasing distance from the stream to which they owe their origin. The constituent pebbles, also, may be fragments of very hard rocks (granite, gneiss, porphyry, etc.), and may be cemented together in such a fashion as to form a rock of great resisting power. Thus the initial alternation of hard nagelfluh and softer molasse beds is a potential cause of accentuated relief.

But the highly diverse present surface of the Plateau is due not to the ordinary surface agents alone, but to the effects of the enlarged glaciers of the Ice Age. During its closing stages, alpine glaciers, whose courses can still be traced, streamed out of their valleys over the Plateau, laid down copious glacial deposits, and modified the drainage conditions profoundly. The glacial deposits, rearranged by running water, and modified by weathering, are often of considerable fertility: the great diversity of the rocks included in the alpine folding should be noted in this connexion. The valleys, widened by the action of the ice, afford important areas of settlement and greatly facilitate communication. The frequent lakes, often large, influence local climate and so the distribution of crop-plants, especially the vine. Considerable tracts, left as swamps and wet moors when the ice retreated back to the Alps, can be drained owing to the proximity of deep ice- and water-worn furrows. Generally, most of the features of importance to the human geographer can be traced back to the recent glaciation.

Our survey of the effects of the glaciation can only be illustrative, not complete, but even so some preliminary notes on the contrasts between the effects of running water and moving ice on land surfaces are necessary. We need not stop to discuss the controversial question as to how far moving ice is in itself an eroding agent. It is sufficient to accept the fact that valleys which have been recently occupied by glaciers show marked differences in shape and characters from those which have been moulded only by running water, and go on to consider the differences between ice and water drainage, and the effects of a combination of the two.

We may begin with one notable feature of ice during a period when the total amount is increasing beyond the capacity of the pre-existing stream valley to allow of its easy discharge. There is abundant evidence, alike within the Alps and on their Plateau margins, that under such conditions the ice tends to rise in the valley till some lowering of the bounding wall allows a portion to escape over a former watershed as a divergent arm, or distributary glacier. As contrasted with running water, which under such conditions effects a catastrophic escape till adjustment of levels occurs, there is evidence that in the case of ice the divergent arm may persist over a long period of time, unless and until the supply of ice diminishes through a decreasing snowfall.

Since the alpine glaciers long since entered on a period of general retreat, this phenomenon does not now occur, at least on any scale. It was once, however, as frequent in the Alps as in the mountains of Ice Age Scotland, with quite similar topographical results.

Another interesting phenomenon can still be observed in the Alps, even if on a small scale, and was once widespread and notable. This is the power of ice to hold up the drainage of a lateral, ice-free valley. The typical text-book example is of course the small Märjelensee, whose waters are held up by the Aletsch glacier. More interesting, perhaps, if less familiar, are the conditions in the Allée Blanche on the Italian side of Mont Blanc. Here the moraine of the Miage glacier, which descends from the Mont Blanc group, has held up the stream of the Allée Blanche, and formed the largely silted-up Combal lake, from which the Dora escapes by cutting a wild and rocky ravine (cf. Fig. 46, p. 153). In this case the upstream glaciers have shrunk more than the Miage, which has a larger gathering-ground. Thus while at an earlier period the whole valley was occupied by an ice-stream formed by the confluence of a number of glaciers, more rapid shrinkage in the upper, as compared with the lower glaciers, has led to the stream formed in the upper valley being successively blocked by ice and by the morainic material

8

which always accumulates round glacier snouts. The stream has in consequence been forced to cut a new course for itself. Clearly, when the Ice Age glaciers deployed on the Plateau, the melt-waters of those with the smaller gathering-ground would find their valley lines blocked by the ice tongues of those of greater size and persistence, and great disturbances of drainage would occur.

It is to such cases as these that many of the peculiar features of the present valleys of the Plateau are due, as we have now to show.

During the last phase of glaciation five glaciers streamed out from the Alps to the Plateau, these taking their rise respectively in the alpine Rhine valley, the Linth, the alpine Reuss, the alpine Aar and the alpine Rhone (Fig. 29). The main Rhine glacier spread out over the area now covered by the Lake of Constance; but in the vicinity of the present site of Sargans it gave off a distributary to the north-east, the further course of which is indicated by the hollow occupied by the Walensee (cf. p. 86). At the eastern end of that lake it was joined by the glacier coming down the Linth valley. The united glacier, after crossing the open, swampy valley now traversed by the Linth canal, reached the area at present occupied by the shallow eastern end of the Lake of Zurich. There divergence again occurred, one glacier arm following the line of the lake, and its effluent the Limmat, and the other the parallel and wider valley to the north-east now occupied by two small lakes and drained by the Glatt to the Rhine (*a* on map).

The glacier emerging from the valley of the alpine Reuss behaved in a quite analogous fashion. Following what is now the Urner arm (Lake of Uri) of the many-armed Lake of Lucerne, it forked near Brunnen, one arm following the Gersau bay of the lake, and the other passing by the valley occupied by the small and largely silted-up Lake of Lowerz and the Lake of Zug, to the north-east of the Rigi (*b* on map).

Everywhere the former presence of such divergent arms of glaciers means a duplication of valleys, one valley forming the existing drainage line and the other being lateral to the present system and devoid of a through stream. Such partially empty or 'dead' valleys afford admirable lines of communication, and, where they can be drained, offer large tracts of potentially fertile land. As regards the second point, the two sections of the valley furrow extending from the Walensee to the eastern end of the Lake of Zurich, and then over the existing minor watershed to the Glatt, present an interesting contrast. The former has only recently been fully drained. In the latter there is much productive ground, and the remains of the lake-dwellings of the little Pfäffikersee remind us how early the suitability of the valley for settlement was recognized. It is interesting to note also that canton Schwyz, which gave its

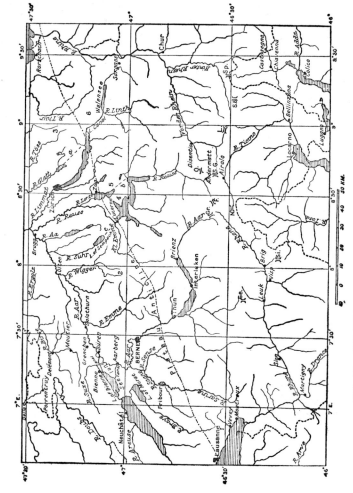

FIG. 29. THE RIVER SYSTEMS OF THE PLATEAU AND ITS MARGINS

1. Mt. Pélerin. 2. The Napf. 3. The Hörnli. 4. The Rigi. 5. The Speer. 6. The Rossberg. These form the chief nagelfluh hills. *a* shows the course of the former divergent arm of the Linth glacier; *b*, that of the former Reuss glacier (see p. 103); *c*, the course of the former main Reuss glacier.

The chief passes within the limits of the map are shown by initials: Ge. = Gemmi, Si. = Simplon, Nu. = Nufenen, Gr. = Grimsel, F. = Furka, S.G. = St. Gothard, O. = Oberalp, L. = Lukmanier, S.B. = San Bernadino, Sp. = Splügen.

name to Switzerland, has its capital of the same name placed near the Lowerz lake in the Urner-Zugersee valley.

More important, under present conditions, is the relation of these dead valleys to lines of communication. We have already (p. 86) indicated the significance of the valley line between Zurich and Sargans as offering a short-cut between the Basel Rhine and the alpine Rhine, avoiding the great north-eastern loop whose apex is occupied by the Lake of Constance. Along this valley passes the railway from Basel and Zurich to Innsbruck and Vienna by the Arlberg route, one of the major routes of Central Europe. More important still is the Lowerz valley, which is traversed by the St. Gothard railway. The Lowerz furrow can be reached from Zurich via Zug, or from Lucerne via the Küssnacht arm of the lake, itself once traversed by another distributary of the Reuss glacier. Thereafter the railway follows the shores of the Urner arm of the Lake of Lucerne to the valley of the alpine Reuss.

The Limmat and Reuss glaciers after their full emergence on the Plateau became confluent and spread out to form a many-lobed mass, separated by but a narrow gap from the lobed end of the great Rhine glacier. The presence of the Limmat-Reuss ice-cushion with its lappets, and their various stages of retreat, have left a deep imprint on the surface. We may note in particular that in the area which extends from the Glatt valley to the Wigger there are a number of parallel troughs, sometimes (Limmat, Lorze-Reuss) occupied by streams draining from the Alps, sometimes (Glatt) by one rising on the alpine edge of the Plateau, sometimes (Aar, Suhr, Wigger) empty in their upper reaches, the streams rising in a secondary watershed. Very curious also is the arc-like valley occupied successively by the Kleine Emme and by the Reuss after it emerges from the Lake of Lucerne. It is clear that the parallel valleys were occupied by the lappets of the Limmat-Reuss glacier and their meltwater streams. The Kleine Emme-Reuss arc is due to a stage in retreat when the meltwaters of a shrinking mass of ice found their former exits blocked by the moraines laid down during the period of advance, and had to round these to find a new exit.

But the point is not to emphasize glacial detail but the fact that the whole of this north-eastern part of the Plateau, because of the former presence of expanded and lobed ends of glaciers emerging from the alpine valleys, has innumerable possible lines of communication. These have also often alpine or sub-alpine continuations, owing to the former existence of divergent glacial arms. With these facts again we must associate the density of the present railway net, the importance of the international routes, and at least in part the development of large-scale industry here. It has, however, to be added that the whole of this north-eastern part of the

Plateau seems to have had a well-developed drainage system before the advent of the ice, owing to the way in which the rampart of the Folded Jura thins out and disappears near Baden (cf. p. 77). The pre-glacial surface showed a steady slope towards the present Aar-Rhine junction.

To the south-west of a line from Olten to Lucerne we find that the Plateau surface differs in several respects from the area just described. Two outstanding features may be noted. First, the Plateau tributaries of the Aar (note the Broye) approach within a few miles of the north shore of the Lake of Geneva, so that by far the greater part of the area drains to the Rhine. Second, the dissection of the surface by streams is less complete, so that considerable belts of upland remain. One of these, the Napf (2), is indicated on Fig. 29 and its curious radial drainage lines should be noted.

The immediate causation of the special features of this part of the Plateau is to be found in the recent glaciation, the Aar glacier, which was confluent with a northern arm of the Rhone glacier, being the agent. But pre-glacial conditions have also exerted some influence. It is here that the blocking effect of the Folded Jura on alpine drainage is most marked. Part of the pre-glacial surface drained to the Rhone, which had cut its way through the southern end of the Jura; part, though apparently much less than at present, to the Rhine after the formation of the Rhine Rift valley in pliocene times, the earlier exit having been to the Danube. The effect of glaciation was to disturb an equilibrium which had been established only with difficulty, and to leave a considerable area with imperfect outlet.

Let us look at some of the details. In the closing stage of glaciation the ice of the alpine Aar sent an arm over the Brünig pass to the Alpnach bay of the Lake of Lucerne. The rest of the ice followed the valley indicated by the lakes of Brienz and Thun, now separated by the Lütschine delta (Fig. 30), and reached the Plateau past Thun, as a purely valley glacier. Near the site of Berne it united with the northern arm of the Rhone glacier, but was separated by a wide gap from the Reuss-Limmat one, so that the Napf was ice-free.

The Rhone glacier emerged from the Alps at what is now the eastern end of the Lake of Geneva, and divided into two. One arm followed the present lake, while the presence of the Prealps and of the mass of nagelfluh now dissected out as Mont Pélerin, north-east of Vevey (1 in Fig. 29) forced the other to take a northerly and north-westerly direction, till it was blocked by the Jura. The consequences are obvious. At the base of the Jura lies a deep furrow marked by the long basin of the Lake of Neuchâtel, continued into the smaller one of the Lake of Bienne (Biel), with a topographical continuation into the valley of the Aar, where this follows the Jura.

The similar but less accentuated furrow indicated by the River Broye and the small Lake of Morat (Murten) results from the former presence of an ice-lobe.

But note that the other arm of the Rhone glacier received an enormous accession of ice, and therefore of eroding power—whether this be ascribed to the ice or to the sub-glacial torrents—in the Arve

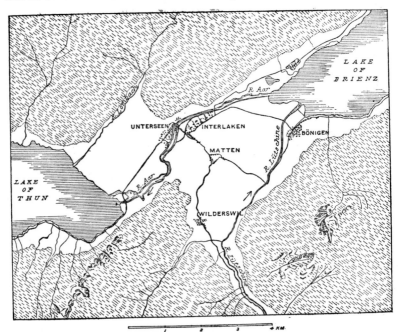

FIG. 30. THE SITE OF INTERLAKEN

The Lütschine is formed by the junction of two glacial torrents, one coming from the Grindelwald valley and the other from the Lauterbrunnen valley. Because of the amount of glacial debris carried it has formed a delta which, in combination with that of the Lombach, separates what was once a single lake into two. Interlaken (567 m.), stands on the flat plain so formed, and is at once sheltered from the north and has access to magnificent mountain scenery.

The dotted line indicates the 660 m. contour, above which the surface rises steeply.

glacier which joined it near the present site of Geneva. This ensured that the post-glacial Rhone should follow (approximately) its pre-glacial course, and left the Neuchâtel-Bienne and Broye-Morat furrows as largely 'dead' valleys, without adequate exits.

One other old valley in this region may be noted. From the neighbourhood of Berne to a point downstream from Solothurn (near Wangen) is a wide furrow, which looks as if it ought to have been the valley of the Aar. Instead, that river at Berne makes a remarkable double turn, cuts its way westward through the molasse in a course marked by incised meanders, joins the Saane valley line, and so turns north to enter the great furrow at the base of the Jura. The Berne-Wangen furrow marks the edge of the ancient Rhone-Aar glacier, and the deposition of morainic matter there compelled the Aar to excavate a new course. As is so frequently the case, the deserted valley affords an excellent line of communication, being followed in part by the main line from Olten to Berne via Herzogenbuchsee.

Even more interesting from the human standpoint are the conditions near the Jura. Because of the imperfect natural drainage of both the Neuchâtel-Bienne and Broye-Morat furrows, flood-water tended to find an uncertain way through swamps to the Aar system. Large tracts of land were thus rendered useless and an important line of communication to the shores of the Lake of Geneva was constantly menaced. The Romans tackled the problem of communications to some extent, but it was not till 1870–80 that a determined effort was made to regulate the drainage. The Aar was diverted into the Lake of Bienne by the Hagneck canal, while the Aar canal takes off from the lake near the town of Bienne and reaches the river at Büren. Between Aarburg, the off-take, and the intake at Büren, little water flows through the old Aar course in normal times. The result has been to drain a considerable tract of land, especially in Seeland ('Lakeland'), or the Swiss Holland, as the area south-east of the Lake of Bienne is sometimes called. The reclaimed lands are fertile, producing, in addition to cereals (including some maize), fruit, market-garden produce, and excellent pastures, two crops of special interest. These are sugar-beet and tobacco. The former is virtually limited to this area (parts of cantons Berne, Vaud, and Fribourg), the latter, grown in the area between the Lake of Neuchâtel and the Broye valley, occurs elsewhere in Switzerland, e.g. in the most southerly parts of Ticino.

To complete our picture of those details of the Plateau which have affected man and his activities we have still to note the areas underlain by the nagelfluh beds. These may be said to influence the topography in two main ways. Where well developed close to the alpine border, they controlled the direction of the ice tongues during the period of retreat, rising like the nunataks of Greenland above the ice-filled valleys, developed in the softer beds. Where they are present over considerable areas out on the Plateau they helped to control the direction of the glaciers deploying from the Alps, and therefore played a not unimportant part in determining the courses of the present streams and lines of communication. In other words, close to the Alps nagelfluh deposits have been so isolated by erosion as to form conspicuous hills or mountains of the type disdainfully called by alpinists 'cow-mountains', because some or most routes up them demand no special agility; nevertheless, as notably on the Rigi (1,800 m., or 5,905 ft.), great cliffs and precipices may bear testimony to the part played by ice in their formation. Out on the Plateau, on the other hand, the presence of thick beds of nagelfluh is indicated by wide, forested uplands, the summits being often plateau-like.

The contrast between the two groups has its basis in the fact that along the alpine border the nagelfluh beds have been influenced by the pressure exerted by the rising Alps, and a certain amount of folding has taken place. Farther out on the Plateau the beds lie as they were laid down. The dotted line on Fig. 29 indicates the course of the so-called Plateau Anticline, which separates the two types of nagelfluh hills.

The Speer (1,934 m., 6 on map) is the highest member of the first group, and the way in which it overlooks the widely-open valley already described as lying between the Walensee and the Lake of Zurich, should be noted. Its presence helped to determine the direction of the Linth-Rhine distributary glacier described on p. 98. The Rigi (4) and the Rossberg (5) again are particularly interesting, because between them passed the arm of the Reuss glacier, whose importance has been already emphasized.

The second group of nagelfluh hills forms a conspicuous feature of the Plateau relief. The deposits extend farthest out over the Plateau and cover the greatest area in two separate regions. One is between the westward-pointing loop of the River Thur and the Lake of Zurich, and accounts for most of the hill country of cantons Zurich and Thurgau, and part of that of St. Gallen and Appenzell (note the Hörnli, 3 on map). The second area lies within the triangle whose points are the towns of Lucerne, Berne, and Thun, and constitutes much of the hill country of the Plateau sections of cantons Berne and Lucerne, notably that formed by the Napf (1,411 m.). The Napf is bordered by the Emmental, which has given its name to the best Swiss cheese.

HUMAN GEOGRAPHY OF THE PLATEAU

We are now in a position to grasp the chief features of the Plateau. We have seen that the great lakes which form its north-eastern and south-western borders overlie areas formerly occupied by the expanded ends of the Rhine and Rhone glaciers. The exits from the Alps of the lesser Ice Age glaciers are marked by smaller lakes, the peculiar shape of that of Lucerne being directly related to the various ice tongues which crossed the site. The still smaller lakes sprinkled over the general surface lie in valleys once occupied by stagnant lobes of ice, while those on the Jura border are related to the northern arm of the Rhone glacier.

The great lines of communication are closely related to the recent glaciation. In the north-west the funnel-shaped depression, wide towards the Alps between Zurich and Lucerne, and narrowing to the area where the Rivers Limmat, Reuss, and Aar join, permits of the gathering up of Plateau and alpine routes, with an ultimate convergence on Basel, a highly important centre from which a number of lines diverge. Again, though the routes in detail are often devious, and the Plateau surface is not uniformly favourable to railway construction, it does nevertheless facilitate communication between the lands bordering the Lake of Constance and those which can be reached from the Lake of Geneva. In connexion with these north-east to south-west lines the position of Berne should be noted. In the southern part of the Plateau the main route must needs be central, in order to avoid alike the lakes of the Jura trough and the alpine foothills. Berne stands at a notable junction of routes, hence its choice as capital, but till the construction of the Lötschberg tunnel route (Berne, Thun, Spiez, Kandersteg, tunnel, Goppenstein, Brig) was at a disadvantage as compared with Lucerne, Zurich, or Lausanne in having no direct access to a transalpine route. Finally, towards the south, the Plateau network is connected to France by routes across the Jura, the Dijon, Frasne, Vallorbe, Lausanne line, leading to the Simplon, being especially important.

Some features of the climate have still to be noted. This is on the whole remarkably uniform throughout, though the north-eastern section is more exposed to the north, and therefore somewhat harsher and damper, save where the Lakes of Constance and Zurich produce local modifications. The special feature is the prevalence of mist, particularly in winter, when a sea of cloud may envelop the whole of the Plateau surface below levels of 800–1,000 m., while the greater heights and the alpine foothills are bathed in bright sunshine. Sursee, on the River Suhr near its emergence from the Lake of Sempach, has an average of 118 cloudy days per annum, and though this is quite exceptional, it is generally true that the Plateau suffers from a deficiency of sunshine.

On the Plateau the average temperature range is 20°C., as compared with the alpine border, where it diminishes to about 18°C., elevation resulting in slightly cooler summers, rather than in any marked increase of winter cold. The mean annual temperature of the lower Plateau stations is of the order of 8°–9°C. (46°–48°F.), the following figures being very typical:

TABLE IV

Station	Height above sea-level	Mean January Temp.	Mean July Temp.
Berne . .	570 m.	−2·3°C. (28·2°F.)	17·6°C. (63·7°F.)
Zurich . .	493 m.	−1·4°C. (29·5°F.)	18·4°C. (65·2°F.)

The influence of the presence of the lake and of the sheltered position should be noted in the case of Zurich.

Because of the Plateau relief those winter inversions of temperature, which are so marked in many of the alpine valleys, particularly that of the Rhone, are not obvious.

Precipitation on the Plateau is generally of the order of 100 cm. (40 in.), dropping to below 80 cm. (32 in.) near the Jura lake area, and rising to 120–160 cm. (47 in.–63 in.) near the Alps. The isohyet of 120 cm. marks approximately the limit of cereal cultivation, and the comparatively small part of Switzerland included, no less than its limitation to the lower parts of the Plateau and its margins and to the greater alpine valleys, especially those of the Rhone and the Rhine, goes far to explain the limited production and thus the need for heavy imports. It may be added that in the High Alps the total mean precipitation, chiefly in the form of snow, rises rapidly to 200–300 cm. (80 in.–120 in.), with a maximum of over 400 cm. (160 in.) in the vicinity of the Monte Rosa group, and not greatly inferior figures in the Säntis area of the north-east.

The extent of the permanently snow-covered area in the Alps has an important effect on the *régime* of the Plateau streams, and thus on hydro-electric power. Those streams which have alpine tributaries show only a winter minimum of flow, being swollen in summer by meltwater. Those which originate wholly on the Plateau have a double minimum, one in late summer and the other in January–February. The latter is due both to the winter temperatures and to the relatively low winter precipitation. Periodicity of precipitation is not very marked, but a summer maximum and a winter minimum can be recognized. Taking the figure of 100 cm. as an average one for the lower parts of the Plateau, it may be said that spring and autumn have each about 25 cm., while the remainder is distributed between summer and winter in the proportion of about 35 to 15. Rain days are frequent, reaching a maximum of 168 at St. Gallen in the north-east, 148 at Berne, and dropping to 130 at Geneva. Such figures go far to explain the general predominance of stock-rearing over crop-production.

The towns show a very curious linear arrangement, closely related to the relief features. Before discussing this, however, it is well, in order to keep a sense of proportion, to recall the fact that of the Plateau towns only four (Zurich, 336,000; Basel, 162,000; Berne, 130,000; Geneva, 124,000) have more than 100,000 inhabitants, and only four others (Lausanne, 92,000; St. Gallen, 62,000; Winterthur, 58,000; Lucerne, 55,000) more than 50,000.

Settlements of any size would tend to arise only on sites which combined the advantage of being market towns and route centres. It may be said that the two are synonymous, since every market town must be a convergence of routes of some kind. But the point is that the resources of the Plateau are not only limited, but generally speaking very uniform, so that this factor acting alone could not in earlier days be of any great importance. On the other hand, the position of the Plateau between Alps and Jura and the check which these present to Central European traffic as a whole, gives the sites commanding the chief passes far more than local significance. Historically important sites would thus be those which combined some local importance as markets with command of natural route-lines. Subsequent growth or stagnation would depend upon the nodal importance in relation to modern means of transport, and the possibility or otherwise of developing considerable industries.

There are three rows of towns—those of the alpine margin; those of the central area; those placed at the base of the Jura. The alpine row may be said to begin on the shores of the Lake of Geneva with Vevey and Montreux, the former a small manufacturing town (tobacco, condensed milk, chocolate, etc.), the latter a general name for a strung-out row of tourist resorts, due to the mildness of the lake climate and the beautiful views of the nearer Alps. The line is continued in Thun, Lucerne, Zug, Rapperswil (on the Lake of Zurich), Herisau, and St. Gallen. Lucerne, despite its manufactures (silk, machinery, etc.) is the great tourist centre of the northern part of Switzerland. It owes this distinction to the beauty of the scenery, the number of minor routes which lead to neighbouring resorts or serve as starting-points for tours in the Oberland, and its command of the St. Gothard route. Thun (a garrison town) is much less important. It is too remote from mountain scenery to attract the tourist, who prefers Interlaken (Fig. 30) or the higher resorts (Grindelwald, Kandersteg, Adelboden, etc.), and too near Berne under modern conditions of transport to be an inevitable stopping-off place like Lucerne.

The central row begins with Lausanne, and is continued by Fribourg, Berne, Zurich, Winterthur, Frauenfeld, with a natural end at Constance, which is, however, German and not Swiss. The great predominance of Zurich is the feature here, and is due to the development of large-scale industry, combined with the command of both local and through routes. Winterthur is an industrial town of the manufacturing belt, of which we shall speak in a moment. Something has been already said of Berne, but Fribourg is particularly interesting, despite its population of only some 26,000. It is a route town and a market town (chocolate and condensed milk industries; cattle market), and like Berne dates from the twelfth century. It stands on the borderland between the German- and French-speaking areas (Fig. 22), and its Catholic university is the spiritual home of Swiss Catholicism. Lausanne, with its lake port of Ouchy, has to the Simplon route something of the relation which Zurich has to the Arlberg one, but is much less favourably placed. Its industries are small, but its educational institutions are renowned, and its command of routes, with the ceaseless stream of tourists which passes along them, makes it an important centre of trade, as compared with the backwater in which Fribourg lies.

The Jura border towns begin at Geneva and extend through Neuchâtel, Bienne, Solothurn, Olten, Aarau, and Baden to Schaffhausen. These are all towns with a considerable amount of industry. Geneva, Neuchâtel (24,000) and Bienne (41,000) are more typical Jura border towns. All engage in watchmaking and all command Jura routes, that reaching Geneva being particularly important, though those to Bienne have been recently improved (see p. 114). Bienne is a growing industrial centre while Neuchâtel is, like Fribourg, a market and university town. Geneva is the south-western gate of Switzerland, commands most of the trade with France and Spain, is the great centre of French culture in Switzerland, and apart from its tourist traffic (mostly through traffic to Upper Savoy) is much frequented by foreigners. Its development as a seat of industry is handicapped by the relief, by the proximity of the French frontier, and by the distance from other centres.

Our survey of the Plateau may be completed by a note on its natural divisions and the characteristics of the industrialized belt. The north-eastern area may be regarded as limited by a line drawn from the vicinity of Baden (p. 77) through the town of Zug to the Alps. Here the vine is limited to sunny slopes and the shores of the Lakes of Constance and Zurich. The considerable large-scale industry has an interesting history. Embroidery on locally-woven linen—a natural woman's occupation in a mainly pastoral area— was an old home industry. The importance of Appenzell (within the alpine border) as a centre even to this day is an indication of the region of origin. Cotton later replaced linen, flax being now little grown, and machines and factories the original handwork in the home. A tradition of delicacy of manipulation, combined with the difficulty of importing raw material, has led to Swiss industry being mainly of the type which absorbs much labour. Thus cotton and silk goods are more important than woollens, and the iron industry is mainly concerned with machinery and scientific instruments, the natural conditions having made the Swiss excellent engineers. Zurich has important silk and machinery works; Herisau is a bleaching town; St. Gallen is the centre of the embroidery trade of canton Appenzell, though this has suffered seriously from American competition. This part of Switzerland is little known to the tourist but is densely peopled.

The central area extends from the line just mentioned to one drawn from Solothurn through Berne to the Alps south of Thun. Here the vine is virtually absent. Industry is almost confined to the Aar towns at the base of the Jura, but extends up some of the tributary valleys. The entrances to the Alps via Lucerne and Thun (Berne) make the tourist industry of great importance but the Plateau surface is mainly agricultural (cf. the Napf area, p. 104).

The south-western region is characterized by the relative abundance of the vine and the appearance of special crops such as tobacco and sugar-beet. There is little industry apart from those already noted which depend on the working up of local raw material (wine-making, condensing of milk, making of milk chocolate, etc.). Tourist traffic tends to be concentrated along the shores of the Lake of Geneva.

THE JURA

This division is of less importance to the human geographer than either of the other two. Within Swiss territory the surface nowhere attains 1,700 m. (cf. the Speer and Rigi on the Plateau), the highest points being La Dôle, 1,678 m. and Mont Terrible, 1,680 m., both in the south-west. Everywhere, however, the drop to the Plateau is abrupt. Only two rivers, the Rhone and the Aar (after its junction with the Reuss and the Limmat) succeed in cutting through the whole folded belt, and this only at its narrowed south-western and north-eastern ends. The Rhine borders the Folded Jura on the north, but does not penetrate into it. Other rivers originate within the chain, and find their way, usually by very devious courses, either to the Saône-Rhone or the Aar-Rhine systems. Of these the largest is the Doubs, but since it flows mainly within France, the Birse, which enters the Rhine near Basel, is more important. By its zigzag course it emphasizes the 'gridiron' arrangement of the Jura ridges, for both it and its tributaries run alternately in valleys parallel to the bars of the grid, and in deep transverse gorges (*cluses*) across them.

Save in the valleys which slope to the southern part of the Plateau, the climate is harsh and humid. Precipitation almost everywhere exceeds notably a mean annual figure of 100 cm., and in the higher regions to the south-west rises to 160 cm. Since temperatures rise slowly in spring this means a deep and prolonged snow-cover over most of the surface, for the wide, continuous valleys characteristic of the Alps and the Plateau are absent here. Despite this fact surface streams and rivulets are few, and on the upper levels both the herdsmen and their flocks have to depend on rain-water stored in cisterns. The apparent anomaly, in a region of high precipitation, is explained by the presence of the limestones, giving rise to underground drainage and the usual karstic phenomena. For the same reason lakes are few and small, and like the wet moors which occur in places are generally associated with the earlier glaciation. Despite the small amount of surface water, the heavy precipitation permits of tree growth, and there is a considerable amount of woodland, both conifers and broad-leaved trees (including the beech) being present, though the upper levels rise above the tree limit (1,400–1,600 m.) and form hill pastures.

Minerals are scanty, as in Switzerland generally. Productive asphalt beds occur in the Areuse valley at Travers, cement stones along the inner border generally, and there is a little iron ore, as at Choindez in the Birse valley downstream from Moutier, especially at Herznach north of Aarau.

Obviously, then, the natural resources are limited. There is comparatively little agriculture, and stock-keeping and forestry form the main rural occupations. The fairly heavy population of the larger valleys is associated rather with the development of industry based on hydro-electric power than with anything the land has to offer. Watchmaking, like the embroidery of canton Appenzell, is now a factory and not a home industry. The two centres of Le Locle and La Chaux-de-Fonds lie in an upland valley near the French border, characterized by its low winter temperatures. Thus the mean January temperature of the former (height 986 m.) is $-2 \cdot 8°$ C., almost identical with that on the summit of the Weissenstein near Solothurn (height 1,283 m.). The two towns are connected by rail to Neuchâtel, while St. Imier in the Suze valley, another centre of the industry, is linked to Bienne.

Before going on to discuss trans-Jura routes, we may note some points connected with the Rhine course between the Lake of Constance and Basel. Here the tabular or unfolded Jura abut upon the Folded Jura, and the Rhine follows a somewhat complicated course. After leaving the lake it found its pre-glacial course blocked by debris, and was forced to cut a new valley through the limestones of the Table Jura, this giving rise to the famous Rhine Falls (water-power) near Schaffhausen. Thereafter the river meanders through molasse beds and morainic material to Kaiserstuhl, where it again traverses limestones, and then cuts its way through the underlying triassic beds (note the salt deposits at Rheinfelden, Augst, and

Schweizerhalle) to Basel. At Laufenburg the Black Forest gneiss reaches the river and accounts for the development of rapids, the rocks having been blasted away to allow for electric installations. Several large and new power stations occur between this point and Basel.

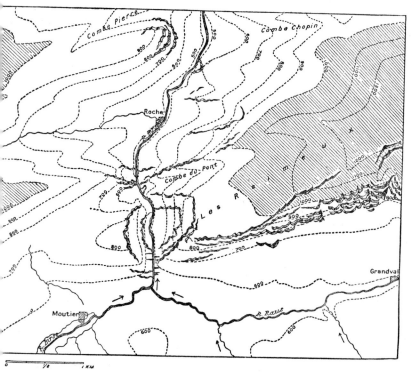

FIG. 31. THE CLUSE OF MOUTIER

The Birse cuts through the Les Raimeux ridge in a narrow gorge, from which open dry valleys or combes, ending blindly above. The Cluse is just wide enough to permit the passage of road and railway (omitted for the sake of clearness) alongside the stream. On the other hand, the Raus tributary runs parallel to the ridge in a wider, flat-floored valley, or Val (note the name Grand*val*), allowing of some amount of cultivation (cf. Fig. 32). The three types of valley, Cluse, Combe, and Val, are characteristic of the Jura.

Heights above 1,000 m. shaded; chief rock outcrops shown. (*From the Swiss 1/25000 map.*)

Basel (162,000) has textile manufactures, especially silk ribbons, and makes dyes, drugs, and other chemicals. In addition to the routes which it commands down the Rhine and through the Gate of Burgundy via Belfort, it has direct access to the Folded Jura by the Birse valley.

The immediate point, however, is to suggest that to reach any of the Swiss alpine routes a crossing of the Jura ridge has to be made, the apparently 'natural' route via the Rhine, Koblenz, and the Aar trans-Jura gorge being indirect. This is even more true of the Rhone gorge, so that the significance of the thinning out of the ridges west of Geneva and north of Brugg respectively is minimized by the position of the narrowed areas. But it is apparent from what has been already said as to the nature of the Jura valleys that any traverse of the folded belt must be circuitous, where the course of a particular stream is followed, and must also involve sooner or later a passage over or through a ridge to reach another river system. Fig. 31 illustrates the first point (cf. also the section, Fig. 32). It

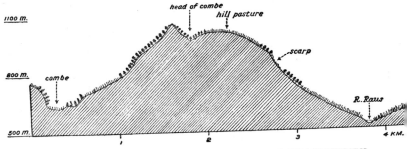

FIG. 32. SECTION ACROSS LES RAIMEUX RIDGE, JURA MOUNTAINS

The section is drawn from the Combe Chopin (Fig. 31) to the Raus valley. It shows the dry combes which run up towards the upper levels, the alternation of pastures and woods, and the presence of fields in the Raus valley.

shows that the Birse reaches Moutier (Münster) after flowing in a longitudinal valley, and unites there with its little tributary the Raus, flowing in the same valley but in the opposite direction. The united stream turns sharply northwards, cutting through a ridge transversely in a series of *cluses*, some only of which are shown. The gorges are wide enough to allow, with some difficulty, for the passage of the road and railway. The latter follows the river to Delémont (Fig. 29), where it branches, one fork descending the river to Basel, while the other, by means of a tunnel through Mont Terrible, reaches Porrentruy, and crosses the French frontier to Delle and Belfort (Paris). But while the Birse thus offers a route from Moutier to Basel, we have still to consider the means of reaching the Plateau surface from the former town. Fig. 33 suggests the three possibilities, which are of much historical interest. The Birse may be followed upstream, where there is the usual alternation of longitudinal and transverse valleys, until a curious gap, the Pierre Pertuis, enables the Suze valley to be reached and followed to

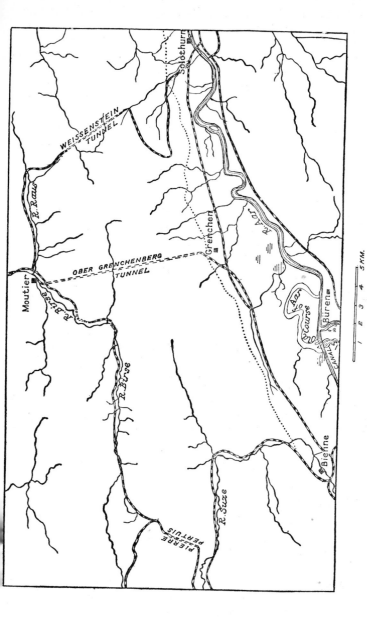

FIG. 33. TRANS-JURA ROUTES FROM MOUTIER TO THE AAR VALLEY

The dotted line indicates the edge of the Jura Mountains towards the swampy Aar valley. Note the course of the Jura rivers and compare Fig. 31.

9

Bienne. This was a Roman route. It carries a railway which required comparatively little tunnelling, but is indirect and has heavy gradients. The second possibility is to follow the Raus till it ceases to offer a route and then tunnel through the Weissenstein ridge (tunnel 2 miles long) to reach Solothurn. This was the old main line and was replaced by the construction of the Ober Grenchenberg tunnel (5⅓ miles, opened in 1916) which leads direct from Moutier to Grenchen (Granges) in the Aar valley, and so to Bienne and Berne. The three stages in the development of routes here illustrate the increasing tendency to revert to lengthy and costly tunnels

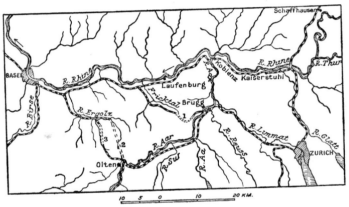

FIG. 34. TRANS-JURA ROUTES FROM BASEL TO THE AAR VALLEY

1. The Bötzberg tunnel. 2. The Lower Hauenstein tunnel. 3. The Upper Hauenstein tunnel.
    Only the main railways are shown. Beyond the limit of the map the railway running south from Olten branches to Lucerne (St. Gothard) and Berne (Lötschberg).

rather than to utilize the devious lines marked out by nature. The particular route just described connects not only through Berne with the important resorts of Interlaken, Grindelwald, etc., but also with the Lötschberg tunnel line.

   Conditions at the north-eastern end of the Jura are very similar, and may be noted briefly to illustrate this point of competition between routes (Fig. 34). Where the spur between the Aar and the Reuss dies down just before the confluence stood the Roman town of Vindonissa, later replaced by Brugg. Vindonissa was a road centre, one road leading to Koblenz at the Aar-Rhine junction, and another across the Jura obliquely to the Rhine near Laufenburg. The direct railway from Basel to Zurich (Arlberg) follows roughly this route, which involves but a short tunnel under the Bötzberg. But Brugg (Vindonissa) has lost much of its earlier importance as a nodal point in favour of Olten, to reach which a longer Jura crossing from the Ergolz valley is necessary. Here again we have an older and a newer route, the latter with a longer tunnel. The older route passes by the Upper Hauenstein tunnel (3) and has heavier gradients than the newer one (opened in 1914) by the Lower Hauenstein tunnel (2), the most direct access to Lucerne and the St. Gothard. It will be noted that in both the cases described the recent improvements not only give better access to Italy, but tap heavy local tourist traffic. The Delle-Delémont-Bienne-Berne route, with its continuation in the Lötschberg line, represents an attempt to draw off the tourist traffic to the Upper Valais from the direct Simplon route, improved in 1914 by the construction of the Mont d'Or tunnel between Frasne and Vallorbe, which cut out the deviation via Pontarlier.

THE ALPINE VALLEYS

On this subject little need be added to what has been already said incidentally. By far the most interesting is the Rhone valley, and Figs. 35, 36, and 37 illustrate some of the main points. The effect of past glaciation is seen in the peculiar U-shape, with the shoulders marking the upper limits of the old glaciers; and of present glaciation in the copious silting, and the fans formed where the lateral glacial torrents enter the main valley. These fans form the favourite sites for valley settlements, which thus escape the cold air which stagnates over the valley floor in winter. The sloping shoulders, above which rise the rocky surfaces unaffected by the earlier glaciation, are similarly warmer in winter than the valley floor (temperature inversion). According to their height they offer sites for permanent settlements surrounded by arable land, or, where they are above the limit of cultivation, for seasonally-occupied huts (cf. p. 70), the adjacent slopes furnishing either hay crops or forming high pastures (alps). In the lower parts of the main and lateral valleys sunny slopes (Figs. 35 and 36) are devoted to the vine, air drainage being probably as important as water drainage in determining the range of the plant. The floor of the Rhone valley has been improved and in the section from Sierre to Martigny has been transformed into a lovely fruit garden where apricots, fine apples, pears, strawberries, and vegetables (especially asparagus) are grown.

The climate of the Rhone valley is particularly interesting. Precipitation is remarkably low, a considerable area, extending from below Sion nearly to Visp, being included within the isohyet of 60 cm. (23½ in.), while even Zermatt, at a height of 1,620 m., has only 75 cm. (under 30 in.) as compared with the average of 100 cm. for the much lower Plateau stations. There is a tendency also to a late summer or autumn maximum, that is, the conditions approximate towards those prevailing in the northern part of the Mediterranean area. Temperatures also are moderate in winter and high in summer, Sion (540 m.) having January and July means of −1·1°C. (30°F.) and 19·6°C. (67·5°F.).

Such facts exert much influence on natural vegetation, cultivated crops and human life generally. Thus while the Jura region, despite the heavy rainfall, suffers from a deficiency of surface water in summer, the Valais with a low precipitation owes to its summer temperatures and the alpine glaciers and snow-fields a water supply which becomes more copious as the need increases. Irrigation is practised everywhere by simple but remarkably effective and ingenious methods, water being carried from the mountain torrents in open channels along the shelves with their fields and pastures. These channels during the summer days carry more and more water as the sun increases in strength, the amount diminishing as the temperature falls. Surplus water is not only easily carried back to the streams at a lower level, but can be used directly for power in saw and flour mills and even for driving churns. There is of course also abundant power for electric installations, and the use of electric light is almost universal not only here but in the whole country.

The vegetation is both varied and diverse. The beech extends only up to the gorge at St. Maurice, shrinking back from the drier upper valley—a reproduction in miniature of its distribution within the Mediterranean region. A variety of wild plants also indicates the Mediterranean affinities of the climate. One of the most interesting is the small shrubby Ephedra, very abundant near Sion. The genus is warm-temperate (Morocco, etc.), found especially in arid regions, and belongs to an aberrant family of Gymnosperms (cone-bearing plants). Other southern types are hyssop, 'smoke' sumach (*Rhus cotinus*), and the savin juniper. Almost more striking is the fact that almond, fig, pomegranate, and even prickly pear (Opuntia) have run wild, introducing a strange note in an alpine valley. Apricots and peaches among fruit-trees are also characteristic of the warmer parts of canton Valais. They emphasize the exceptional features of the canton. It should be noted that some of the plants named appear also in canton Ticino and in the southern valleys (Val Bregaglia and Val di Poschiavo) in Grisons; but their presence there is not remarkable since these areas belong to the southern slope of the Alps. It is the fact that Valais is separated from Italy by the loftiest chain of the Swiss Alps that makes its vegetation so remarkable. We have already noted the great height to which cultivated crops ascend (p. 66); it may be added that the tree limit rises to the astonishing height of over 2,200 m. (cf. the Jura where it is only 1,400–1,600 m.

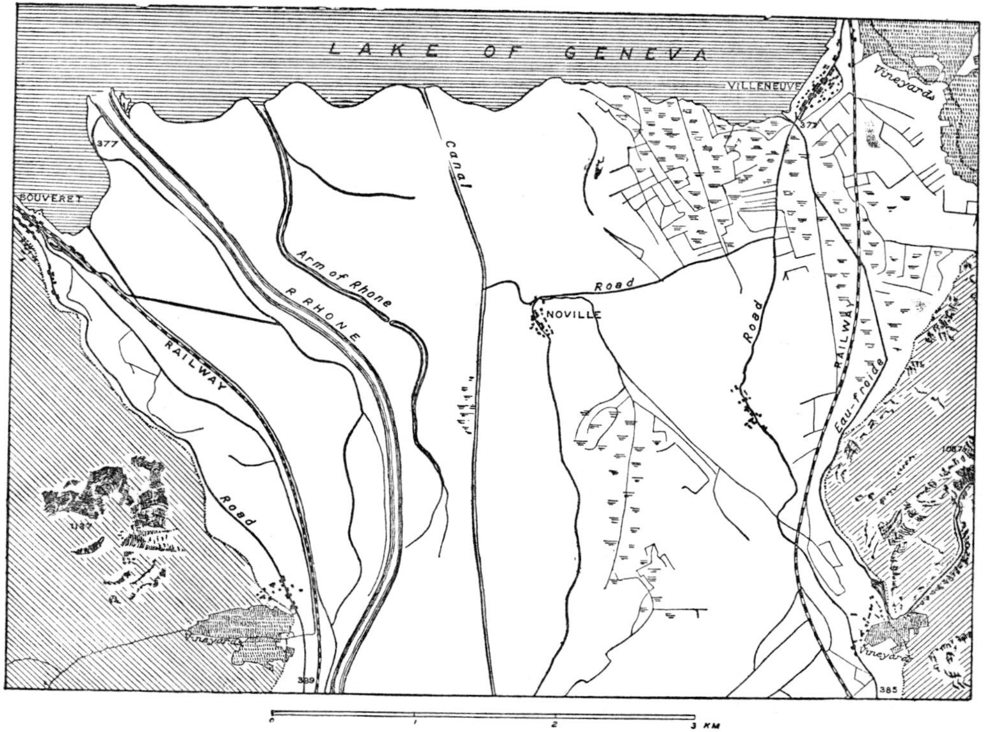

FIG. 35. THE ENTRY OF THE RHONE INTO THE LAKE OF GENEVA

The great size of the delta is associated with the amount of debris brought down by the Rhone from the glaciers of its upper valley. Note the swampy alluvial flats with their drainage ditches, and the vineyards on the sloping fans of the lateral torrents. Areas above 400 m. are stippled, rocky surfaces shaded; the spot heights show the gentle slope of the delta, as compared with the rapid rise of the bounding hills. (*From the Swiss 1/25000 map.*)

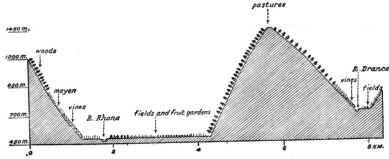

FIG. 36. SECTION FROM THE RHONE TO THE DRANCE VALLEY ABOVE
MARTIGNY

To the left of the diagram is the steep, wooded slope which forms the
right bank of the wide, U-shaped Rhone valley. Note that while the left
bank is wooded throughout, the sunny, southward-facing right bank is
wooded only in its upper and steeper part, and below carries first a mayen
or spring pasturage, with huts, and then vineyards. The valley floor is now
mainly cultivated. In the higher Drance valley vineyards again appear on
the southward-facing slope. (*From the Swiss 1/50000 map.*)

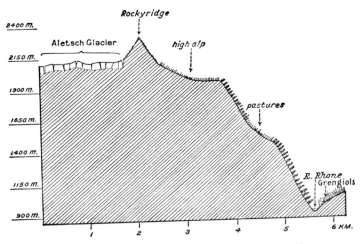

FIG. 37. SECTION ACROSS THE UPPER RHONE VALLEY

The section is taken midway between Mörel and Fiesch, and shows the
village of Grengiols, placed on a left-bank alluvial fan. Another village,
surrounded by pastures, is placed where a slight easing off of the right-
bank slope occurs, due to a stage in glacial retreat. The upper alp, with its
seasonally occupied huts, overlies the broad shelf which marks the former
upper limit of glaciation. Above this shoulder the right which forms the
parting towards the Aletsch glacier is rocky and devoid of signs of glacial
sculpture. (*From the Swiss 1/50000 map.*)

STATISTICAL SUMMARY

AREA AND SURFACE

Total area 15,940 sq. miles or 41,295 sq. km.; 10 per cent belongs to the Jura, 30 per cent to the Plateau, and 60 per cent to the Alps.

The land utilization can roughly be divided into four: one-quarter unproductive, one-quarter alpine pastures, one-quarter forests, and one-quarter cultivated land (grassland and arable).

The woods are made up of about 30 per cent broad-leaved trees, chiefly beech, and 70 per cent coniferous, spruce being the most widely distributed species. Forests are distributed over the surface in the proportion of 20 per cent in the Jura, 25 per cent on the Plateau, and 55 per cent in the Alps. Wood consumption exceeds national production.

Of grain crops wheat covers the greatest area, followed by oats and rye (especially in Valais). Production fell steadily from the middle of the nineteenth century to the war periods during which it rose. Great efforts were made after the 1939–45 war to maintain the arable area at a grand total of about 300,000 hectares (in 1939 the total area was about 200,000 hectares). Of other crops potatoes are produced in quantities normally sufficient to meet the demand; but sugar, tobacco, wine, fruit, garden produce, etc., require to be largely supplemented by imports.

The predominance of grassland, affording rich pasture, is reflected in the amount of live stock kept, and particularly in the great numbers of dairy cattle. Cattle exceed 1,500,000 head; pigs over 600,000; goats about 200,000; but there are under 200,000 sheep. Horses, mules, and donkeys, once used largely for transport in the mountain regions, now number less than 150,000. The number of roads open to motor traffic is constantly increasing.

There are more than 200,000 holdings of an average size of only 15 acres. Only 15 per cent of the farmers are tenants.

EXTERNAL TRADE

Imports in 1938–9 averaged about 1,760 million Swiss francs (then 25 to the £) and exports 1,300 million francs. But the profits of the tourist industry, as well as the capital investments in foreign countries must be added as invisible exports. There was an import of 480 million francs of foodstuffs but an export of only 75 millions (mainly cheese). Raw material imports were valued at 650 millions, exports at only 85. Imports of manufactures were 600 millions whilst exports amounted to 1,140 millions (watches, machinery, chemicals, textiles).

The chief suppliers of the imports were, in order, Germany, France, U.S.A., Italy, Great Britain. Exports went to Great Britain, France, U.S.A., and Italy.

The relatively small fuel imports, despite the fact that there are but small coal deposits of a very low value, is associated with the great development of hydro-electric power. The maximum capacity of the power stations is some 2·5 million kW.

POPULATION

The 1941 census showed a total population of 4,265,703, giving an average density of 264 per sq. mile, or 340 per sq. mile of productive land. In 100 years the population has doubled. One-third of the inhabitants live in towns of over 10,000 inhabitants. The four towns of over 100,000 inhabitants account for about three-quarters of a million people. But about 820,000 live in communes of under 1,000. Because Swiss people live in relatively small settlements, foreigners often have the impression that Switzerland is a country of farmers and herdsmen. But in 1930 only 21 per cent of the working population was engaged on the land (including forestry and fishing), whilst industry absorbs 45 per cent, commerce 10 per cent, and hotels only 5 per cent (but many more part-time).

Four languages are officially recognized. German is spoken by 73 per cent, French by 21 per cent, Italian by 5 per cent, and Romansch (in the Grisons) by 1 per cent of the population.

REFERENCES

MAPS

Switzerland is one of the best-mapped countries in the world, and the maps are readily accessible. There are five official maps of the whole country: 1. The Dufour map, 25 sheets, scale 1/100000. 2. The general map, 4 sheets, 1/250000, based on the Dufour map. 3. The Siegfried Topographical Atlas, 546 sheets, Jura and Plateau on scale of 1/25000, Alps on scale of 1/50000. 4. The 1/100000 uniform with the World map on this scale, in one sheet. 5. The 'Neue Landeskarte der Schweiz' on the 1/50000 scale. Certain topographical plans on the scale of 1/5000 and 1/10000 are also available.

In addition to these purely topographic maps, there is an Economic map of Switzerland on the scale of 1/300000 prepared by Dr. Hans Carol, of the Geographical Institute of the University of Zurich and published by Kümmerly-Frey of Berne. There are also good maps in the *Schweizer Mittelschulatlas*.

BOOKS

The best study is J. Früh, *Geographie der Schweiz*, in 3 vols. (St. Gallen, 1929–38). A one vol. work is W. Leemann, *Landeskunde der Schweiz* (Erlenbach, 1939), and a good booklet is O. Flückiger's *Die Schweiz, Natur und Wirtschaft* (Zürich, 1934). A summary of the economic geography of Switzerland is given in Chisholm's *Handbook of Commercial Geography*, revised by L. D. Stamp, 1937, and of general geography in Em. de Martonne, 'Europe Centrale', *Géographie Universelle*, Tome 4, 1931.

On the Geology and Morphology consult A. Heim, *Geologie der Schweiz*, 3 vols. (Leipzig, 1918–22); Penk and Brückner, *Die Alpen im Eiszeitalter*

(Leipzig, 1909). On the Climate and Vegetation, J. Maurer, R. Billwiller, and C. Hess, *Das Klima der Schweiz* (Zürich and Berne, 1923-9). The various guide-books such as Baedeker are also valuable. The Swiss geographical journals are *Der Schweizer Geograph* (Berne, 1923-45), followed by *Geographica Helvetica* (Berne, 1946 onwards).

PART III

ITALY

CHAPTER VI

ITALY: STRUCTURE, RELIEF, AND NATURAL DIVISIONS

General Survey—Apennine Tectonics—Post-Oligocene Changes and their Effects—Southern Peninsular Italy—Central Italy—Other Elements

GENERAL SURVEY

ITALY shows much apparent simplicity of form, for it appears to fall naturally into three divisions. To the north lie the plains, drained mainly by the Po, the only really large Italian river, and, save where they slope eastwards to the northern Adriatic, girdled by mountains. The narrow peninsula, traversed by the Apennines and dividing into two secondary peninsulas in the south, seems to form a natural second unit, while, though Corsica is French, the islands of Sicily and Sardinia, with the Tuscan archipelago and the smaller groups within the Tyrrhenian Sea, appear to constitute a third element.

The total area, in round figures, is 310,000 sq. km., or about 120,000 sq. miles, and is thus closely comparable to that of the British Isles, while the population of 43,000,000 is not greatly inferior to that of Great Britain. Despite the presence of the northern 'continental' portion, Italy also shares to some extent the maritime character of Britain, for 80 per cent of the surface is less than 62 miles from the sea. Further, so long as the Mediterranean was the world sea it had a peculiarly favourable position in relation to maritime trade routes, and the piercing of the Suez Canal restored this to some extent. First the alpine passes and then the alpine tunnels and railways, also, have always made the lands which are now Italian the natural intermediaries between continental Europe and the Mediterranean. Finally, the water frontier of some 4,100 miles (6,660 km.) exceeds greatly in length the land frontier of some 1,290 miles (2,078 km.), and the 1919 frontier changes strengthened the latter from the strategic aspect as well as considerably extending the national territories (by 23,300 sq. km., or nearly 9,000 sq. miles).

In more detail we may note that the great flattened arc of the Alps, continued into the plateau of the Carso (Karst), forms a girdle round the northern section of the plains. In the west the frontier with France rises to or beyond the crest to the advantage of France. Beyond the complex Swiss frontier, already discussed, the frontier with Austria crosses the Reschen Scheideck (Resia) and Brenner passes, and includes all the feeders of the Adige, Piave, and Tagliamento before turning southwards to the sea north of Trieste. To the south of the plains the Apennines continue the mountain girdle. Separated, according to the usual interpretation, by the deep gap of the Cadibona pass (465 m.) from the Ligurian Alps, they bend round to enter the peninsula, and traverse it throughout, running broadly parallel to its south-easterly trend. In this section coastal lowlands occur, now on one shore and now on the other, in a fashion which almost justifies the hasty conclusion that we have here a central mountain axis with bordering plains. Finally, the island form and the relation to the deep Tyrrhenian Sea seem to make Sicily, Sardinia, and the Tuscan archipelago a natural unit.

But even though this tripartite division of the Italian lands has certain merits, it obscures the real complexity of structure and detailed topography. Thus the conception of the plains as a single unit, floored by unmodified recent deposits, and so sharply contrasted with their folded and complex borderlands, fails to take account of all the facts. Near Turin the surface uniformity is broken by the appearance of the Monferrato Hills (716 m.), where tertiary beds, which have been involved in the mountain folding, appear, and not only introduce an alien element into the landscape, but also a new structural note. Similarly, between Verona and Padua, in mid-plain, there arise the igneous Berici and Euganean Hills (603 m.), equally alien in character, and of early tertiary age as compared with the much more recent volcanic areas of peninsular Italy.

Peninsular Italy itself is far more complex than any summary allusion to mountain backbone and marginal lowlands can suggest, while Sicily and Sardinia differ in almost every respect, structural no less than geographical. The former is but a separated part of the peninsula, containing elements identical with those found in Calabria; but Sardinia is built largely of crystalline rocks. Nor, altogether apart from the narrowness of the Strait of Messina, can the island form of Sicily be regarded as a distinguishing feature, for in the geological yesterday both it and the southern part of the peninsula were represented by an archipelago, and it is a mere geological accident that Calabria now forms part of the peninsula while Sicily remains separated from it. Sardinia, on the other hand, is continental in aspect.

Since then a mere division into the three elements of hill-girdled northern plains, peninsula with mountain backbone and Tyrrhenian islands fails to take account of the facts of geographical importance, some attempt must be made to discuss the structure of Italy. It should be realized, however, that much uncertainty and difference of opinion still exists. The description can only be cursory, and must be restricted to an attempt to give an intelligible—if somewhat provisional—interpretation of the existing relief features.

APENNINE TECTONICS

Fig. 38 indicates Kober's view of the main tectonic features, that is, of the nature of the mountain-building processes and, particularly, of the relation of the Alps and Apennines. According to him the Apennines are not a continuation of the Alps, but form part of the Dinarides, and are folded towards the east. The Western Alps, represented by the outer zone and the zone of Pennine nappes, come down to the sea in the region of the Franco-Italian frontier, but are separated from the Apennines proper in the region of Sestri Ponente, at the head of the Gulf of Genoa, by a narrow East Alpine belt which extends into Corsica. The Apennine folded belt, which dates from early oligocene times, though both antecedent and 'posthumous' movements occurred, extends from Genoa throughout the peninsula, into the secondary one of Calabria, with a continuation into northern Sicily. As in the Alps, overthrusting has occurred, with the development of nappes, but the outermost zone (A1), that facing the Adriatic, has not been greatly displaced. This zone is best developed in the Abruzzi, where it consists of mesozoic limestones. It is bordered on its outer side, throughout its extension, by unfolded tertiary beds, corresponding to the molasse beds of the Swiss Plateau, but in distinction to the outer Alpine Zone (p. 36), it is not thrust over these.

The lowest nappe of the three recognized by Kober is exposed only in the 'window' (x) of the Apuan Alps of Tuscany, where the metamorphosed limestones forming the marbles of Carrara and Massa are of much economic importance. The next, or Tuscan, nappe (A2) includes a great variety of rocks, of different ages, from palaeozoic to tertiary, and varying in character from crystallines to limestones, radiolarian cherts, conglomerates and sandstones. This nappe constitutes a large part of the northern Apennines. Finally, the third or uppermost nappe is the Ligurian one (A3), including, save for the Carrara 'window', the Apuan Alps, Monte Pisano east of Pisa, the hills between Siena and Grosseto, and generally what are called the Sub-Apennines, characterized by their metalliferous rocks. The rocks are sandstones, serpentine, conglomerates, and eruptive rocks, and the Ligurides seem to extend into Elba. According to Kober they represent the rock-sheet which was earliest and most frequently disturbed by mountain-building processes, and in

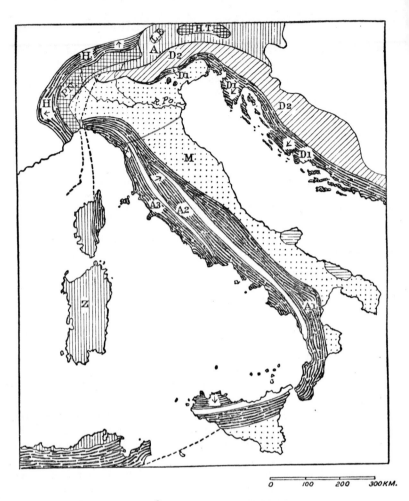

FIG. 38. TECTONIC MAP OF ITALY

In the Alpine girdle to the north the Western and Eastern Alps are shown in generalized fashion (see Figs. 12 and 13 for details). In the Western Alps H is the zone which includes the Helvetian nappes, and PN the Pennine nappes. The Eastern Alps also contain two main elements. To the north are the Austrid (A) nappes, built of the Tirolid and Grisonid nappes shown in Fig. 13, the lower (West Alpine) nappes being exposed in the windows of the Lower Engadine (L.E.) and Hohe Tauern (H.T.). To the south lie the Dinarides, built of an outer (D1) and inner (D2) zone, and continued into the Balkan peninsula.

The Apennines consist of an outer, little-displaced zone (A1) and three series of nappes. Of these the lowest (x) is exposed only in the window of the Apuan Alps; then comes the Tuscan nappe (A2), and the uppermost or Ligurian nappe (A3). M is the belt of young unfolded beds, the Monte Gargano peninsula and Apulian limestone plateau being indicated by shading, and the volcanic hills of the north-eastern plains by cross-hatching. Z = the crystalline rocks of Sardinia and Corsica. For fuller explanation see text. (*After Kober, modified.*)

their present form are but the residue of vast rock-masses once widely thrust over the Tuscan nappe, and now mainly removed by erosion. With the extent and frequency of folding within them is associated great volcanic activity, though the volcanoes of Tuscany have long passed into the quiescent stage.

This description, even if it helps to give some idea of the character of the Apennines, is yet mainly of interest to us in that it serves to supplement the sketch already given in the case of the Alps of modern views as to mountain-building processes. In the case of Switzerland some discussion of the subject appeared essential, for the recognition of the main elements of the Eastern and Western Alps, and of the origin of the contrasts between them, does help us to understand the main relief features. But in a study of Italy it has to be admitted that the effects of the mountain-building processes play a quite subordinate part in determining the existing land-forms. It may indeed be said that epeirogenic (p. 31) movements have been far more important than orogenic ones, and, combined with volcanic outbursts of geologically recent date, fracture and collapse, have been the main factors in giving the lands their present characteristics. In these respects Italy resembles Greece rather than Switzerland, that is, is truly Mediterranean and not alpine.

The slow secular movement has been predominantly in the upward direction since tertiary times, or, in other words, the lands have increased at the expense of the sea. On the other hand, in the Greek area the collapse of the Aegean has been at least in part quite recent, so that the sea has gained upon the lands, though there also great elevation of parts of the lands has taken place.

POST-OLIGOCENE CHANGES AND THEIR EFFECTS

The evidence upon which is based the statement that Italy has shown a secular though interrupted movement of uplift since the close of tertiary times is found in the present position of marine deposits. Sea-shells occur in glacial material to the south of the Lake of Como at a height of 370 m. above present sea-level. Even more striking is the fact that, e.g., in Calabria in the south of the peninsula, marine beds of pliocene origin lie at various levels up to 1,300 m. From the distribution of these over the surface of the peninsula it has been deduced that a large part of what is now Italy was submerged during that period. Fig. 39 shows, with some uncertainty as to detail, the distribution of land and water then. But before we examine this figure some other points have to be noted.

As already stated the main Apennine folding seems to date from oligocene, and apparently early oligocene, times. Thus all pre-oligocene rocks, including eocene beds, are folded. But rocks older than mesozoics are exposed over only a small part of the surface. Crystallines appear in the Peloritani Mountains of north-eastern Sicily, and in the Sila and Aspromonte uplands of Calabria (Fig. 41). These were formerly described as parts of the sunken Tyrrhenian Massif, regarded as represented also by much of Sardinia and part of Corsica. On Kober's view of the tectonics of the Apennines, however, they are rather rocks involved in the Apennine folding and exposed by long-continued denudation. Palaeozoic (permo-carboniferous) rocks, in part metamorphosed, occur in Tuscany to a limited extent. Thus the general absence of large areas of old crystalline rocks is a notable contrast with Switzerland and the alpine borderlands of Italy.

Limestones of triassic, jurassic, and cretaceous age cover a larger area, especially in the central Apennines and in the south, being largely replaced in the northern Apennines by eocene limestones. But for a reason which will appear in a moment the landscape of peninsular Italy is not dominated by massive limestones to the extent to which this account would suggest. It is in point of fact the widespread presence of late tertiary beds of a more readily weathered type, such as sandstones, marls, clays, and conglomerates, which is the outstanding feature of the country, and helps to give it its geologically youthful appearance.

The distribution of these beds is interesting, because of the light which it throws on the history of the land surface. In the first place, and in marked contrast with the Alps, oligocene conglomerates (lower molasse, p. 96) occur far within the folded area, especially in the northern Apennines. This means that the mountains were being worn down as they rose. On them lie unconformably miocene sandstones, marls, and clays (upper molasse), indicating renewed elevation and subsequent denudation. Thus already in mid-tertiary times the Apennines had been reduced to a mere skeleton of a mountain chain, and the folded areas had been interpenetrated by deposits of later date than the main (early oligocene) folding.

Another striking feature is presented by the cauldron subsidences on the Tyrrhenian border, which form continuations of the area of collapse represented by that sea. Two of these can be recognized, apart from the Gulf of Genoa to the north. One occurs in Tuscany and Latium, the other is represented by the Plain of Campania and the Gulfs of Gaeta, Naples, Salerno, and Policastro. Both areas are associated with a strong development of vulcanism. Farther south the fractures were of the transverse Greek type, rather than of cauldron nature. Thus alike in the north-west, in Tuscany, and in the south, the continuity of the chain was broken. In Tuscany the collapse affected only the area nearest the Tyrrhenian Sea, the centre of disturbance. Here a series of islands appeared (Fig. 39, 1), separated from each other by straits, and from the main Apennine chain, which remained intact, by a wider belt of sea. In the south, owing to the combination of the cauldron movements and transverse

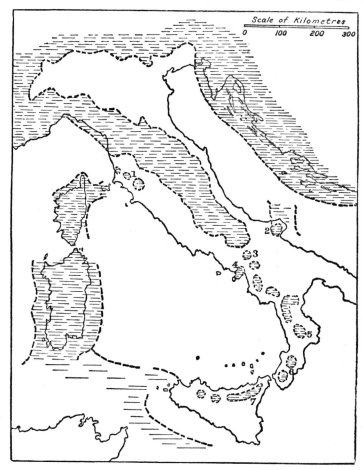

FIG. 39. DISTRIBUTION OF LAND (SHADED) AND WATER IN THE ITALIAN AREA DURING PLIOCENE TIMES

The figure 1 is placed against the area which now forms the Sub-Apennines; 2 against the Monte Gargano peninsula; 3 against the Matese group; 4 against the Sorrento peninsula; 5 the Sila massif; 6 the Serra-Aspromonte massif; 7 the Peloritani Mountains of Sicily. (*Based on Fischer and Rovereto.*)

aulting, the whole width of the chain was affected, and it became series of fragments, separated by sunken areas. In both cases the ormer straits and arms of the sea are often indicated on the present map by relative depressions, lying between the more resistant masses which formed the earlier islands.

Further, while active or quiescent volcanoes are associated with the Tyrrhenian side of the Apennines, that is, with the area of collapse, and are as a rule absent on the outer side, there are two exceptions in the southern area, where faulting occurred as a repercussion of the Tyrrhenian collapse. One is the great cone of Etna on the southern side of the continuation of the Apennines into Sicily; the other is the extinct volcano of Monte Vulture on the northern border of Lucania, along the line of the relative depression indicated by the River Ofanto, which enters the Adriatic near Barletta, and the River Sele flowing into the Tyrrhenian to the south of Salerno (Fig. 41).

We are now in a position to examine in detail the conditions which existed in pliocene times as shown in Fig. 39. At that time the northern plains, the home to-day of so large a proportion of the Italian people, were still beneath the sea. The existing peninsula was represented by a much narrower and shorter one, plus an island girdle extending into the north of what is now Sicily. The peninsular section was linked to the Alps by a narrow neck in what is now the region of Genoa. It consisted only of the axis of the present northern and central Apennines. The section towards the Tyrrhenian Sea was submerged save for islands or shoals, now represented by the so-called Sub-Apennines of Tuscany, that interrupted hill-girdle already mentioned made up of the Apuan Alps, Monte Pisano, and the hills west of Siena, with a continuation into the promontory of Monte Argentario. It has also to be remembered that even the pliocene peninsular area had not the uniformity which the diagram seems to suggest. As already seen, the folded rocks within it had been previously exposed to prolonged erosion, with deposition of the products of the weathering processes in inner basins.

In the south the semicircular archipelago shows that the whole width of the Apennines was fractured and largely submerged. The isolated land area to the east of the island girdle corresponds on the present-day map to the curious peninsula of Monte Gargano. Like the limestone plateau of southern Apulia, apparently at least largely submerged in pliocene times, Monte Gargano consists of slightly-folded mesozoic limestones, mainly of cretaceous age. Similar rocks reappear in the Tremiti Islands to the north and in Pelagosa to the north-east (Fig. 40), and we have already seen (p. 21) that a submarine ridge extends across the Adriatic here. According to Kober these limestone areas probably belong to the Dinarides and not to the Apennines.

It is thus clear that before the post-pliocene uplift, that is, before the Italian lands acquired any approach to their present form, the

Apennines were already a shattered ruin. At most they formed a disarticulated framework round which the present peninsula was built up. The description given disposes alike of the idea that the existing peninsula can be regarded as a unit, and of the simple conception of it as existing as a central mountain area of folded rocks with marginal lowlands made of younger, unfolded beds. Before the uplift occurred there was a marked contrast between the southern

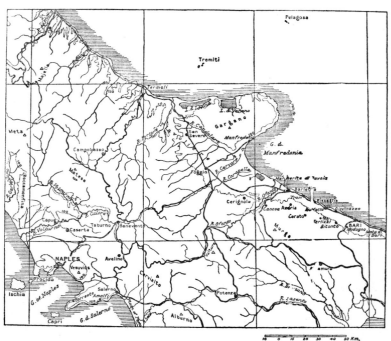

FIG. 40. PART OF SOUTHERN PENINSULAR ITALY, SHOWING CHIEF TOWNS AND LINES OF COMMUNICATION IN APULIA

This map should be compared with Fig. 59. The railway lines running north and south of Naples, omitted here, are shown in that figure. The contour is that of 100 m. The Vallo di Diano (cf. Fig. 41), which is traversed by a railway, lies immediately to the east of Monte Alburno. (*Based on the 1/1000000 map.*)

and central peninsular areas, and in the latter between the Adriatic border, uniformly depressed, and the Tyrrhenian one with its cauldron subsidences, its active volcanoes, and its marginal islands. The immediate effect of the uplift, which was accentuated to the south, was to obscure, but not to obliterate, the initial contrasts between the outer (Adriatic-Ionian) and inner (Tyrrhenian) borders. The long gulf which now forms the northern plains was narrowed and so shallowed that it could be readily filled up by glacial and alluvial deposits. From Piedmont to Sicily a strip of marine pliocene deposits was added to the lands, thus increasing the width of the original peninsula in the north and centre. In the south they filled in, or at least shallowed, the strait between Monte Gargano and the fractured Apennines, preparing the way for the attachment of the former to the Italian lands. The uplift was also sufficiently great to reduce the straits between the parts of the archipelago to shallow basins, readily converted into dry land by fluviatile deposition, and thus lead up to the conversion of the former islands into a continuous land-mass, of curious form, united by young deposits to the extremity of the pliocene peninsula. It will be noted that the continuity of the border of late tertiary beds along the Adriatic shore (Fig. 38), except for the 'alien' Monte Gargano peninsula, means that the coast-line is mainly smooth and devoid of harbours.

The greater initial complexity of the Tyrrhenian border, with its localized subsidences and volcanic activity, has produced very different conditions. Here there is neither a uniform coast-line, nor yet a continuous strip of uplifted pliocene rocks. The rocks which form the shore-line are indeed of very varied nature. Thus it is made of folded Apennine elements in parts of Tuscany, as in the peninsula of Monte Argentario; in Latium, as near Civitavecchia; in Campania, as in the Sorrento peninsula and the promontory between the Gulfs of Salerno and Policastro; and on the western coast of Calabria and the northern one of Sicily. Elsewhere, as notably round the Gulf of Naples, recent volcanic deposits occur on the shore, or, as in the Pontine and Maremma plains, the rivers are still engaged in building the land out seawards with the help of their load of debris. Thus as compared with the east we have a much greater variety of rock types, and a much more varied coast-line, yielding a number of potential harbours, especially in the days of small boats. Further, the process of attaching the pliocene Tuscan islands to the pliocene peninsula took place in gradual stages, sea-gulfs becoming large inland lakes, and these being gradually reduced in size with the development of the river systems. Changes in the extent of the residual lakes and in the relations of the river systems have continued into historical time. Some of the old lake beds are of high fertility, and their presence facilitates communication within the mountain area. Other highly fertile areas are found in some of the regions of vulcanism, while the old rocks of Tuscany contain metallic ores, otherwise rare in Italy. The combination of such facts has made the western coast of peninsular Italy, throughout historical time, of much greater importance than the Adriatic one. But despite these contrasts the fundamental division of the Italian peninsula must be between the north central area, within which the Apennine belt remained continuous during pliocene times, and the southern area, shattered by cross-faulting, and more extensively submerged. To the former, with its outer girdle of young rocks, is attached on the west the Sub-Apennine area; the latter, or Southern Peninsular Italy, shows much complexity of detail. With it we may conveniently begin.

SOUTHERN PENINSULAR ITALY

The southern limit of the pliocene peninsula may be taken as indicated on the present map by the mountain groups of Maiella and Meta, in the south of the province of Abruzzi and Molise. The Matese group, separated from the Meta by the depression in which flows the upper Volturno river (Fig. 40), represents the first member of the island girdle of Fig. 39. Southern Peninsular Italy, as thus defined, is built of three main elements, linked together by the uplifted marine pliocene beds and by post-pliocene alluvial deposits. These three are the volcanic area round Naples; the fragments of the folded Apennines represented by the pliocene island girdle; and the limestones of Monte Gargano and the Apulian tableland (Murge). From the geographical standpoint this complex origin is of great importance, both because of the varying agricultural value of the different rock types, and because of its effect in dividing the area into a number of well-defined regions.

The activity of Vesuvius is believed to date only from the end of the pliocene period, and in the Phlegraean fields to the west of Naples minor oscillations of sea-level have taken place in historic times, as is shown by the famous Serapeum at Pozzuoli. The point of immediate interest, however, is to note that the increase of the lands in this area since the pliocene uplift is due to two main causes. One is the actual surface discharge of volcanic material into a shallow sea, and the second is river action. Thus much of the Plain of Campania, which gives its name to the province, has been built up by the alluvium brought down by the River Volturno, which has filled in a shallow bay between two areas of volcanic rocks (cf. Fig. 41). Here, then, we have land still in the making, both in the geological and in the geographical sense, for the lowest parts of such alluvial flats, though drained and greatly improved in places, are still too malarious for settlement.

The fragmentation of the Apennines means that no continuous mountain chain separated the Tyrrhenian shore, either from that which abuts on the Adriatic or from that of the Ionian Sea, including the Gulf of Taranto, which divides the secondary Calabrian peninsula from that of Apulia. Let us note the significance of this statement. The Calore tributary of the River Volturno traverses an important depression within which lies the historic town of Benevento (Fig. 40).

The lowland has always formed a valuable line of communication. It carries the railway from Naples to Foggia; it was crossed by the ancient Latin way from Capua on the lower Volturno to what is now Taranto. Near Ariano, east of Benevento, marine pliocene beds lie at a height 1,200 m. above sea-level; this means that the lowland is a former strait, now uplifted. Further, though in the neighbourhood the railway crosses the watershed between the Tyrrhenian and the Adriatic seas by the help of tunnels, yet we are not here in 'Apennine' land but in a region floored by soft, young beds.

Farther south, again, the block of high land lying between the Gulfs of Salerno and Policastro, and containing the Alburno and Cervati Mountains, is separated from an inner group, with Mt. Volturino, by the long depression called the Vallo di Diano, traversed by the Tanagro tributary of the River Sele—this is again a former strait, now uplifted and filled in. The upper River Agri, a river which flows to the Gulf of Taranto, approaches the Vallo di Diano (Fig. 41); it also occupies a well-defined basin. In Calabria this tendency for the land to be divided into hill blocks, separated by well-marked lowlands, once marine straits, is even more marked. Fig. 60 on p. 197 shows the important Crati lowland. The river (note the town of Cosenza) rises within 10 miles of the Tyrrhenian Sea, from which it is separated only by a narrow coastal range, flows north through the lowland, and then turns on itself to run north-east to the Gulf of Taranto. Still farther south the Catanzaro depression is all but continuous from sea to sea, and separates the former islands indicated by the crystalline massifs of the Sila and the Serra-Aspromonte. The parting between east and west streams here is under 250 m. in height.

In regard to the third structural element we have to note that the former island of Monte Gargano is separated from the Apennine area by the large lowland called the Tavoliere di Puglia. This reaches the sea in swampy and lagoon coasts both to the north and to the east, in the Gulf of Manfredonia (Fig. 40), and is floored in part by uplifted marine pliocene beds, and in part by quite recent deposits. Southwards it is continued, beyond a low parting, into the valley of the River Bradano, which enters the Gulf of Taranto. The whole depression represents the former belt of sea which inter-vened between the fractured Apennines to the west and the 'Dinaric' lands represented by the limestones of Monte Gargano and their continuation in the Murge tableland. The relation of the Tavoliere-Bradano depression to the Benevento one mentioned above should be noted.

The result is that in this southern area we find a definitely Greek type of land, showing a great variety of relief and rocks, divided up into a series of blocks. Though unattractive in places, as in the lowlands of Apulia, in the karstic upland of the Gargano peninsula and the similar but lower Murge tableland with its continuation into the peninsula of Otranto, as well as in the Sila and Serra-Aspromonte uplands, it displays elsewhere areas of high fertility, within easy reach of the sea, so limited naturally both by relief and by a change in the nature of the rocks as to favour concentration of effort. Thus the city-states of Magna Graecia—note, as an example, Sybaris at the mouth of the River Crati—were placed on or near the coast in areas offering local advantages of site and situation.

Some other features of geographical importance, related to the structural features, may be noted. The fracturing and collapse, as already seen, is associated with active vulcanism; but other and more deadly evidence of crustal instability is found in the frequent earthquakes—another feature shared in common with the Greek lands. There are two further menaces to man and his works. The recent and notable elevation of soft, unconsolidated beds above sea-level, and the fact that these overlie rocks of quite different character, such as the granites of Calabria, cause landslides to occur on a scale of which we have no experience in our own country. The slides often occur along the line of junction between different rock-types, and both here and in other parts of the peninsula are of such common occurrence that the Italians have a special name for them—*frane*—meaning a crumbling surface with a tendency to slide downwards. A further consequence, both of the uplift and of the nature of the uplifted beds, accentuated by the rainfall *régime*, is the heavy load of debris carried by the rivers. As this is thrown down in the inner basins or on the coasts, swamps, marshes, and lakes are formed, the natural breeding-places of mosquitoes. Once these are infected with the parasite their presence means malaria, which despite all that has been done remains a plague in southern Italy, where it has always been more general and more severe than in other parts of the country.

CENTRAL ITALY

The part of the peninsula lying to the north of the Matese group forms what may be conveniently called Central Italy. Its northern limit may be taken for our present purpose as a line from Spezia to Rimini, and three outstanding features fall to be noted:

First, the Apennines, whether of moderate height, as in the north (Monte Cimone, 2,163 m.); or broad and relatively lofty as in the Abruzzi, where the Gran Sasso group reaches 2,921 m. in Monte Corno, the highest summit of the range, Monte Vettore in the Sibellini group on the border of the Marches 2,422 m., Monte Velino to the south 2,487 m., and Monte Amaro in the Maiella 2,795 m., form a definite and continuous barrier. Owing to the trend of the range the barrier effect is twofold; it separates the Po plains from the peninsula, and the eastern and western coasts from each other. The northern (Etruscan) section of the Apennines is, it is true, traversed by a number of passes, varying in height from 700 to 1,100 m., and offering no great difficulty. Yet to-day this section is crossed but by four railway routes, the Parma-Spezia, Bologna-Pistoia (Florence), Bologna-Prato (Florence), and Faenza-Florence lines, most of the traffic being concentrated on the third one. The extreme density of the railway network over the plains, and its relative density in the lower Arno basin, compared with these three unbranched connecting strands is a very obvious indication of the topographic barrier between the two. Conditions in the broad Abruzzi section are even more striking. The main railway is coastal from Rimini southwards, and it sends off a large number of branches; but only a few of these cross the whole width of the mountain belt, and then by curiously indirect routes. The lines from Pescara to Rome and from Ancona to Orte afford the only fairly direct connexion between the east and west coasts, and their intricate courses in the mountain section make clear the difficulties which are encountered.

The second outstanding feature is that already noted—the earlier shattering and collapse of large tracts of Apennine land to the west, towards the Ligurian and Tyrrhenian seas, as shown by the existing alluvial basins and depressions. But the virtual continuity of the areas of collapse from the Arno basin in the north, throughout the whole length of the Tiber and even southwards to the district round Naples, is concealed, not only by the presence, especially in Tuscany, of strands of exposed Apennine land, forming minor hill ranges, but by the third feature. This is the great belt of extinct volcanoes (Fig. 41) which, beginning with Monte Amiata (1,734 m.) in southern Tuscany, extends through Latium, where its presence is indicated mainly by the crater lakes, Bolsena, Vico, and Bracciano, the elevation being generally moderate, is continued south of Rome in the Alban Hills, again with similar though smaller crater lakes, and may be regarded as coming to an end in the Roccamonfina cone (M. S. Croce, 1,005 m.), which appears to block the opening of the lower Garigliano (Liri) valley (cf. Figs. 40 and 59). Beyond the Plain of Campania, the fumaroles of the Solfatara and the fiery lavas of Vesuvius show us that we have reached the area of active vulcanism. Further, while Monte Amiata is nearly 35 miles from the sea, and the Alban Hills over 15, at Naples the volcanic area is coastal. This means that the volcanic belt has a less marked easterly trend than the present coast-line. The section between Monte Amiata and the Roccamonfina cone is indeed separated from the sea by a belt, narrowing southwards, formed in part by fragments of Apennine land, as at Monte Argentario, C. Linaro near Civitavecchia, and the Lepini Hills, which approach the shore at the head of the Gulf of

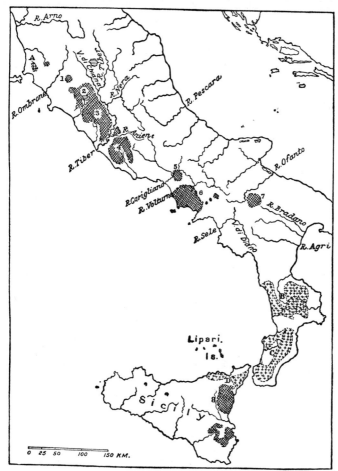

FIG. 41. THE VOLCANOES OF PENINSULAR ITALY, WITH THE CHIEF AREAS OF CRYSTALLINE ROCKS

The chief cones, active or extinct, are indicated by numbers: 1. Mt. Amiata. 2. Lake of Bolsena. 3. Mt. Cimino. 4. Alban Hills. 5. Roccamonfina. 6. Vesuvius, etc. 7. Mt. Vulture. 8. Etna with the Iblei Mountains to the south.

A indicates the position of the crystallines of Tuscany. B, the Sila massif, penetrated by the Crati lowland (Fig. 60). C, the Serra-Aspromonte massif. D, the Peloritani Mountains of Sicily.

Gaeta, but to a much greater extent by recent alluvium and redistributed volcanic deposits, forming naturally the coastal swamps and marshes.

The main contrasts between southern and central peninsular Italy as defined above are now apparent. In the south the active volcanoes, the notable articulation of the shores of the Gulf of Naples, the minor evidence of continuing earth movements in the Phlegraean fields and of fresh outbursts of volcanic activity such as that which gave rise to the cone of Monte Nuove in 1538, leave us in no doubt as to the recent origin of the present features and of their instability. In the central area, although the land-forms, including the present coast-line, are geologically recent, a measure of structural stability was attained before the beginning of historic times. The complexity of origin was concealed by a mantle of debris spread over the whole. This, combined with the moderate uplift, increased the land areas greatly at the expense of what had once been shallow seas, studded with islands of older rock. South of these seas, island volcanoes developed, of the type of the present Lipari Islands. With the uplift and the spread of alluvial deposits the former sea was converted into bays and long lakes, and progressively filled in. The two great river systems of the Arno and the Tiber developed highly complex courses, linking together the former lakes by gorges through ridges, and finding devious exits to the sea. In detail their courses have changed considerably during the historic period, and though the basins through which they pass offer opportunities both for extensive cultivation and for the construction of easy lines of communication, it has yet to be remembered that marshes, both coastal and inland, areas of interior drainage and of uncertain flow, and the flood menace mean that the land is not, as it were, ready-made but requires continuous human effort before its advantages can be fully utilized.

It is interesting to relate the features just described to the historic contrast between this Roman area and the city-states of Magna Graecia. We have seen that the central area has a greater extent of —at least potential—agricultural land than the south, while the bordering hills and marshes gave such natural protection as was necessary for the first origin of a political entity of any size. Because of the long, winding river-courses with their intercalated basins, opportunities for the construction of land-routes occur on a scale not represented in the south. Finally, and most important, despite the relative narrowness of the peninsula, which reaches some 160 miles at its widest between the elbow at Ancona and the Piombino peninsula, the sea is actually 'remote'. The last statement may appear at first sight fantastic. It should be noted, however, that at present, apart from the ports of Spezia and Leghorn, there is no important port on the west coast between Genoa and Naples, and none on the east between Venice and Brindisi, except Ancona and Bari, which are chiefly important for local traffic. On the west coast, it is true, possibilities are not lacking, and Civitavecchia should be noted particularly; but the belt of volcanic hills, the coastal marshes, and the changing coast-line (cf. Ostia and Pisa) have always formed obstacles to the construction of permanent ports. More important, in reality, than the physical difficulties, is the concentration of effort and population on the borders of the inner basins, above their swampy and unhealthy floors, and the ease with which these basins can be connected by land-routes. Rome was almost from the start a road centre; Florence did not become really important till the obstacles of the land-route between the Arno and the Tiber by the swampy, flood-devastated Val di Chiana had been overcome, and even so had a severe struggle for an adequate sea-outlet. In short, for the Greeks of the south the unimpressionable sea was the obvious, the only easy means of communication; the road, with all that it means of permanent occupation, of the persistent surface imprint, was the Roman symbol, and was the direct consequence of the characteristics of the first Roman lands. Where the land changes ceaselessly as a result of those inner forces which are wholly beyond man's control, it is the sea which takes on the aspect of constancy. Where it changes only as a result of river action, which can be modified by man, it is but a step further to build causeways which ignore minor topographical features as completely as do rectified and canalized rivers, and fulfil man's purpose more effectively than these. Where productive areas are coastal, strictly limited in extent landwards, and bounded by unproductive veldts, the natural unit is the self-sufficing city-state. Where they are inland and extensive, and easily linked together, domination from a centre becomes possible and an entirely different type of community develops. It is noteworthy, further, that within the peninsula the Romans had experience of all the different types of difficulty which the road engineer has to face—broad and fairly high mountain ranges; those defiles on their flanks which are often a greater obstacle than the actual pass; marshes; rivers, varying seasonally from mere trickles or chains of pools to raging torrents; unstable surfaces always tending to slide, and so forth. Thus their advance into continental Europe involved only the further application of knowledge previously gained.

OTHER ELEMENTS

So far we have been mainly concerned with the complex history of the Apennine chain, and with the attempt to show that the contrasts between the northern and southern sections of the peninsula are too great for it to be regarded as a unit. Incidentally, the description has helped to justify the earlier statement that the Tyrrhenian islands have too little in common to be grouped together. Sicily

and the Lipari Islands share with the Naples area the presence of
active volcanoes. The former, like the adjacent part of the peninsula,
contains a prolongation of the fractured Apennines, and, to a minor
extent, of the exposed crystalline rocks which cover so much of the
surface in Calabria. It is, however, a special feature of Sicily that the
belt of uplifted tertiary rocks which borders the Apennines on their
convex side is here greatly developed and forms much of the surface.
Sardinia is aloof and different alike in its structure and in its purely
geographical features, and must be regarded as an area apart. Elba
and the Tuscan archipelago belong to Tuscany and are best considered along with Central Italy.

The other Italian lands may be thought at first sight to present a
relatively simple problem, consisting as they do mainly of the
northern plains and the alpine girdle. But a difficulty arises from
the position to be occupied in the scheme by Liguria, the area
separated from the plains by the Ligurian Alps, by the mountain
strip between Savona and Genoa, which Kober (p. 125) regards as
a continuation of the Eastern Alps, and by the Ligurian Apennines
in the more limited sense, that is, east of Genoa. Here we have a
very typical Riviera coast, the hills rising close behind the shore.
The area is usually included, without question, with Central Italy,
but there are various objections to this course. The narrowing of
the mountain belt, especially in the area just west of Genoa; the
low and easy passes across it (note the three railway routes, that to
Genoa being doubled); the presence of notable ports (Genoa and
Savona) in addition to a multiplicity of small fishing-stations; the
mild winter temperatures, associated with the presence of citrus
fruits far to the north of their limit on the west coast of the peninsula
(region of Alban Hills), and the well-developed winter tourist industry, are all special features. The sea plays a large part in the life of
the people, but the economic connexions with the plains and across
them with transalpine Europe are far closer than with Central Italy.
It seems justifiable to consider the region rather as an annex of the
north than as an isolated part of the centre, more especially as the
characters of the coast-line change so suddenly and so definitely
near Spezia.

This gives us three main areas to be considered in detail—the
Alpine Borderlands, with the included vast stretch of the Northern
Plains and the marginal area of Liguria; Central Italy, including the
provinces of Tuscany, Umbria, the Marches (Marche), Latium,
with Abruzzi and Molise; Southern Italy, including the provinces
of Campania, Apulia, Lucania, Calabria, and also Sicily. Sardinia,
forming a separate unit, is annexed to this division.

CHAPTER VII

THE ALPINE BORDERLANDS, THE NORTHERN PLAINS, AND THE MARGINAL AREAS

Frontier Changes—The Eastern Alps in Italy—The Western Mountain Region—Liguria—The Northern Plains—Town Sites in the Plains—Climate and Agricultural Products

FROM the administrative standpoint Italy is divided into ninety-two provinces, each controlled by a prefect and named after the chief town. Atlas maps, however, as a rule name and show the boundaries only of the sixteen regional divisions or compartments. These in the main correspond to historic entities and bear familiar names, though at the present time they have no administrative or legal character. The fact that they have had in the past historic importance means that they correspond more or less definitely to natural divisions, i.e. have readily recognizable physical boundaries. Thus for the geographer they are of much greater importance than the provinces, and their distribution over the surface is of interest.

FRONTIER CHANGES

Before the war of 1914–18 the three most northerly departments, Piedmont, Lombardy, and Venetia (Venezia), each included an alpine in addition to a plains section. But in the last-named the alpine section was relatively narrow. A great block of Austrian territory, including the upper Adige (Etsch) and its tributaries as far south as the gorge near Ala, the upper end of Lake Garda with certain of its feeders, the upper valley of the River Chiese, and the headstreams of the River Brenta, was thrust like a wedge towards the plains, separating the alpine sections of Lombardy and Venetia (Figs. 42 and 43). The most northerly points of Lombardy were in the neighbourhood of the Splügen and Stelvio passes. Eastwards Venetia had a crest frontier along the Carnic Alps, to the south of the upper Drave (Drau) valley. In the intervening section the pre-1919 frontier crossed the very important line of communication which leads from Innsbruck over the Brenner to Verona, as well as the minor ones indicated by the steamer route on Lake Garda, and the cross-route from Trento to Padua (Venice) by the Val Sugana (River Brenta). The 1919 frontier was thrust up to the Reschen-Scheideck or Resia pass, whence it followed the crest of the Oetztaler Alps to the Brenner, continued along the crest of the western part of the Hohe Tauern, and, turning south, crossed the open Pustertal (Valle Pusteria) to the east of the saddle at Dobbiaco (Toblach), so that a small part of the upper Drave became Italian (Fig. 44). It then rejoined the old frontier along the crest of the Carnic Alps. The frontier is thus essentially a crest one, the object of the small deviation in the Valle Pusteria being to give to Italy access to the important tourist resort of Cortina.

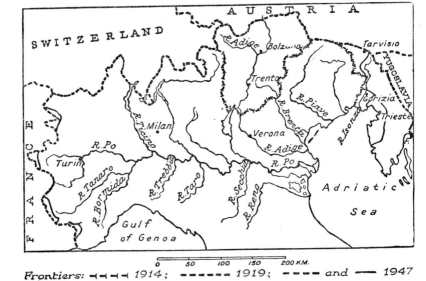

Frontiers: ⊣⊣⊣⊣ 1914; ▬ ▬ ▬ ▬ 1919; ▬ ▬ ▬ and ▬▬▬ 1947

FIG. 42. THE OLD AND NEW FRONTIERS OF ITALY
Trieste is now to be a Free Territory.

The second block of new territory lay to the east of the old Venetia. The pre-1919 frontier took off from the Carnic Alps well to the west of the Isonzo, leaving that river, with the town of Gorizia, within the Austro-Hungarian Empire. But after the first World War it was moved eastwards so that it crossed an important gap made by a feeder of the Gail, itself a tributary of the Drave. East of the gap the frontier turned south, dividing Italy from Yugoslavia in the region of the Julian Alps, and giving to the former the whole of the Carso, the peninsula of Istria, and the two great islands of Cherso and Lussin, with some smaller ones. These limits, demanded for the sake of the security so obviously menaced in the days when Austria-Hungary was a great military power, led to the inclusion in Italy of large numbers of German-speaking people in what was formerly south Tyrol, and of a number of Slovenes, with some Croats, in the east.

At first regarded as a part of Venetia, the new lands later formed separate departments. The old Venetia became Venezia Euganea (note the Euganean Hills, Fig. 47); the more westerly area Venezia Tridentina, with the two provinces of Bolzano (Bozen) and Trento; the eastern one, Venezia Giulia and Zara, consisted of the two major provinces of Gorizia and Pola, with smaller ones grouped round the cities of Trieste and Fiume, and the isolated enclave of Zara on the Adriatic coast of Yugoslavia. As a result of the 1939–45 war the bulk of Venezia Giulia, together with Fiume, Zara, and all Italian islands off the Yugoslav coast, have been handed over to Yugoslavia with the area around Trieste becoming an international zone.

The mountain section of Venetia thus falls into the Eastern Alps. Bearing in mind what has been already said as to the southern protrusion of Swiss territory in canton Ticino, it is clear that this is also true broadly of the mountain section of Lombardy. Thus from the Lake of Como eastwards, apart from those minor extensions of Swiss territory over the crest in canton Grisons, already discussed, Italy includes a section of the southern slope of the Eastern Alps. Thus it contains the southern slope of the snowclad Oetztaler Alps (Weisskugel, 3,746 m.) and of the western Hohe Tauern, where the Dreiherrnspitze ('peak of the three overlords'), 3,505 m., once the frontier between Salzburg, Carinthia, and Tyrol, now stands on the Austro-Italian frontier. Within the country also lie the lofty Ortler (Ortelio) peaks, 3,905 m., with the Stelvio pass, the wonderful rock scenery of the Dolomites, and the Presanella-Adamello groups (3,550 m.). The whole area shows a remarkable complexity of valley lines and may conveniently be studied as a whole.

After the war of 1939–45 minor changes were made in the French frontier when the communes of Tenda and Briga and four other small areas were ceded to France.

THE EASTERN ALPS IN ITALY

On Fig. 38 are shown the main structural elements of the Eastern Alps in Italian territory. To the north are the Austrids (A) or East Alpine nappes in the limited sense, consisting of a lower (Grisonid) and upper (Tirolid) series, thinning out westward in the root zone (p. 36). Within this belt, as already explained, Pennine nappes are exposed in the windows of the Lower Engadine (L.E.) and Hohe Tauern (H.T.). In the region shown, the Austrids consist largely of crystalline rocks, but bear sedimentaries 'on their backs'. Together with the Hohe Tauern window they give rise to the highest peaks and form the central zone of the Eastern Alps. To the south, though not in reality showing the parallelism which this schematic diagram suggests, lies the Dinarid belt, 'overturned' towards the south and characterized by the great development of massive limestones. This forms a continuation of the eastern Adriatic mountain zone, and is built up of a lower series (D1), which includes the Carso and gives rise to hill country of only moderate elevation, and of an upper one (D2) within which the rocks are of more varied type and the mountains of greater elevation.

We shall not attempt to elaborate the facts indicated on this diagram, but confine the description to the main topographical features. From the Bernina region, where the description ended in the account of canton Grisons, a broad zone of Grisonid crystallines extends eastwards over the upper Adda area, and then north-eastwards over the upper Adige and by the Passeiertal (Val Passiria) towards the Brenner. Within this belt, however, the Ortler group is developed from triassic limestones and not from crystallines. To the north the Tirolid Oeztaler Alps are built of crystalline rocks, but limestones appear towards the saddle of the Brenner. The crystalline belt is continued in the Hohe Tauern.

The next point is that across the Tonale pass (Fig. 43)—the pre-1919 frontier—between the upper Oglio and the Val di Sole (occupied by the River Noce, a feeder of the Adige), the western section of this central belt extends southwards in the Adamello and Presanella groups. This southern extension is bounded to the east by a zone of great structural disturbance called the Giudicaria line. It obtains its name from a district round the upper Chiese, a river which enters Lake Idro and ultimately joins the Oglio. But the Giudicaria line in the structural sense can be traced from Lake Idro north-north-east to the bend of the Adige at Merano. It separates the Austrids or central belt from the Dinarids or southern belt, and thus crystallines from massive limestones, and shows a rough parallelism to the Adige between the gorge at Ala and the junction of the Adige and Isarco near Bolzano. Within the triangle thus defined, having its apex at Merano, the beautiful Brenta group (3,176 m.) with its snows and glaciers, is the most striking feature. But the whole area, with its typical limestone scenery, and its very complex gridiron type of valleys (cf. the Jura) is of great interest and much frequented by tourists. It should be noted that here the Dinarids extend far to the north, while, conversely, the Austrids extend far to the south in the area west of the upper Chiese, so that the whole alpine belt is peculiarly wide and complex.

East of the Adige the continuation of the Dinarids forms the Dolomites, built of triassic limestones cut up into fantastic forms by erosion, and showing a beauty and variety of rock scenery un-equalled elsewhere in the Alps. The way in which the rocks rise bare and sheer, and of every variety of tint, from the green and

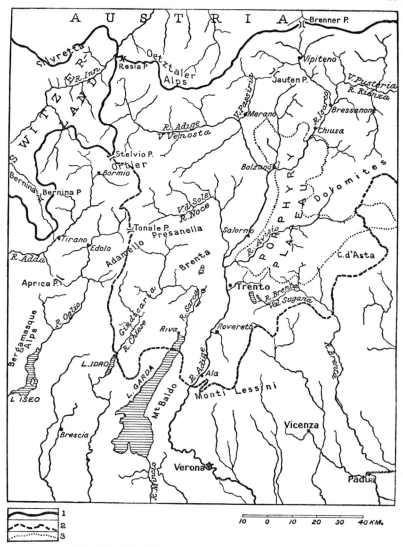

FIG. 43. THE UPPER ADIGE AND SURROUNDING AREA

1. Present frontiers. 2. Pre-1919 Austro-Italian frontier. 3. Approximate Limits of Porphyry Plateau. (*Based on the 1/1000000 map, with additions.*)

flowery pastures below, is an unforgettable sight. The Austrians constructed roads which made the whole area fully accessible to the tourist, and, as already stated, the new frontier was, in part, so drawn as to give Italy the advantage of this well-organized industry.

11

The Dinarid belt in this region does not, however, consist only of the Dolomites in the limited sense; two other elements have to be considered. One is the great mass of exposed eruptive rocks, forming the porphyry plateau (Fig. 43). This lies on the left bank of the Adige, extends from the neighbourhood of Chiusa (or Klausen=defile) on the Isarco to that of Trento on the Adige, and eastward interpenetrates the Dolomite limestones. Through the plateau the Isarco, on its way down from the Brenner pass, has had to cut a difficult path. Not till the year 1314 was a practicable way made here, so that against the lowness of the Brenner saddle (1,370 m.) we have to put this difficulty of access from the south. For a prolonged period a circuitous approach was necessary, as distinct from the apparently direct one by the Adige-Isarco valley.

The second point is that to the south of the Dolomites and of the eastward extension of the porphyry plateau, there appears a belt of crystalline rocks, with the Cima d'Asta group (2,848 m.). This belt is bounded sharply to the south by the Val Sugana, beyond which lie the mainly calcareous Monti Lessini (2,236 m.) and Tredici Comuni, pushed out peninsula fashion into the plain, and having as it were a prolongation in the Euganean and Berici Hills to the south. The Tredici Comuni form the most southerly protrusion of the Dinarid belt towards the plain, and bearing in mind what has been said as to its northerly extension into the Adige bend at Merano, it is clear that this belt attains its greatest width along the line of the Adige from Merano to Verona, while it is continued in the porphyry plateau up the Isarco towards Chiusa. In other words, the Dinarids are widest along the politically disputed belt, which is that which, under modern conditions, is traversed by the lowest and most direct transalpine route, the Innsbruck-Verona railway and road.

Eastward, beyond the Val Sugana, the Venetian Alps, or Alps of Friuli, continue the Dinarid belt. Their border towards the plain runs in a flattened curve, with a northerly trend, towards the Isonzo (Fig. 44), beyond which we come to the relatively low Carso plateau, with its underground drainage system and great caves. Since the northern border of the Dinarid belt similarly runs slightly to the south of east, we have a very notable narrowing of the whole belt in the region of the Isonzo headstreams. This has an important effect on lines of communication, and again occurs in a region politically disputed. But the narrowing does not, as one might suppose, notably facilitate the crossing of the whole alpine belt. This is partly because of the curiously indirect course of the rivers in the Venetian Alps; much more, however, is it due to the fact that the central belt to the north shows no single direct saddle equivalent to the Brenner. It is true that the routes which pass on the one hand by Udine to Venice and on the other by Gorizia to Trieste (Fig. 48) have an ultimate connexion with the Semmering. Not only have they other connexions in addition, however, but that with the Semmering is indirect, involving a crossing from the Mur valley to the Drave.

The Venetian Alps are again calcareous but less lofty than the peaks of the Dolomites. They have been heavily faulted, apparently

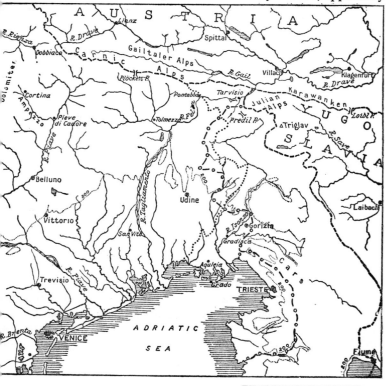

FIG. 44. OLD AND NEW FRONTIERS OF ITALY IN THE NORTH-EAST

The pre-1914 frontier between Italy and the Austro-Hungarian Empire is shown by the dotted line, the 1919 frontier by broken lines and the 1947 one by a continuous line. The 200-metre contour has been indicated. It may be regarded as the southern limit of the Venetian Alps towards the coastal lowland. For the main railways see Fig. 48. (*Based on the 1/1000000 map, with modifications.*)

a result of the collapse of the north Adriatic, and with this faulting is associated the indirectness of the valley lines already noted. Thus while when their lowland border is considered it seems as if we might generalize and say that they are drained by tumultuous transverse streams, of constantly varying *régime*, plunging downwards towards the plains with their heavy load of silt, this statement has to be qualified so far as the interior is concerned. In particular, the Piave, in the vicinity of the town of Belluno, and the Tagliamento, in that of Tolmezzo, both flow for a time in valleys definitely longitudinal and not transverse to the chain.

We have still to consider the conditions to the north. The Hohe Tauern are bounded to the south by the Pustertal or Pusteria valley (see Figs. 43 and 44), occupied first by the Rienza, a feeder of the Isarco, and then by the Drave. This valley lies near, but not precisely within, the line of junction (Drauzug) of the central or crystalline belt and the Dinarids. The line is continued not into the valley of the Drave but into that of its tributary the Gail, the two rivers running parallel till their junction at Villach in the basin of Klagenfurt. South of the Gail valley rise the Carnic Alps, the natural old and present frontier, and the boundary between areas of Italian and German speech. They rise to heights of 2,800 m. and consist of a variety of rocks, including crystallines and some limestones. Eastwards, beyond the Italian frontier, they are continued into the Karawanken; southwards they abut on the calcareous Julian Alps, the highest peak of which, Triglav or Tricorno (2,863 m.), is within Yugoslavia.

Returning finally to the western area we have to note that, beyond the Oglio, the chain of the Bergamasque Alps (Fig. 43) separates the Valtellina (Upper Adda valley) from the plains. It consists of a northern crystalline and a southern calcareous section, without any obvious line of demarcation.

We must turn next to the valleys, of which the longitudinal ones are specially noteworthy, being as strikingly developed within the Italian area as in that which remains Austrian. Little can be said as to their causation, for this has not been fully worked out; as already stated, however, the Pusteria valley seems to have some relation to the junction zone between the central (Austrid) and southern (Dinarid) belts. Whatever their origin, however, there can be no doubt of the geographical importance of the valleys. In the first place their frequently open nature, the effects of glaciation (cf. what has been said as to the Upper Rhone valley, p. 115) and their mild climate make them the chief areas of settlement. Their resources as usual are varied, but the great extension of vineyard and orchards (Valtellina and Val Venosta) is an important feature in addition to the timbered slopes and the pastures above.

Secondly, particularly in the inter-war period, there has been great development of hydro-electric power, stimulated by the high price of imported coal. The Adige valley has been intensively developed and contains some large modern power-stations. Hydro-electric installations are not of course limited to the longitudinal valleys, the Isarco near Bolzano being used in a large scheme. A the same time a change of direction on the course of a stream from transverse to longitudinal, as in the case of the Piave, or the downward plunging of lateral transverse streams into a wide, overdeepened longitudinal valley, as in the Valtellina, gives special opportunity for utilizing water-power. The power may be used locally, as for electrifying railways or supplying factories, but is generally transmitted to the cities of the plain, while the discharged water may also be used for irrigation there.

Finally, where convenient exits occur, the longitudinal valleys form parts of through routes whose significance has varied greatly at different periods. Beginning with the Valtellina, we find that Tirano at its head (railway to Lecco) has a number of possible exits; but the two to the north are high and difficult. One leads by the Bernina railway (p. 92) to the Engadine, the other by the Stelvio pass road, the highest motor-road in Europe (2,758 m., or 9,049 ft.) to the Val Venosta. Another exit is eastward by the Aprica pass to Edolo on the Oglio, whence a railway leads to Milan and Brescia, or the Tonale pass (p. 144) road may be followed to the north. Traffic here is mainly local and tourist.

The Val Venosta has not only lower exits but for long afforded ways of avoiding the difficult Isarco defile. Thus the Adige may be followed to the Resia (Reschen-Scheideck) pass (1,510 m.), an easy but circuitous route. A more direct exit to the north is by the Passiria valley from Merano (Jaufen pass, 2,094 m.), which leads to Vipiteno (Sterzing) on the Brenner route above the defile. Both passes are crossed by motor-roads. It should be noted, however, that the Resia and Brenner passes alike lead only to the longitudinal Inn valley, the northern calcareous Alps still forming a barrier before Germany is reached. The railway circumvents this obstacle by following the Lower Inn in its north-easterly course to Kufstein, but the old routes were by the Fern or Seefeld passes (the latter crossed by the Mittenwald railway) and thus more directly to the north.

Eastward the Pusteria valley (River Rienza) joins that of the Isarco in the small basin of Bressanone (Brixen), again above the defile, and in early days afforded another means of reaching the Brenner saddle, while avoiding the obstacle. From Venice the Piave route could be followed past Belluno, and via the Ampezzo valley to the saddle at Dobbiaco, and then down the Rienza to Bressanone. This was the medieval way from Venice to Germany (*Strada di Allemagna*). During the 1914–18 war a railway was begun by the Austrians, later finished by the Italians, connecting Dobbiaco via Cortina in the Ampezzo valley to Belluno and thus to Venice. This railway revived the importance of the ancient way.

East of Dobbiaco the Pusteria valley railway crosses the Austrian frontier and, following the line of the Drave valley, runs to Villach and Klagenfurt. At Villach the Drave and the Gail converge, and a tributary of the latter (cf. p. 142), with the town of Tarvisio (Tarvis), is separated from the Fella tributary of the Tagliamento by only a low pass (Tarvisio or Safnitz, 797 m.). This allows for the exit of the railway to Udine and Venice. This line has cross-connexions in its plain section with Gorizia and Trieste, but the direct route to Trieste (see Fig. 48) from Klagenfurt (Vienna) runs farther east, through the Karawanken tunnel, into Yugoslav territory. From Tarvisio the Predil pass (1,162 m.), of historic importance, leads to the Isonzo and is crossed by a road.

The Carnic Alps are not traversed by any railway, and the Plöcken pass, or Passo di Monte Croce (1,363 m.), from the Gail valley to the Tolmezzo basin of the Tagliamento, is only crossed by a motor-road. This emphasizes the importance of the range as a barrier.

Something may be added as to the towns of this alpine region.[1] Merano (25,575), at the entrance to the Val Venosta, that is, where the Adige turns towards the south, and also where the Passiria valley takes off, lost some of its initial importance in favour of Bolzano when the Kuntersweg through the Isarco defile was constructed (p. 146). Apart from being a local market centre (wine, fruit, grain, live stock), Merano is chiefly important as a health resort. Hot and oppressive in summer, it has winters which, though cold, are dry, windless, and sunny. Bolzano (41,722) has, with the advent of hydro-electricity, become an important metallurgical centre with aluminium, cryolite, and magnesium plants. The town is also noted for its fruit and before 1914 had large Austrian and German markets. The climate permits the more delicate types (peaches, etc.) to thrive, and as they are grown sufficiently near their limit to make it desirable to produce only the best kinds, it is necessary to devote much care to their cultivation. Trento (37,280) has textile and metallurgical industries. It is thoroughly Italian both in appearance and in speech, and its initial importance was due to its command of the diverging routes of the Adige to Verona and the Val Sugana to Venice. In the latter case a low saddle separates a small feeder of the Adige from the Brenta. Trento is also connected by road with the Giudicaria (p. 144). The importance of Belluno (10,083) has been already noted.

It may be added that the Adige area presents a peculiarly difficult problem from many different points of view, and the two aspects on which so much stress has been laid, those of security on the one side and on the other of language distribution and its historical implications, are by no means the only ones. To the Austrians of

[1] An interesting article is Griffith Taylor, "Trento to the Reschen Pass", *Geographical Review*, 1940, p. 215.

the industrial towns and to many Germans the region represented all—and more—that canton Ticino does to the Swiss townsfolk. To be able to find themselves at home in a land with a sunny climate, southern vegetation, and superb scenery, had a psychological effect, the intensity of which is perhaps not fully appreciated, though it may be realized partially by recalling what California and Florida mean to the Americans of the eastern United States. To the northern folk the frontier on the Brenner represents the barred gate of a Garden of Eden.

THE WESTERN MOUNTAIN REGION

Of the Western Alps in Italy little need be said, since the range has been already fully discussed. With the thinning out and final disappearance of the southern calcareous (Dinarid) belt, the crystalline rocks of the Pennine nappes (Fig. 38) are exposed towards the plain in a great semicircle, extending from Lake Maggiore to Cuneo. The mountains carved out of them rise with great abruptness from the plain of Piedmont, culminating in the three peaks of Monviso (3,843 m.), which gives birth to what is regarded as the Po head-stream, the Gran Paradiso (4,061 m.), and the Monte Rosa group (4,638 m.). The first two form as it were the pillars of the great gateway through which Turin is reached. From the crystalline massifs already described (p. 38) this belt of the Pennine nappes is separated by the so-called zone of Briançonnais, which extends from the Ligurian Alps along the curve of the mountain chain, that is, at first north-west to the town of Briançon, then north and finally north-east towards the two St. Bernard passes and the Rhone valley. It consists of sedimentaries of carboniferous and later age, and we have already noted some of its features in the vale of Chamonix and the continuation of that valley towards Martigny (p. 87). It lies largely within French territory but has a notable effect on the features of the frontier region; for within it the chief passes are developed (Fig. 45). This is because while most of the tributaries of the Po rise in the belt of the nappes, and have thus a short and rapid course down the slope to the plain, two of its headstreams have been able to work their way back into the sedimentary zone. There they not only display a multiplicity of tributaries, but these approach the similarly branched headwaters of the streams on the French side, the resultant lowering of the crest giving rise to the passes. One of these rivers is the Dora Riparia, and of its headstreams one gives access to the Arc over the Mont Cenis pass (2,097 m.); another also to the Arc by the Col de Fréjus under which runs the Mont Cenis railway tunnel; a third to the Durance by the Mont Genèvre (1,954 m.). The other river, the Dora Baltea (cf. Fig. 46) penetrates through the sedimentary zone to the crystalline Massif of Mont Blanc, and gives access via Aosta to the Little St. Bernard (2,157 m.) which leads to the Isère as well as to the Great St. Bernard (p. 89).

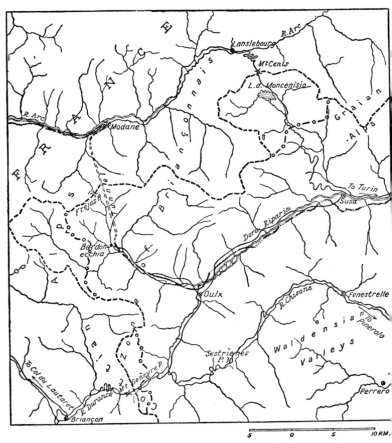

FIG. 45. PART OF THE ZONE OF THE BRIANÇONNAIS, WITH THE MONT CENIS PASS AND TUNNEL

The way in which the headstreams of the Dora Riparia overlap those of the Arc should be noted, also the position of the passes. Note the new areas awarded to France in 1947 in this region. The Italians have also agreed to co-operate if a new railway is built from Briançon to Modane, via Bardonecchia. (*Based on the 'Nuova Carta d' Italia', 1/250000, with modifications.*)

The sedimentary zone has also another if indirect effect. The streams which course down the steep slopes of the nappe belt and unite to form the Po of Turin, are relatively unsuited to the Italian type of settlement, while the plain is both near and more attractive. On the other hand, beyond the steep Italian slope, there stretches westwards into French territory a great mass of high ground, containing a French-speaking population adapted throughout a long period of historical time to a mountain environment. The result is that the valleys of the upper Dora Riparia and Dora Baltea, the latter with a long west-to-east section centring round Aosta, are occupied by French-speaking people, the way over the crest and down the valley in each case being easier than Italian upward extension from the plain. The province of Val d'Aosta forms almost

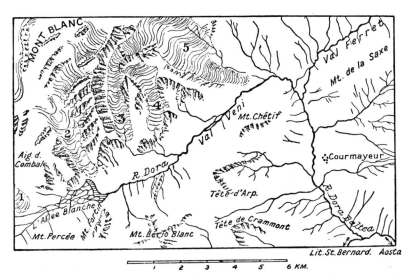

FIG. 46. THE ITALIAN SIDE OF MONT BLANC AND THE SOURCE OF
THE DORA BALTEA

1. End of the shrunken Allée Blanche glacier. 2. Miage Glacier. 3. Brouillard Glacier, separated from 2 by the rocks of Mont Brouillard. 4. Fresnay Glacier. 5. Brenva Glacier.
The Dora Baltea is formed by the junction near Courmayeur of two alpine torrents, flowing in opposite directions. Below, the stream is joined by the Thuile from the Little St. Bernard pass. Note the small Combal lake, where the drainage of the Allée Blanche is blocked by the moraine of the Miage Glacier, and cf. p. 97. (*From the French 1/1000000 map.*)

a rectangle, three of its sides being made up of the massifs of Monte Rosa, Mont Blanc, and Gran Paradiso, whilst on the south the valley opens on to the northern plain. This province is governed by a freely elected council of the valley, and the French and Italian languages are given equality, but it remains part of Italy and under Italian law. The Waldensian valleys, with Pinerolo as the border town towards the plain, can also be reached from the Mont Genèvre pass, and are similarly French-speaking (Fig. 45).

The contrast with the conditions just described in the case of the Eastern Alps is striking, and may be associated with the absence of the southern calcareous belt. In the eastern area the gentle slopes of the Calcareous Alps, with their open and yet sheltered valleys, enticed Italian-speaking people upwards towards the central belt, which could likewise be readily reached from the north by German-speaking mountain folk. In this western area French-speaking mountain folk found their way over the passes where valleys suitable for permanent settlement occurred on the Italian side; but these upper valleys were cut off from the plains by the intervening steep slope, and the clash between two different types of social polity was much less serious than in the east. Further, the general limitation of the passes to the narrow sedimentary belt, intercalated between two areas of hard crystalline rock, makes transalpine routes few and direct. There is not that lateral interlocking of routes which is associated in the eastern area with the interpenetration of the crystallines by the calcareous belt, and there complicates the frontier question so greatly.

The Dora Baltea valley, it may be added, separates the Pennine Alps from the Graian, the Dora Riparia the latter from the Cottian, and the Col d'Argentera or Larche (1,995 m., connecting the southern Stura with the Ubaye tributary of the Durance), the latter from the Maritime Alps, which are separated from the Ligurian Alps by the Col di Tenda (1,873 m.).

In the Maritime Alps, which include the crystalline massif of Mercantour (p. 38), the frontier is now at the watershed. The range is lofty, forming a barrier zone with a remarkable contrast in climate and vegetation between the two sides. The political frontier crosses the Col di Tenda and reaches the sea at the bridge of St. Louis, nearly midway between Ventimiglia, at the Roya mouth, and Menton. The bridge crosses a deep gorge made by a small coastal stream. To the east extends the Italian Riviera di Ponente, included within Liguria, and to the west the French Riviera, without any obvious difference in climate or natural features. The Italian language extends westward at least as far as Nice, and there is a large Italian element in the French Riviera generally. The railway opened in 1928 from Cuneo (Turin), branching at Breil to Ventimiglia and Nice, is interesting as throwing light both on the character of the mountain belt and on the complexity in detail of the frontier here. Cuneo (18,882) on the Stura (Fig. 47) in Piedmont, has silk mills and an important market for chestnuts in the autumn and for silkworms. The sweet chestnut is a very important economic tree on the hill border of the plain, whilst within the plain and on its margins the mulberry is grown for silkworm rearing. A feeder of the Gesso, a Stura tributary, gives access to the Col di Tenda, which is traversed by means of road and railway tunnels, 5 miles long (Mont Cenis tunnel, $7\frac{1}{2}$ m.). The Italian part of the railway, however, has altogether 46 tunnels, with a total length of 16 miles, and as many again in France, indicating the difficulty and cost of railway construction here.

LIGURIA

Beyond Breil we enter Liguria, the department which slopes from the mountain border to the coast, and extends from the St. Louis bridge to beyond Spezia. The appearance of the olive and of citrus fruits (*agrumi*) on the coastal strip recalls what has been already said as to the climatic contrast between the plains and this sheltered area. But the oranges at least are not grown wholly as a commercial fruit crop. Some are small kinds which are preserved (candied), and orange-trees also are extensively planted as an advertisement of the mild climate and to attract tourists.

To the east of the Col di Tenda, and extending to the deeply-notched Cadibona pass (465 m.), which allows of the passage of the railway to Savona (Fig. 47), are the Ligurian Alps. They are of complicated structure, including a small crystalline massif in addition to a prolongation of the Briançonnais zone, and reach a height of 2,600 m. From the Cadibona to the Giovi (472 m.) pass behind Genoa lies the lower and narrower belt usually regarded as the beginning of the Apennines, which, according to Kober, is an extension of the Austrids (p. 125). Its geographical importance can scarcely be over-estimated. In addition to the Giovi, now traversed by two lines of rail, and the higher but more direct road pass of the Bocchetta (772 m.), the Turchino pass (532 m.) gives another access by rail. The narrowing and lowering of the mountain belt is associated with the collapse of the seaward margin, already noted, which brings Genoa and Savona into relatively close contact with the plains. Genoa is indeed their western outlet, as Venice is the eastern one. Just as the coast of the western (Ponente) Riviera trends north-east, so the eastern (Levante) Riviera trends south-east. Both, particularly the Riviera di Ponente, contain a long series of health resorts (Bordighera, San Remo, etc.); on the Riviera di Levante the finest scenery occurs beyond the peninsula of Portofino (Rapallo, Santa Margherita, etc.).

In striking contrast to these Riviera coasts, with their villas, great hotels, gardens, and intensive cultivation, is the industrial belt at the apex of the triangle. Genoa, with a population of 512,313, is not only the most important port of Italy, surpassing Naples, but also the rival of Marseille. Its advantages are obvious: it has at once access to the plains, themselves the area of convergence of the great transalpine routes, and a good position for Mediterranean trade.

Thus its economic hinterland extends into Switzerland and beyond and it carries on a large part of the coasting trade of the Mediterranean, as well as being a calling-place for ocean steamers, both on the Atlantic and eastern routes. But its disadvantages are just as obvious. The greatest is the lack of space for development, whether inland or laterally. Further, while the harbour has the advantage of being free from the menace of silting (contrast Venice) it is unsheltered as compared with the large natural haven of Spezia though recent artificial additions to the port enable the larges vessels afloat to be accommodated. Another drawback arises from the nature of Italian trade, which demands the import of bulky goods, such as coal (but cf. p. 148), raw cotton, grain, phosphate for fertilizers, mineral oil, and so on, while the exports are mainly valuable goods of lesser weight and bulk. It will be noted that the steepest slope and heaviest haul is that from the coast, the slope towards the plain being gentler and the return trains less heavily loaded. This of course increases freight charges, many wagons having to return empty.

The city is superbly placed on a semicircle round the harbour and industrial development has meant rather the growth of satellite towns to the west than actual expansion. These satellites lie to the west because immediately to the east the Apennines broaden out notably, and for over 50 miles, till the Parma-Spezia line is reached (Fig. 48), there is no other transverse route. Again, the Monferrat hills impede cross-traffic behind Savona, so that despite the low gap of the Cadibona pass that town is not a serious rival to Genoa. The latter is mainly a port and trade centre, but has metallurgical and engineering industries. These are mainly connected with ship building carried on particularly at Sampierdarena—part of Genoa —and at Savona. Although heavy industries predominate at Genoa there are also paper-making, potteries, sugar-refining, vegetable canning, soap-making, and other trades. The removal of the naval base and arsenal to Spezia resulted from the better harbour at the latter.

THE NORTHERN PLAINS

Fig. 47, combined with what has been already said, makes clear the general features of the plains, the most densely-peopled part of Italy, containing about 40 per cent of the population on 16 per cent of the surface. They are characterized alike by the number of their large towns, their highly-developed industry, and their agricultural wealth. In origin, as has been seen, a filled-up arm of the sea, their height above sea-level varies from 100 to 300 m. in the north, and farther south from 40 to 100 m., so that a comparatively small depression would again submerge them.

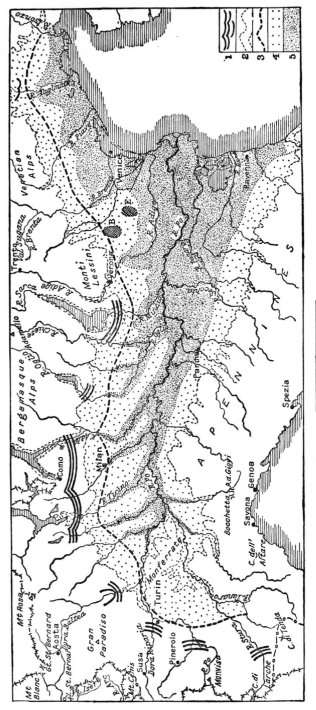

FIG. 47. THE NORTHERN PLAINS

1. The morainic amphitheatres. 2. The contour line of 200 m. 3. The line of the fontanili. 4. Fluvio-glacial terraces. 5. River alluvium.

B=the Berici, and E=the Euganean volcanic hills.

As the figure suggests, four types of landscape can be recognized, with a more or less definitely zonal arrangement. In the first place, the openings of the greater alpine valleys show remarkable morainic amphitheatres, sometimes of considerable height and regular form, sometimes greatly modified by later stream action. These mark the areas where the Ice Age glaciers stagnated on the margin of the former sea. In striking contrast to the Swiss glaciers (p. 98) the Italian ones were not confluent, their expanded tongues being quite separate the one from the other; owing to their steep slope and great carrying power they deposited enormous masses of debris at the sea border. Of these morainic amphitheatres we may note those due to the terminal moraines: of the Stura glacier; of the Po glacier from Monviso, which extend between Savigliano and Pinerolo; of the Dora Riparia glacier from the Mont Cenis region, which rise 900 m. above sea-level and 500 m. above the valley-floor and extend down the valley over a distance of over 20 km., or nearly 13 miles; of those of the Mont Blanc and Monte Rosa glaciers, which form a great barrier across the opening of the Dora Baltea valley near Ivrea. In the last the lateral walls of the semicircle rise to 450 m. above present river-level, while the frontal part is broken up into hillocks interspersed with small lakes. Farther east the moraines lie to the south of the alpine border lakes, and their presence has led to various modifications of the drainage. Thus Lakes Lugano, Orta, and Varese have had their former exits blocked by the morainic material, and now drain by indirect routes to Lake Maggiore, while the Adda leaves Lake Como by the Lecco arm. The concentration of the whole drainage into the two rivers of the Ticino and Adda, some 40 miles apart at their exits from the lakes, gives the morainic barrier here greater continuity than elsewhere, but the height is lower than to the west, the maximum being about 378 m. At its exit from the Lake of Iseo the Oglio has similarly to cut through a belt of moraine. The tongue of the enlarged Adige glacier did not follow the present river-valley but that of the Lake of Garda, and the expanded lower end of the otherwise narrow and fiord-like lake is encircled by a border of morainic hills. These are much dissected by the Mincio but rise to heights of over 200 m. The last important morainic belt is that which occurs on the Tagliamento to the north-east.

In front of the moraines lies an 'outwash' plain, formed by coarse sand, gravel, and pebbles, the latter sometimes cemented together to form a kind of conglomerate (*ferretto*). These deposits are porous, so that rainwater sinks in, while they are sufficiently resistant to allow the rivers to cut miniature 'gorges'. In consequence both of the coarseness of the deposits and of the dryness of the surface this upper terrace is rather unproductive. Parts of it have been reclaimed and planted with vines and mulberries, but much is bush or heath land. It is somewhat scantily peopled and the alternation of ridges and valleys is unfavourable to transverse lines of communication.

Near the edge of this terrace the infiltrated water, which penetrates until it encounters a deeper clayey layer, tends to gush out at the surface in springs, sufficiently numerous to form the line of the *fontanili*. The lower terrace delimited by this line of springs is built of finer deposits, is extremely productive, and has abundant irrigation water available. Roads and railways are easily constructed, and the possibility of linking together the transverse streams by canals facilitates communication by water.

Finally, the Po and its larger tributaries are fringed by fine-grained alluvium, through which the rivers meander in constantly changing courses. Narrowing rapidly westward, where it disappears to the east of Turin, this alluvial belt widens funnel-like towards the Adriatic, where it extends southward up to the Apennine border and northward stretches along the shore of the north Adriatic, thus prolonging the plains eastward till they disappear against the edge of the Carso. Since none of the Apennine tributaries and some only of the alpine ones are clarified within lakes, and since, further, the ancient glaciers have left an enormous mass of easily transported material, the plain is constantly extending seawards, the land having gained on the sea notably in historic times. But in all the lower part of the plain the rivers tend to flow on their own flood plains at a level higher than that of the surrounding lands. Here, therefore, as in all areas of similar character, they are the enemies of man. They menace his lines of communication, they push his settlements back beyond the danger zone, they threaten constantly the agricultural land which he has drained laboriously and protected by embankments. Though the Po is navigable for large boats to the Ticino confluence and for barges to Casale, above the Sesia confluence, it is a poor line of communication, constantly tending to change its course, and varying greatly in its discharge. Here, therefore, we have an area which can be made productive, but only at the price of sustained effort; not one generally suitable for occupation by primitive folk, but giving ample space for expansion once experience and capital are available.

TOWN SITES IN THE PLAINS

The presence of these four zones, and the contrasts between them, exert great influence both on the use which can be made of the land and on the sites of towns. Thus, on or near the morainic belt, sub-alpine towns tend to arise at the junction zone of hill and plain, especially where an alpine valley debouches on to the plain.

Among their advantages are access to the trans-alpine routes and to the mountain zone with its timber and live stock industry; water-power; the possibility of local specialized production, especially of wine, silk based on the cultivation of the mulberry, almost everywhere the less exacting fruit-trees, such as walnuts, peaches, etc., with, in certain areas, the olive for olive oil and even (shores of the Lake of Garda) a limited and dwindling production of citrus fruits, with winter protection. The water-power, used to generate electricity, the local supplies of raw material and the possibility of importing more, facilitate the growth of industry. Thus we find a great belt of border towns of varying size. Among them may be mentioned (Fig. 48) Saluzzo, Pinerolo, Ivrea, Biella (Italy's chief woollen town, 24,328); Varese (23,348); Como (Italy's chief silk centre, 42,569); Bergamo (engineering, silk, and woollen industries, 73,534); Brescia (iron, armaments, and textiles, 92,583); Verona (a great market centre and nodal point, with varied industries, 185,724). The series ends with Gorizia (36,794).

The factors determining the varying sizes of these towns are of interest. In the west we have the small centres which always tend to rise where upland meets lowland, owing to the need for exchange of products. But the great size of Verona and Brescia, followed by Bergamo and Como in descending order, is a special feature which can be directly related to the structural features already described. In the west, where crystalline rocks rise with more or less abruptness from the border of the plain, the contrast between mountain and plain life is equally abrupt, and the former area is of limited productivity and scantily peopled. But Verona, as we have seen, marks the area where the calcareous belt is widest, extends farthest into the plain, and is most completely dissected by valleys which invite settlement. Brescia has similarly behind it the highly-dissected area to the west of Lake Garda, and Bergamo the low southern border of the Bergamasque Alps. As the Dinarid belt tails out westward towards Lake Maggiore so the productive hinterland of the border towns diminishes, and the towns themselves decrease in size.

Leaving for a moment the plain towns proper we may turn to the southern border, which is very clearly divided into an eastern and a western section. West of Piacenza the Apennine belt thins out, or according to Kober, disappears towards the narrowed prolongation of the Eastern Alps. From near Piacenza—a bridge-town of the Po —to Rimini the border-line between hill and plain forms a very definite south-easterly trending line, made clear on the poorest map by the row of towns strung along the railway, which follows the line of the old Emilian way (Fig. 48). To the west there is a striking contrast. On the one hand, the narrowing of the Ligurian mountain belt gives the plain a notable extension to the south, while on the

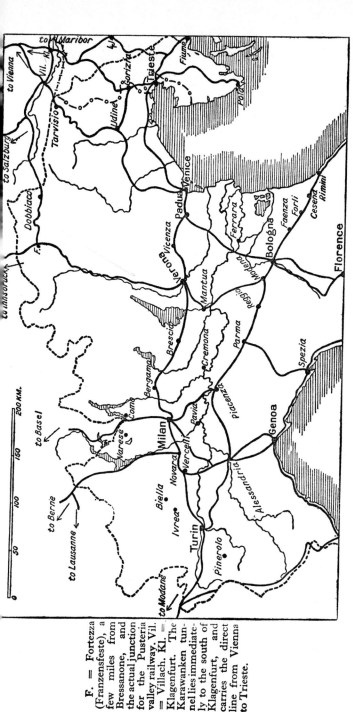

F. = Fortezza (Franzensfeste), a few miles from Bressanone, and the actual junction for the Pusteria valley railway. Vil. = Villach. Kl. = Klagenfurt. The Karawanken tunnel lies immediately to the south of Klagenfurt, and carries the direct line from Vienna to Trieste.

FIG. 48. THE MAIN RAILWAYS OF NORTH ITALY AND THEIR CONNEXIONS

The chief trans-frontier connexions to France, Switzerland, Austria, and Yugoslavia are shown by arrows. The western routes converge on Turin and Milan, each linked to the network of the plains, and via Alessandria to Genoa and so to the western coastal line; also via Piacenza to the route at the base of the Apennines, continued into the eastern coastal line, and with cross-connexions to Spezia and Florence. Verona and Padua are the converging points of the eastern international routes. The network to the north-east is the result of the Austro-Hungarian development of lines to Trieste and Fiume.

other the low Monferrato hills interrupt its surface. The River Tanaro, in origin presumably a small southern tributary, has been able to cut its way back through this easily-eroded tertiary upland, and thus draw off water from the Po headstreams (note the angle of capture at Bra), so that the Stura is a Tanaro feeder, while the parallel Maira flows direct to the Po. It is the renewed vigour given to the Tanaro by these captures which has led to the development of the valleys which facilitate the construction of railways between the plain of Piedmont and the Ligurian coast, and the position of Alessandria (57,949) near the junction of the large Bormida tributary with the main Tanaro stream should be noted. Although Lombardy is continued in a narrow strip south of Pavia to the Apennine crest, yet broadly it may be said that the western area falls within Piedmont, while the eastern is included in Emilia. The latter is an east-to-west strip, the shorter axis extending, roughly speaking, from the Apennine crest to the Po, consisting of an upland border, narrow to the south-east, where the boundary does not reach to the crest of the Apennines, and widening towards the north-west, and a very low-lying plain section, which is wide towards the Adriatic and narrows greatly to the north-west.

Only a narrow belt of fluvio-glacial deposits fringe the Apennines, and the rivers, which have a very variable water content, emerge from the narrow valleys and deposit alluvial cones on the border of the low plain. The towns are usually placed some little distance from the streams, and slightly above plain level. The most important rivers are the Reno (Bologna); the Panaro and the Secchia, with Modena lying between them where they approach; the Taro (near Parma on its own river); and the Trebbia (Piacenza). Of the towns the chief are Rimini (31,505), Cesena, Forli (33,505), Faenza, Imola, Bologna (232,980), Modena (50,541), Reggio nell' Emilia (49,069), Parma (65,126), Piacenza (49,527). The great importance of Bologna, one of the chief railway junctions of Italy, with an ancient university, is due to its command of the main route to the south (Florence) and its multiple connexions with the railways of the plain, in addition to its position on the longitudinal thoroughfare of the southern part of the plain. Generally, however, the size and antiquity of the towns of this belt results from their relation to the very important line of communication which links them together, and to the fact that they have a double hinterland—the plains on one side and the highly important area of central Italy on the other. The latter is reached now by rail or road through the passes of the Etruscan Apennines, but in earlier days chiefly by the more circuitous route through the Roman Apennines followed by the Via Flaminia.

Since the Apennine streams are of far less value for generating hydro-electric power than the alpine ones, large-scale industry is less developed here than to the north. Nor is the mulberry grown on the same scale, industries based on the local production of hemp replacing the silk-spinning of the north. Generally, however, the towns owe their size and historic importance to the agricultural products of the Emilian plains, which include much grain, sugar-beet, live stock (Bologna sausages), hemp, the vine, and a variety of fruit-trees. It is worth note that the inhabitants of Bologna—like those of Dijon in Burgundy—have the reputation of being both epicures and great eaters, as contrasted with the frugality of most Italians, the adjacent lands yielding a great variety of food-products.

It may be added that the small Uso river, between Rimini and Cesena, is believed to be the ancient Rubicon, the boundary for the Romans between the upland basins and the valleys of central Italy and the strange new world of the plains; but the stream has undergone some modification since classical times.

Turin (608,211), at the confluence of the Dora Riparia and the Po headstream, may be said from one point of view to be the beginning of the row of towns placed on the lower terrace; but it is exceptional in several respects. It stands where the zonal arrangement is ceasing to be marked, and has the Monferrato hill country to the east, while the other towns of the series have before them the slope downward to the alluvial plain of the great artery. Turin gathers up not only the western routes from the Alps but those leading to the Ligurian coast; in aspect it is modern and cosmopolitan rather than Italian. The second industrial centre in Italy, Turin has various branches of engineering industries, notably the manufacture of motor-cars, and also textile industries, including cotton, woollen, rayon, and jute. The Monferrato upland is devoted mainly to vines, the sparkling wine of Asti (*Asti spumante*) being specially renowned. Because the conditions there are so favourable, vineyards are less developed on the plain section, which is given up to grain with mulberry and fruit-trees.

Eastward, large towns tend to occur below the line of the fontanili, where the land at once becomes more productive and less dry, Vercelli (32,397), on the Sesia, Novara (52,269), Magenta, near the Ticino, Milan (1,068,079), Vicenza (48,279), Padua (90,325), Treviso (43,949), Udine (54,638) are examples. The great predominance of Milan, but little smaller than Rome and thus the second town in Italy, is noteworthy. Its wonderful cathedral—Gothic but very different from the Gothic buildings across the Alps—is equally symbolic of its significance as a link between Central Europe and the south, and between the older Italy and the newer. With far more artistic treasures than Turin, it is yet not like Ravenna or Florence, primarily a tourist town, but a modern commercial city,

closely linked to Switzerland and Germany. It is needless t
emphasize its command of routes, or its importance as a centre c
trade and of the intellectual (university and many institutes of learn
ing; book-publishing) and artistic, especially musical (Conservatori
manufacture of musical instruments) life of the plains. Among it
varied industries are included engineering (motor-cars, watches an
clocks, etc.), while in addition to being the chief silk market
Europe and the headquarters of the Italian rayon and hemp indus
tries, it has numerous silk and cotton mills. Its influence extends i
all directions, giving rise to a high local density of population; man
minor industrial towns occur in the neighbourhood, as, for exampl
Monza to the north.

The fact that the town is not placed near a large river is a featur
shared with other settlements in this area; for the rivers are bot
dangerous and useless. They choke their beds with alluvium, s
that these become too narrow to carry flood water, which is cor
strained to seek new, lateral courses. Constant repetition of th
process produces what American geographers call a 'braided river
that is, one with a broad bed with a multiplicity of narrow, inter
lacing channels, separated by islands and banks which may be con
pletely submerged in the single surging flood at certain seasons.
the Tagliamento (cf. Fig. 44) is the typical example of this condition
the Ticino, Sesia, Adda, etc., also show it, and it prevents th
establishment of large settlements close to the rivers.

Padua, the second largest town of this belt, is an important centr
of communications, linking up transverse and longitudinal route
Its famous university is but a little more recent than that of Bologn
both dating from the early thirteenth century.

The zone within which these towns stand is characterized espec
ally by mixed cultivation, vines and mulberry-trees rising from th
midst of the wide corn-fields. Irrigated meadows are mainly devote
to hay crops, and these can be mown as many as six times durin
the warmer part of the year. Rice is also grown, as near Novara, bu
is more characteristic of the belt nearer the Po and thus damper
The main areas of rice cultivation lie near Pavia and Ferrara. It
in this lower area, also, that watered meadowland is most wide
spread; while, on the other hand, vines tend to diminish because
the damp subsoil.

Since what has been said of the vagaries of the alpine tributari
applies equally to the Po, the cities of the alluvial belt tend to avo
too close a proximity to the river and its larger feeders. Pav
(40,208), Cremona (54,564), and Mantua (36,489) form an interestin
series. Pavia, connected to Milan by canal as well as by road a
rail, is on the Ticino, where it becomes controllable before i
confluence with the Po. Cremona lies east of the Adda confluenc

but Mantua, on the site of an ancient Etruscan town, is placed where the Mincio expands into three lakes, which, with marshes on the fourth side, give it much natural protection. Thus it was the most southerly element of the Austrian Quadrilateral (Verona, Peschiera, on Lake Garda, Legnago, on the Adige, Mantua).

Ferrara (58,187), the largest town of this row, stands to the south of the river, a little back from the right bank of the main stream and near two small distributaries. Its castle commands the Po crossing and also the transverse route from Padua to Bologna, which is pushed westwards by the need of avoiding the deltaic marshes and lagoons of the coast. Extensive reclamation works have been undertaken in the vicinity, and the cultivable land has been greatly increased in area.

Finally we come to the coastal towns, which are of great interest. From Rimini, where the Apennines abut on the shore, till the Carso is reached beyond the Isonzo mouth, the coast-line is formed by deposits brought down by the great alpine rivers, and transported by the marine currents which sweep round the curving shore in a direction from north-east to south-west. The chief rivers are the Po, Adige, Brenta, Piave, Tagliamento, and Isonzo, and the fine mud which they carry in suspension is precipitated where fresh water meets salt. As on similar coasts elsewhere (e.g. the Baltic), long and narrow mud-banks tend to form offshore, on which wind and waves pile up sand. Thus spits are formed parallel to the shore, and are broken by the exits of the diverging, deltaic streams. Such spits are called *lidi* locally, and the famous Lido, the bathing-station outside Venice, is but a particular example. Behind is a mud-floored lagoon, sheltered from the waves by the spit, particularly favourable to the growth of zostera or sea-grass, which supplies food and shelter to many small marine animals which in their turn are preyed upon by fish. Thus we have the possibility of a port, entered through the gaps in the seaward bank, and of the rise of fishing-stations round the lagoon.

But the process of deposition is continuous. Fresh mud is continually raising the floor of the inner part of the lagoon, so that it shallows, and in place of being vivified—*laguna viva*—by tidal water (cf. p. 11), and by the boats which float on its surface, it becomes a muddy, dead shallow—*laguna morta*—a breeding-place for mosquitoes. The size and number of the offshore spits also increase, the width and depths of the openings between them decrease, and the lagoons become converted into what the Italians call *valli*, all but cut off from the sea and showing an alternation of relative deeps and shoals or banks. The lagoons of Venice (Fig. 49), of Grado and Marano (Fig. 50), the valli of Comacchio, and the smaller valli south of Ravenna, illustrate stages in the process. With the disappearance of any expanse of open water the valli are converted into marshes (*paludi*), destined to fill up in course of time, even if man does not hasten the process.

It is a natural deduction that ports on this coast are doomed to be short-lived. Adria on the Po delta is now some 14 miles from the sea, but was once a port: Ravenna (29,070), whose marvellous Byzantine buildings speak to its former sea traffic across the Adriatic, is now 5 miles distant at the nearest point, and the connecting canals have little significance. Aquileia (Fig. 50) is now a small and poor inland township, for long ravaged by malaria, and though from the coast to the south a channel runs through the lagoon to Grado on the outer spit, Grado is only a fishing- and bathing-station. Venice (170,830) is the only site on this lagoon coast which has retained importance as a harbour. Founded as a refuge on islands round the old course of the Brenta, its original resources were salt and fish, with the possibility of glass-making from local sands. The crusades first made clear the significance of its easy access to the Adige transalpine routes (p. 149), and prolonged and sustained efforts were made to ward off the fate which has overtaken the other ports. The Brenta was turned to the south of the lagoon, the Sile and Piave to the north-east. But decay came finally, not from within, but from without, with the shifting of the trade routes from the Mediterranean to the outer seas. When the piercing of the Suez Canal brought the vivifying current back to the inner seas, Venice proved quite unfitted to deal with modern steamship traffic, so that a new harbour had to be constructed on the mainland at Porto Marghera. Here and near by at Mestre, chemical, coking, metallurgical, and engineering industries have developed. The volume of trade is about equally shared between the ports of Venice and Porto Marghera, though the passenger traffic is mainly confined to Venice. Great efforts have been made to remove the old reproach that Venice had sunk from her former proud position to become a mere tourist centre.

CLIMATE AND CROPS

To this general account of the plains we may add a few notes upon the climate. As already indicated, mean winter temperatures are low, January means being but little above freezing-point (Milan 0·2°C., or 32·4°F., Turin 0·5°C., Alessandria 0·5°C., Bologna 1·5°C.), rising at Venice to 2·5°C. Further, one must not exaggerate the winter warmth of the sheltered belt at the base of the Alps, for even on Lake Como January means only reach 3°; the sub-alpine stations are definitely cold (Bolzano 0°, Belluno −1°). On the other hand, the rise at the Riviera stations is relatively enormous. The January mean at Genoa is 7·5°, higher than at Rome or Foggia (both little over 6°), and higher winter temperatures do not occur till

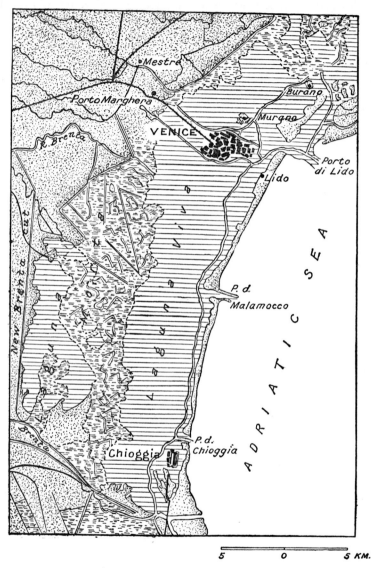

FIG. 49. THE LAGOONS OF VENICE

Note the largely silted *laguna morta* and the open *laguna viva*, some of the deep water channels of the latter being shown. The sandspits or *lidi* which form the seaward boundary are broken by gaps which serve as entrances. Note particularly the Porto di Lido. The New Cut, which carries waters of the Brenta away from Venice, is shown. (*From the 'Nuova Carta d'Italia', 1/250000.*)

Naples and the south are reached. The heavy winter transplain passenger traffic which results from the search by northerners fo warmth and sunshine helps to pay for the cost of railway construc tion (cf. the new Cuneo-Ventimiglia route, p. 154), and also in par compensates for the loss due to the nature of the goods traffic.

Summer temperatures, however, are similar both over the plain and on the Riviera coast, Genoa, Alessandria, Milan (Fig. 51) Venice, all having means which vary comparatively little above o below 24° (75°F.). The people of the plains are thus subjected to

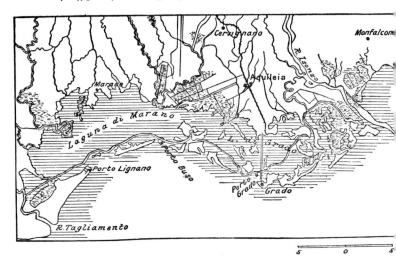

FIG. 50. THE POSITION OF AQUILEIA

This map shows the deltaic coast region between the Isonzo and the Tagliamento. As in the case of Venice the outer island fringe is broken by gaps or *porti*, and the Porto Grado has a deep-water channel to the mainland. Aquileia is now an inland town. (*From the 'Nuova Carta d'Italia', 1/250000*.)

a moderately continental temperature range, not such as to hampe effort seriously at either season, but with a contrast sufficiently grea to stimulate. Their greater energy as compared with the inhabitan of the more enervating south (cf. Palermo in Fig. 51), the grea development of industry and their highly efficient agriculture an all associated facts. Owing to the generally steep mountain slope summer temperatures drop rapidly towards the margins. Turi (height 275 m.) has a July mean of 23°C. as against 24°C. at Mila (147 m.), the subalpine towns means of 20°–21°C.; but such figur give little idea of the rapidity of the drop as the high summer resor are reached. Thus fresh, cool air is available for the townsfolk ther

Precipitation is low in relation to summer temperatures, thoug this is made up for in part by its fairly even distribution throughout the year (Fig. 52), and much more by the facilities for irrigation. A considerable area has total figures of 500–800 mm. (roughly 20–30 in.), Turin 859 mm., Alessandria 648 mm., Bologna 668 mm., Venice 750 mm., being typical figures. But the total fall increases rapidly towards the mountain border (Milan 1,007 mm., or about 40 in., Vicenza 1,208), as it does to the south of it (Genoa 1,314), and on the eastern coast of the Adriatic (Trieste 1,085). As the winter temperatures suggest, snow is not infrequent (average

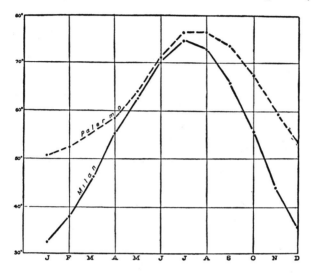

FIG. 51. TEMPERATURE CURVES (DEGREES FAHRENHEIT) FOR MILAN AND PALERMO

Note the steep gradient at Milan due to the continental feature of hot summers and cold winters. The average July temperature there is only 1·8° F. less than at Palermo, which is more than 7° of lat. farther south; but the average January temperature is 18·1° F. less than at Palermo.

number of snowy days 8½), and the snow cover sometimes persists for some days at a time.

The climatic type favours grain production on a very large scale, and the various reclamation schemes, here as elsewhere, have had for one of their aims the making of Italy independent of foreign supplies. Great progress has been already made in increasing the area under wheat. The high summer temperatures and the abundant supplies of water, however, favour maize as against wheat, and large amounts are grown in the damper areas. In marked contrast to other parts of Italy, maize (*polenta*) forms the staple of the diet

of the poorer peasants. Another indication that the plains are continental rather than Mediterranean is found in the abundance of
milk, butter, and cheese (Parmesan, Gorgonzola, etc.), rare commodities elsewhere. The dairy cattle are fed for the most part not
on mountain pastures as in Switzerland, but from the irrigated
meadow-lands. Thus the transhumant movements so characteristic
of the south do not occur, and in place of the typical Mediterranean
antagonism between shepherd or goatherd and cultivator there is

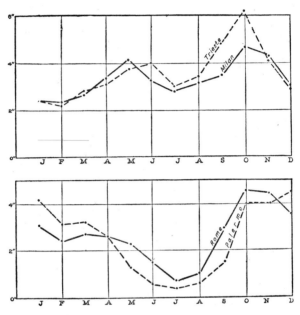

FIG. 52. MEAN MONTHLY PRECIPITATION AT TRIESTE,
MILAN, ROME, AND PALERMO (INCHES)

At Trieste and Milan every month has more than 2 in. rainfall, the maximum fall in each case being in October, with a
secondary maximum in early summer (May to June); the
minimum is in February. Totals (round numbers) are 43 in.
and 40 in. respectively.

At Rome three and at Palermo five months have less than
2 in., July at Palermo being virtually rainless (0·3 in.). The
maximum fall is in October–November at Rome, and in
December at Palermo. Rome has a total fall of about 32 in.
and Palermo of 30 in.

a systematized agriculture in which crops and stock both play their
part. The large live stock industry includes horse-rearing, especially
in Lombardy.

From the plains proper the olive is excluded, and if the vine is
widespread, cultivation is most intensive on the better-drained hilly

reas (Monferrato, Euganean Hills, Apennine slopes in Emilia, etc.).
ugar-beet and rice in Italy are mainly confined to the plains, the
tter being grown along the swampy north Adriatic coast as well as
1 the Po areas already mentioned. Its absence elsewhere, however,
 not so much a climatic effect as a result of the malaria danger, less
 the plains partly because high cultivation seems to check the
reeding of mosquitoes owing to the amount of salts dissolved in the
rainage water.

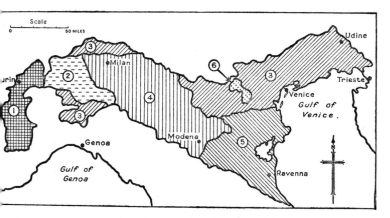

FIG. 53. AGRICULTURAL REGIONS OF THE NORTHERN PLAIN (*after Robertson*)

1. Meadow and Wheat Region
2. Western Po Rice Region
3. Marginal Cereal Region
4. Meadow Region
5. Industrial Crops Region
6. Berici and Euganean Hills

CHAPTER VIII

CENTRAL ITALY

General Survey—Origin of the Relief—The River Systems—
Distribution of Population, Cities, and Products—San Marino

GENERAL SURVEY

CENTRAL ITALY consists of the section of the peninsul lying between the northern Apennines and the southern are where the continuity of the chain is broken in the upland basins, and intersecting valleys. For the sake of convenience w have regarded it as made up of five departments: Tuscany, whic corresponds to the former duchy; Latium, Umbria, and the Marche the last with the tiny republic of San Marino on its northern borde which were included in the Papal States; and Abruzzi and Molis formed by the union of two elements of the earlier Kingdom of tl Two Sicilies.

The Marches, comprising the slopes from the comparative narrow Roman Apennines to the Adriatic, include the ancie Flaminian Way and the modern lines of communication to tl eastern section of the plains, and constitute, as the name indicates, border zone between the hilly peninsula and the northern lowland The Papal States extended here across the Apennines in Romagn corresponding to a part of Emilia. Abruzzi proper is a lofty uplar intersected by deep valleys, offering great resistance to throu routes and thus aloof and for long backward and primitive. Tl natural drawbacks were accentuated, prior to the unification Italy, by the political conditions, which made it a frontier ar towards the Papal States. The Bourbons deliberately neglect communications, and brigandage was for long rife. Despite position, indeed, the upland then displayed definitely 'souther features; poverty, insecurity, apparent over-population, isolati with all that it means in the maintenance of local customs, trar humance with the associated depression of agriculture, being characteristic. Since the unity of Italy was achieved, and especia under the Fascist *régime*, great efforts were made to develop co munications and improve conditions generally. Historically, ho ever, Abruzzi has been mainly a protective bastion to the m advanced western area. Molise comprised the gentler and m fertile slopes towards the south and east. Umbria is essentially passage land between the mountainous east and the undulating a diversified west.

This leaves us with the two great historic units. Tuscany was the seat of the Etruscan civilization, based, in part, upon the minerals of the so-called Sub-Apennines, which include copper, silver, lead, zinc, mercury, antimony, and so on, apart from iron. None is now of great importance save the iron of Elba. If Latium, the broad plain, gave Rome an original agricultural basis, the rise of that power depended fundamentally on the peculiar relief conditions, and on the genius of those who first learnt to take advantage of them by the construction of the great system of roads which diverged from the city. Thus the details of the topography demand careful consideration.

Before, however, we pass to these one or two general points may be noted. The first is the relative position of Central Italy in the kingdom. Although Rome (1,094,710) is the capital and the first city of Italy and has grown with great rapidity in recent years, yet Latium as a whole is thinly peopled. The mean density of the whole, including the city, is only 154 per sq. km., or 399 per sq. mile, as against figures like 264 per sq. km. or 699 per sq. mile for Liguria and 253, or 655 per sq. mile, for Lombardy. This statement is true of Central Italy as a whole, the figure in the case of Umbria dropping to 85 per sq. km., or 220 per sq. mile. In other words, there are not here the dense agricultural populations either of the northern plains or of Campania and Sicily, nor is there the development of large-scale industry which accounts for the great towns of Liguria and Lombardy. Apart from Rome, only Florence (271,975), and Leghorn or Livorno (109,188) surpass the 100,000 limit. Leghorn is the only considerable port, and is handicapped by a poor harbour. On the other hand, both historically and actually, Central Italy, with its beautiful hill towns, its intensive cultivation of wheat, vine, and olive, its artistic treasures, its highly individualized people, is the most typical Italy. It forms the region in which the *genius loci* found its first and fullest expression, which gave birth to the greatest men of the country, from which have radiated, and still radiate, some of the strongest influences in the history of civilized man. The importance of Rome rests less on its position as a link between north and south than on its symbolic value. It is not in any real sense the heart of the kingdom, for the north and south have their own centres, and the Italian language had its birth in Tuscany; but it is much more. As a world centre, commanding the allegiance of millions, it was a potent factor in promoting the development of the modern State, giving the necessary nucleus of dignity and tradition, making its appeal to all the separate elements, and adding as a unifying element the proud consciousness of heirship to a great past.

ORIGIN OF THE RELIEF

The broad structural features have been already discussed, and the essentials may be briefly recalled. The Central Apennines include the area which remained above sea-level in pliocene times, contain a large limestone element, and are bordered on the east by a strip of young unfolded beds. Within Tuscany the original folded Apennines were fractured and largely submerged, their shattered remnants forming the hill country, variously called the Sub-Apennines and the Anti-Apennines. These include the *Catena Metallifera*, or mineral-bearing range, which extends parallel to the coast from near Leghorn to the vicinity of Grosseto, and includes igneous rocks, believed to have been of submarine origin and to represent the first (early tertiary) manifestation of volcanic activity in the Tyrrhenian area. On the other hand, the volcanic hills of southern Tuscany (Fig. 41), extending southwards from about lat. 45° to the border of Latium, and including Monte Amiata, etc., are of post-pliocene age and resulted from sub-aerial eruptions, that is, from the welling-out of lava at or near sea-level. This belt is continued in the still younger volcanic belt of northern Latium where the Bolsena, Viterbo (Cimini), and Bracciano hills, with their persistent crater lakes, rose on the littoral during the post-pliocene recession of the sea. Beyond the Campagna volcanic activity continued into historic times in the Alban Hills, forming the transition towards the still active volcanoes of the south.

This then is the structural basis of the present relief. The next point is to grasp the implications of the post-pliocene uplift. This meant the addition to the peninsula of the Sub-Apennine area and of the volcanic belt, and the conversion of former straits into inner lake basins. The earlier shore has been traced in the north to the west of Florence (Firenze), and southwards in an undulating line, with a rough parallelism to the present coast, to the west of Lake Trasimeno, east of Orvieto and west of Terni and Tivoli (Fig. 54). Between it and the corresponding edge of the younger volcanic deposits to the west lies a furrow through which, as we shall see, the Tiber flows for a part of its course.

Before considering this highly complex river system, however, we have to note a striking contrast between it and the Arno. Both rivers rise far to the north and at no great distance from one another. But the Arno, after a—literally—circuitous course through what were once inner lake basins, cuts through or rounds the obstacles formed by the shattered fragments of the Apennine folds, and finds a direct western exit to the Ligurian Sea. Here it forms a common delta with the Serchio. Very different is the course of the Tiber. In its upper section it has a generally southward course, and passes

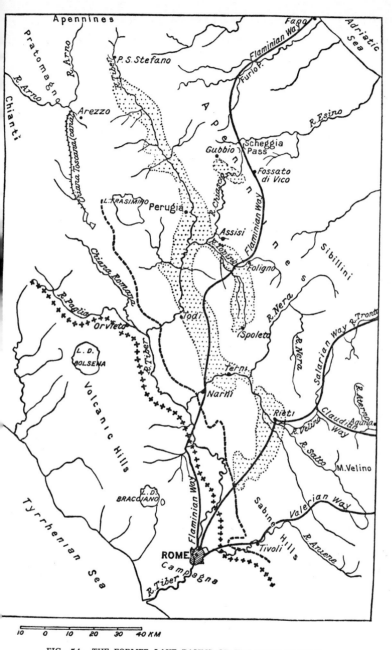

FIG. 54. THE FORMER LAKE BASINS OF THE TIBER SYSTEM

The broken line indicates the old coast-line and the crosses the approximate limit of the volcanic belt. Note that the Tiber flows during a part of its course in the furrow between the former coast-line and the edge of the volcanic belt. The basins are dotted. (*Basins, old coast-line, and limit of volcanic belt from Maull after Rovereto.*)

through what was once a vast inner lake basin (Fig. 54). Near Todi
it bends sharply, cuts its way through an Apennine ridge, and at an
earlier period reached the sea south-east of Orvieto. But the development of the volcanic hill country, combined with the uplift, blocked
this exit, forcing the river to turn once again and enter the furrow
just mentioned. This is followed till, after rounding Monte Soratte,
the last great outpost to the east of the volcanic hills of northern
Latium, it finds an exit across the Campagna between the Bracciano
and Alban Hills, forming, like the Arno-Serchio, an extensive
deltaic stretch (Fig. 55).

But this is not all. The damming effect of the volcanic belt, with
the resultant prolongation of the course of the main stream, means
that the westerly drainage of the lofty central Apennines is forced
to find an indirect exit to the sea, mainly through the Tiber. Within
the mountains the headstreams tend to have a longitudinal course,
corresponding generally to the direction of the folding. But the
presence of the inner lake basins, and the influence of the master
stream of the Tiber, give them extremely indirect courses after they
emerge from the mountain belt, so that a small-scale map presents
the appearance of an inextricable tangle, particularly as man has
modified the drainage.

One is tempted to generalize and say that between the Central
Apennines to the east and the Sub-Apennines and the volcanic belt
to the west, there is a great lowland, constituting much of Umbria
with a continuation by the Val di Chiana into the east-to-west basin
of the lower Arno. But such a statement does not represent the
facts accurately. Lowland Umbria is not one continuous basin
neither the Tiber nor its tributaries follows continuously the old
lake basins which occur within it. Indeed, the narrow, gorge-like
sections, cut through hill belts, which occur on both main stream
and tributaries, suggest that the river system in its essentials is older
than the formation of the lake basins.

From the human standpoint some important consequences result
from the complex conditions. The inner basins, because of their
uncertain and incomplete drainage, their liability to flooding and the
malarial danger, are unfavourable to settlement, so that the towns
tend to be placed on the marginal slopes. Perugia (31,839) and
Assisi (Fig. 56), facing each other across the Tiber valley, are
striking examples, while the low mean density of population in
Umbria speaks to the wide areas in the basins unsuited to close
settlement. Again, the details both emphasize and supplement what
has been already said as to the part played by Umbria as a passage
way. It is not, as might be supposed, an area through which routes
can be constructed in any direction. The rivers, now meandering
through wide, swampy basins, now pent in narrow valleys, at times

in tearing flood and at others shrunken in their wide beds; the unstable, sliding rocks—both forbid this. The Romans carried the Flaminian Way well to the east with a bold disregard of rivers as guiding lines. The railway from Rome to Florence, which leaves the Tiber valley at the Paglia confluence, follows the latter valley for a time, and then skirts Lake Trasimeno on its way to Arezzo and the Arno, takes a route which was only feasible after long-continued struggle with the uncertain drainage of the Val di Chiana—Lake Trasimeno area.

Generally, in the confused topography of the western section of Central Italy we find a multiplicity of hill sites giving security, water-supply, slopes suitable for intensive cultivation, with access to the more dangerous low ground of the basins which offers possibilities for farming of the more extensive type. The Etruscan cities no less than the medieval and renaissance ones were the natural response. The linking of such scattered settlements into a unit depended upon the building of artificial causeways, for the swampy, constantly-changing coast-line, no less than the characteristics of the rivers, made communication by water unimportant.

THE RIVER SYSTEMS

Bearing these general facts in mind, we may now note some of the details of the hydrography. The Tiber (Fig. 55) rises as a mountain stream on the slopes of Monte Fumaiolo (1,408 m.), near the junction of the Etruscan and Roman Apennines, approximately in the latitude of Florence and in a longitude somewhat to the *west* of Rome. After receiving a number of mountain tributaries it enters, downstream from Pieve San Stefano, a long, narrow basin, once a lake (Fig. 54), which extends southward over a distance of more than 130 km., ending to the south of Terni, which lies near its eastern border. To the south of Perugia this basin forks, giving off an eastern branch, which forms the long arm on whose eastern and south-eastern borders stand the towns of Foligno and Spoleto. But the main section of the basin is not continuously occupied by the Tiber, which, as already stated, south of Todi turns sharply to the south-west, cutting through Apennine ridges, and entering the long furrow whose upper section is occupied in part by the River Paglia. That stream has feeders coming from the Val di Chiana, the region of uncertain drainage between Arno and Tiber, with the large, shallow Lake Trasimeno, with only an artificial outlet, on its eastern border. The lake represents a persistent remnant of the large bodies of fresh water formed during the post-pliocene uplift.

The further course of the Tiber has been already outlined, so that we may turn next to its left-bank tributaries. To understand

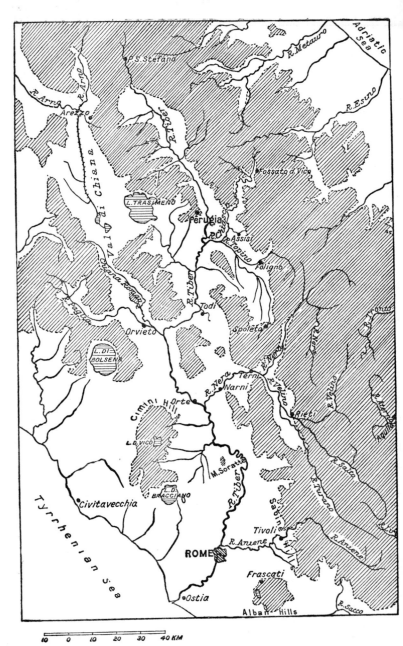

FIG. 55. THE TIBER VALLEY AND ADJACENT AREAS

Heights above 400 m. are stippled. (*From the 1/1000000 map.*)

the courses of these we have to note the former presence of two other lake basins in addition to the large one already described. Both, even at the time of their greatest extension, were comparatively small. The smaller and more northerly has the town of Gubbio on its north-western and that of Fossato di Vico near its south-eastern margin. The larger is the basin of Rieti. Both, it will be noted, like the Foligno-Spoleto arm of the central basin, lie close to the high ground of the Central Apennines, so that the emergent mountain streams have to find their way through them. Within the mountains these streams tend to flow in parallel valleys, longitudinal to the fold-lines. The basins, if the matter may be put so, drag them out of their initial direction and impose a very indirect journey to the Tiber.

The first important stream is the Chiascio, which rises near the Scheggia pass (591 m.), and abandons its mountain course to enter the Gubbio-Fossato di Vico basin, much of which it drains. But in place of following that basin throughout its length, that is, north-westward, it cuts its way south-westward through hilly country to the central basin, joining the Tiber downstream from Perugia. On its way it receives the Topino, another mountain stream, similarly diverted by the Foligno-Spoleto basin, and gathering up the drainage water of the basin in embanked and regulated feeders, connected with the ditches and channels which form a network over its floor (Fig. 56).

Farther south the Nera has headstreams which again flow in the longitudinal valleys of the Central Apennines, but it is drawn into the central basin near Terni. It then cuts its way past Narni in a narrowed valley parallel to that of the Tiber downstream from Todi, and joins that river near Orte. On its way to Terni it gathers up the drainage of the Rieti basin by means of the Velino, which has on its course the Marble Falls (water-power) as it cuts through a ridge to join the Nera. The Velino is once again a mountain stream, flowing in a valley parallel to that of the upper Nera but farther east, the river flowing south instead of north like the upper Nera. Before it joins the Nera near Terni the Velino describes a complete semicircle through the Rieti basin, which is but partially drained, two small lakes persisting as a remnant of the earlier conditions. Not far from Rieti the Velino is joined by the Salto, flowing in a south-east to north-west direction through the mountain belt, in a valley which corresponds with that occupied by the upper Liri. The latter, flowing in the opposite direction to that of the Salto, follows a fairly direct course to the sea to the south, entering this as the Garigliano at the Gulf of Gaeta. As compared with it the water carried by the Salto is taken in a north-westerly direction to Terni, and so follows a very circuitous route before it finally reaches the sea in the main stream of the Tiber. The Roman disregard of river-lines (cf. Fig. 54) has thus a natural origin in the nature of the drainage in the area where their first engineering feats were accomplished.

The last of the eastern feeders to be mentioned is the Aniene, which, breaking through the Sabine Mountains at the Falls of

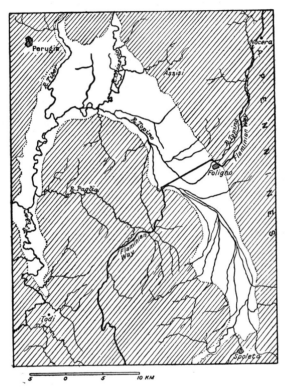

FIG. 56. PART OF THE CENTRAL BASIN OF THE TIBER, SHOWING DRAINAGE CONDITIONS AND THE COURSE OF THE FLAMINIAN WAY

Heights above 400 m. are stippled, so that the un-shaded areas do not correspond in detail to the lake basins of Fig. 54, which are those areas floored by recent lacustrine deposits. (*Based on the 'Nuova Carta Stradale d'Italia'*.)

Tivoli, runs direct to the Tiber at Rome. Apart from the falls its main interest is that its short and direct course reminds us that in the latitude of Rome we are south of the old lake basins of the central area, and also that the Central Apennines cease here to be eastern and occupy a median position in the peninsula. A further notable point is that a feeder of the Aniene flows in a north-westerly direction between the Apennine border and the Alban Hills, that is within a continuation of the furrow occupied by the Tiber before it enters the Campagna. Across a low water-parting this furrow is continued into the valley of the River Sacco, a tributary of the Liri, which thus opens up a route from the Campagna of Rome to Naples (Fig. 57).

The next point is to note that the greater streams flowing to the Adriatic have the same tendency as the western streams to show a longitudinal upper course, and then to turn sharply and flow in gorge sections down the steep eastern slopes of the mountains, and thereafter in gentler and more open valleys across the lower coastal belt, which has the main railway on the narrow plain which margins the low hills. Three representative examples of these rivers may be given. A feeder of the Candigliano tributary of the Metauro, which flows northward, approaches, across an intervening valley occupied by a tributary of the Esino, the southward-flowing headstream of the Chiascio (Fig. 55). This Candigliano tributary joins the main stream where that is flowing transversely, and before its entrance into the difficult Furlo defile, below which it joins the Metauro. This was the route utilized by the Flaminian Way (Fig. 54), which reached the coast at Fano. The railway avoids the Furlo defile by making a circuit via the upper Metauro. The upper Tronto (Figs. 54 and 55) flows in a northerly direction parallel to the upper Velino, here running in a southerly direction. The Tronto then turns sharply and breaks its way to the sea past Ascoli. This was the route followed by the Salarian Way.

The third example is the most striking. The Aterno (Fig. 55) has a long north-west to south-east upper course, parallel to but some distance to the east of the south-east to north-west course of the Salto. It includes the high basin of Aquila (700 m.; population 20,573), rich in fruit-trees, including vine, olive, and almonds, turns sharply to the north-east as the Pescara, after receiving a tributary from the lower Sulmona basin, breaks through the hills in a narrow valley, and enters the Adriatic at Pescara, west of Chieti (Fig. 40, p. 131). The Pescara valley corresponds in direction to the Aniene valley to the west, and the present railway, no less than the Valerian Way (Fig. 54), indicates the significance of this fact. Both skirt the northern border of the drained Fucino lake, of karstic character, without outlet, and lying in a basin which forms a kind of lateral appendix to the upper Salto valley. The point of special interest, however, is that the bend on the Velino, where the latter leaves its longitudinal valley to turn towards the Rieti basin, makes it possible to connect this valley with the Aterno-Pescara one. The New Claudian Way took off from the Salarian Way at the Velino bend

and crossed to Aquila, joining the Valerian Way where that follows
the Pescara. In essentials the railway takes a similar course, so that
Rieti (Terni, Perugia) is linked to Aquila and to the transverse
Rome-Chieti route.

We have still to consider the western streams north of the Tiber,
of which the Arno is of course much the most important. Though

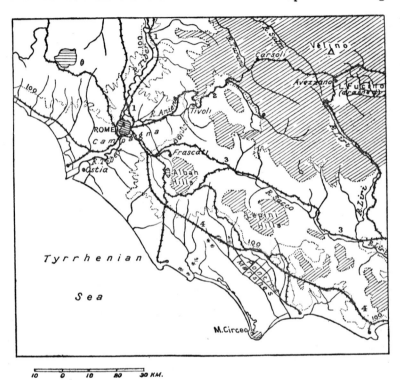

FIG. 57. THE ENVIRONS OF ROME AND THE CHIEF RAILWAYS

Heights above 600 m. are stippled.
1. Rome to Florence railway. 2. Rome to Chieti. 3. Old line from Rome
to Naples. 4. New direct line from Rome to Naples.
Mt. Velino is shown but the river Velino is beyond the limit of the map
(cf. Fig. 54).

it also passes through a series of basins, formerly lakes, the conditions are much less complicated. The river (Fig. 58) rises on the
slopes of Monte Falterona (1,649 m.) and the Cima del Casentino
in the Etruscan Apennines, enters a small upper basin, breaks
through a hill belt and reaches the large Arezzo basin, continued
southwards in the Val di Chiana. Through this basin it flows in a
semicircle, following almost a south to north direction between the

Pratomagno (1,592 m.) hill group and the Chianti Hills. The former, famous for its beautiful woodland scenery, has the suppressed monastery of Vallombrosa on its slopes, while the latter are noted for their red wine, sold in the familiar flasks encased in Tuscan straw-work.

At its westward bend the Arno receives the Sieve, which drains the small basin of Borgo San Lorenzo, traversed by the railway to Faenza (p. 136); it then breaks through hill country to enter the fertile Florence basin. This extends from south-east to north-west, the town, with Etruscan Fiesole on the slopes above, lying on the south-eastern border, while Pistoia (29,532) is on the north-western

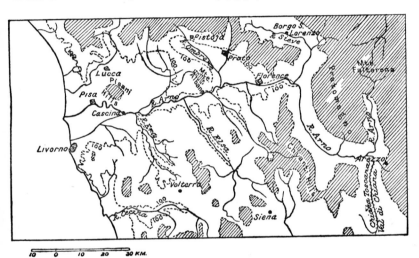

FIG. 58. PART OF NORTHERN TUSCANY WITH THE ARNO BASIN
The 100 m. contour is shown and heights above 400 m. are stippled.

one. The basin is traversed by the two streams of the Bisenzio and the Ombrone Pistoiese. On the former lies Prato, while the Ombrone opens up the transapennine route via the Reno to Bologna (p. 162). This is a difficult route, on which it is impossible to maintain high speeds, and a new and more direct railway connecting Florence with Bologna via Prato and the Bisenzio valley, instead of via Pistoia and the Ombrone, has been constructed. The new line includes the famous Apennine tunnel, 11½ miles long. It leads from the Bisenzio headstreams to the Setta valley, from which the valley of the River Savena is reached by a second tunnel. Ultimately, the Ancona-Bologna line is joined just short of the latter town.

After crossing the southern margin of the basin, the Arno cuts through Monte Albano in a gorge, and finally rounds Monte Pisano to the south and enters the sea past Pisa (49,471), once a port. It forms, as already stated, a common delta with the Serchio, which, after leaving the Apennines, has Lucca on its southern bank, cuts through the western end of Monte Pisano and flows over the wide, marshy, coastal plain, with many ditches and drainage channels. Leghorn lies to the south of this deltaic strip, where the hills approach the coast, and there is no important river to carry silt.

The only other long river of Tuscany is the Ombrone Grossetano, which rises in the southern end of the Chianti hills, has the hill town of Siena placed above a right-bank tributary, and passes Grosseto through a thinly-peopled, malarious coastal plain, where, however, drainage and reclamation works were carried out on a considerable scale by the Fascists. Volterra, another of the hill towns of Tuscany, and one of the twelve cities of the Etruscan confederation, stands on the parting between the Era tributary of the Arno and the Cecina river, but is approached from the latter. Volterra has salt and alabaster works, and the River Cecina traverses the *Catena Metallifera* (p. 174), with its varied mineral deposits. To the south of its valley are the *soffioni*, or steam-jets of Lardarello from which boracic acid is obtained.

DISTRIBUTION OF POPULATION, CITIES, AND PRODUCTS

This detailed survey gives the basis for the generalizations with which this chapter opens, and in particular accounts for the relatively low density of population. Apart from Rome, which, despite its seven 'hills', is not a hill town in the strict sense, the areas favourable to settlement are the lower slopes, whether those of the eastern side of the Central Apennines, of central Tuscany, or of the margins of the inner basins. In the last the bordering hills of the Arno basins, because of the central position of the basin of Florence, with its converging routes, and the large extent of productive land, are much more densely peopled than those of the Tiber. As contrasted with the hill country the highlands and the lowlands are as a rule little suited for close settlement. The mountains, particularly those of Abruzzi, have little to offer save some mountain pasture and limited woodland, the sweet chestnut, as in the north (p. 154), yielding an accessory food-supply. But, as is so generally the case in the Mediterranean area, the mountain pastures bring with them many problems. The fact that they can only be seasonally utilized means that lowland areas, often at a considerable distance, must be depended on for winter feeding-grounds, and that has often involved the neglect of cultivation and drainage there, increasing the risk of malaria, while the passage of the flocks through the area intervening between the summer and winter pastures gives rise to difficulties.

The present diminution of transhumance in Abruzzi (see Chapter IX) is in part a consequence of the campaign against malaria and of the efforts to increase the area under grain.

The lowlands, particularly but not exclusively the coastal swamps, are unfavourable mainly on account of malaria. Up till about forty years ago the areas particularly ravaged in Central Italy were parts of the Maremma on the coast of Tuscany between the peninsulas of Monte Massoncello and Monte Argentario; the Campagna and Pontine marshes in Latium, together with the coastal strip north-west of Civitavecchia; and the coastal lowland of Abruzzi and Molise. The two first-named areas show some interesting features.

Monte Massoncello and Monte Argentario are of importance to the physical geographer, the former because it represents an island completely united to the mainland by silt deposition, and the latter because it shows a stage in the process. Here two sand-spits (Italian *tomboli*) link the hilly island to the coast, the intervening shallow salt-water lagoon (*stagno*), which is rich in fish, being crossed by a third embanked belt of land which carries the railway and road and has on it the small town of Orbetello. At the base of Monte Massoncello lies the port of Piombino, which has large blast furnaces and steel works dependent on iron ore imported from Portoferraio in Elba. Farther south the swampy deltaic plain of the Ombrone has been in the past almost uninhabitable on account of malaria. Here, then, we have a coast which, if less notably than that of the north Adriatic, is extending steadily seawards, and at best can only slowly and at the price of continued effort be utilized by man.

In the Roman Campagna, on the other hand, man has not been guiltless of making matters worse. In the early days of Rome the area was certainly productive and yielded considerable supplies of corn. Its degeneration into a waste, the condition from which it is only now recovering, is believed to have been due in large part to economic causes. The growth of the city and the associated development of the great 'ways' in all directions at once increased the need for corn and rendered possible a dependence upon distant areas. The cultivating peasants were displaced by the owners of the large estates (*latifundia*), who preferred stock-rearing (with summer migration to the Abruzzi highland) to corn production. A not dissimilar process occurred in the central valley of California in our own days, where wheat production was displaced by cattle-raising carried on by corporations which bought up large tracts of land, though here intensive cultivation of specialized crops has followed as a third stage in development. In the case of the Campagna, malaria, depopulation, and insecurity followed on the disappearance of the small cultivator. There is no doubt (cf. p. 171) that intensive cultivation, with all it implies in drainage and the working and manuring of the soil, does diminish malaria, while, conversely, neglect increases the risk. The Campagna is, however, floored with somewhat impervious volcanic deposits, which are specially unfavourable in that they hold up the water, so that the surface tends to be alternately swampy and dried out, according to the season, and it has been suggested that this condition is more marked now than it was in early Roman times. It does not appear that the problem has been fully worked out, though conditions in, e.g., the cattle lands of South Africa suggest that over-grazing and neglect may lead to a permanent loss of fertility. It is thus possible that there has been an actual change in the soil of the Campagna. Great efforts are now being made to render it healthy and productive, and a considerable measure of success has been attained.

Very interesting also were the bold attempts made under the Fascist *régime* to drain and render healthy and productive the Pontine Marshes (Fig. 57). The figure shows that the Marshes are bounded seawards by a small river (the Sisto), which flows in a southerly direction, entering the sea across a dune-fringed stretch of land midway between the promontory of Monte Circeo and the town of Terracina (shown by a dot on the map). In early days the area was well peopled and remarkably productive, largely because of the fine silt brought down by the torrents from the Lepini Hills behind, during the winter months. It has been supposed that at some date prior to 300 B.C. the outlet of the Sisto river was obstructed, perhaps owing to seismic uplift, with the result that the basin became water-logged and the Marshes were formed. Despite efforts constantly renewed throughout the centuries, and indicated on the map by the canal lines, the area remained derelict and occupied only by a few fever-stricken herdsmen, tending the flocks of African water buffalo. The Fascists commenced reclamation here in 1926 and by 1938 the work had been finished over five-eighths of the total area. Great drainage schemes were completed and large areas of woodland cleared and roads, farms, villages, and model towns built. Fodder crops and some sugar-beet were being grown with wheat before 1939.

The detailed survey given justifies also the earlier statement that Central Italy has but limited access to the sea. On the west Pisa and Leghorn on the one hand, and Ostia and Civitavecchia on the other, show that here, again as in the north Adriatic, man is engaged in a losing fight with nature. Civitavecchia has only local importance as the port of Rome, and though Leghorn ranks fifth among Italian ports both in tonnage of vessels and of goods entering, its single strand of rail, and the absence of any dense network behind it, show that it is not in any sense the inevitable outlet for a large area. It was developed by the Medici as the outlet of Florence in the sixteenth century, and is one of the few exceptions to the rule that the notable towns of Central Italy have a long history behind them.

On the east coast the absence of large havens, with the partial exception of Ancona (57,068), is not the only drawback, for the Central Apennines are both a notable obstacle to cross-traffic and greatly limit the extent of the hinterland. Ancona's connexions with the interior and west, via Fossato di Vico, are very indirect, and the most direct east-to-west route (Pescara-Rome) has no notable port at either end.

The paucity of ports of any size and the resultant limitation of overseas traffic, combined with the small amount of locally-produced raw material, and the scanty power resources, explain the characteristically limited development of large-scale industry. That again gives the reason why so many of the towns offer the appearance of having had a past greater than the present, for other parts of the country have under modern conditions taken over the functions which they once performed. The frequent persistence of city walls, former fortifications, and of ancient buildings generally, which attracts the tourist to so many of the hill towns, may be associated with the fact that the present population is often not large enough to fill the old circuit, and there is thus no need to destroy the old to make room for the new. A characteristic combination of beauty —of site and plan as well as of buildings—and of squalor, dirt, and poverty results, well exemplified in such cities as Perugia or Assisi.

As regards agriculture the climate is favourable to varied production without giving overwhelming importance to any particular crop. In the west, January mean temperatures approximate to 8°C., July ones to 25°C., the rainfall is usually over 800 mm. (Rome, 805 mm., or nearly 32 in.; cf. Fig. 53) and occurs at all seasons with a summer minimum and an autumn and early winter maximum. In the east, January temperatures are a little lower, about 6°C., July ones slightly higher, total precipitation about 750 mm., with a more definite winter maximum. Citrus fruits are excluded, cotton is not grown, and though the mulberry is cultivated for silkworm-rearing to some extent in Tuscany and on a smaller scale in the Marches, there is no notable production of raw silk. Ascoli Piceno, however, is the principal centre for the breeding of silkworms and nearly 70 per cent of Italian silkworm eggs come from the Ascoli province. Wheat is generally the predominant cereal, but is of the soft type; in Tuscany spring-sown wheat is grown thickly to give the lanky stems valued in the straw-plaiting industry. On the damper lands maize replaces wheat, and it is also grown extensively in the east. The olive is grown almost everywhere save where elevation or swampy lands prohibit it, and with the vine for wine is the most characteristic crop, especially in Tuscany. There is no dairying industry comparable to that of the north, and though sheep are reared and the old woollen industry of Tuscany persists, as at Florence and Prato, most of the raw material is imported. Cotton goods are manufactured at Leghorn, Pisa, Pistoia, Lucca, and Ancona, but again with imported raw material. This statement is indeed generally true of industries based on raw materials of plant or animal origin, save in such cases as wine-making, flour-milling, the making of olive oil, and straw-plaiting, which depend upon home production, though up to the present there has been a large import of wheat.

As already indicated, the region produces a considerable variety of rocks and minerals, the iron of Elba being particularly important and iron industries fairly widespread. The great difficulty is power, for Central Italy has no large developed resources of water-power, no true coal, and but limited supplies of lignite, as, e.g., at Spoleto. Thus large iron- and steelworks, as well as armament factories and chemical works, have been established at Terni (37,295), because of the power of the falls (p. 179), and an interesting minor source of power is the use of the steam-jets of Lardarello (p. 184) to generate electricity, transmitted to the ironworks of Piombino and elsewhere. Among the useful rocks mention should be made of the potter's clays and earths, widely distributed in Tuscany, the Marches, and Umbria (note the pigments burnt sienna and umber), which form the basis of old-established industries. Florence is also famous for its mosaics (fragments of marble and ornamental stones being used) jewellery, and other artistic products. The heavier industries, such as engineering and chemicals, are confined to the new suburb of Rifredi.

The predominance of Rome and Florence among the cities is a natural consequence of the topography. The former, as already seen, is essentially a route centre developed from a refuge; the latter has greater local resources, but is in a pocket so far as the country as a whole is concerned, and has always been handicapped by the difficulty of maintaining a sea-outlet. Rome has expanded greatly beyond the original limits in new industrial suburbs to the east, north-west, and west, but an appreciation of the value of tradition has led to a careful preservation of the historic sites, with much clearance of later structures to expose them more fully. If it is they which make the strongest appeal to most visitors, yet one must not forget the significance of two other great buildings, placed on opposite sides of the Tiber—St. Peter's, visible far across the Campagna, with the great mass of the Vatican behind, and the proud flaunting of the Vittorio Emmanuele monument, built of intent on the slope of the Capitoline Hill, and commemorating the unity of Italy, as St. Peter's and the Vatican symbolize the wider influences which radiate from the city. It is this long sequence of historical structures throughout the ages which justifies the epithet without which no description of Rome is regarded as complete; Jerusalem and Athens, its much older rivals, do not convey the same impression of continuity and permanence. At Athens the Acropolis, with its great buildings, rises from a town which is essentially modern and has comparatively little to mark the millennia between the period of its greatness and its resurrection in our own day. Jerusalem must needs make its chief appeal to the spirit and the imagination, for it has not much to gratify the eye of the flesh, save the beautiful mosque.

To the previous account of the routes which radiate from Rome it should be added that the railway which follows the coast northwards past Civitavecchia, Grosseto, Leghorn, Pisa, Spezia to Genoa and beyond, corresponds in essentials to the Aurelian Way and its continuations. On the other hand, the great southern road, the Appian Way, after crossing the Campagna and skirting the Alban Hills, followed the coast in the region of the Pontine marshes, while the railway via Capua takes advantage of the Sacco-Liri valley (p. 181), approximately the direction of the Latin Way. But a newer line (completed 1927) between Rome and Naples follows virtually the line of the Appian Way and is considerably shorter than the older railway. It enters the plain of Campania by tunnelling through the hill on its northern border (Monte Massico, 811 m.), and reaches Naples via Pozzuoli (Figs. 57 and 59).

The tiny republic of San Marino (area 59 sq. km., or 23 sq. miles; population 13,948) merits a word or two. Essentially a rock fortress on Monte Titano, a conglomerate hill on the north-eastern slopes of the Apennines, with an encircling belt, it produces some corn and wine, rears cattle and quarries the stone of its hill. Founded originally as a convent refuge, it has retained its independence because of its isolation and insignificance. A narrow-gauge electric railway connects it with Rimini.

CHAPTER IX

SOUTHERN PENINSULAR ITALY AND THE ISLANDS

General Survey—The Peninsular Area—Sicily—Sardinia—
Climate, Occupations, and Products—Distribution of Population,
Towns, and Communications

GENERAL SURVEY

WITH the southern part of the peninsula, which for the
sake of convenience we have taken as including Campania,
Calabria, Apulia, and Lucania, and the islands, great and
small, we come to a world apart, strikingly different from the
remainder of Italy. Sicily, separated from the Calabrian sub-
peninsula at the Strait of Messina merely by a sunken fault-zone,
shares most of the features of the mainland, while the minor islands
and island groups of the Tyrrhenian Sea represent particular
elements of the adjacent land surfaces. Sardinia has as special
features a lower density of population than any other part of Italy,
and the presence of those metallic minerals which, save in Tuscany,
are elsewhere so rare. In other respects, however, it also is definitely
southern in character.

Southern here means Mediterranean, and the area is indeed the
typically Mediterranean part of the kingdom, which elsewhere is
mainly Central European or transitional. It is Mediterranean in
latitude, the Calabrian peninsula extending slightly south of lat. 38°,
eastern Sicily well to the south of lat. 37°, while Sardinia stretches
from north of lat. 41° to south of lat. 39°. The latitude affects
climate, which is markedly Mediterranean in character. It may be
noted that Siracusa in Sicily is virtually in the same latitude as
Carthage, or, in other words, a part of the island lies to the south
of a part of the Atlas Lands. The reciprocal relation of Carthage
and Rome to Sicily and the Atlas Lands was but the historical
response to a general similarity of conditions in the two.

The position brings the Italian area astride the main Mediterranean routes, and the effect of this is accentuated both by the
major dissection of the lands—the island form of Sicily and the
'heel and toe' secondary peninsulas of the mainland—and by the
minor articulations of the actual coast-line. The latter feature gives
sites for a multiplicity of ports, great and small; while the former
ensures for these frontages, not only on the great west–east Mediterranean thoroughfare, but also on the minor seas—Adriatic, Ionian,
and Tyrrhenian. The effect of position is indicated both in the past

history: in the numerous Greek colonies of Sicily and the peninsula; the long story of Palermo as a Carthaginian, Roman, Arab, and Norman centre; the importance of Amalfi in the early Middle Ages when for a time it rivalled Genoa and Pisa; and in the present-day significance of Naples. Further, if, whether considered as a Mediterranean or as a world port, Naples has at present no rival within the region, it is yet characteristic that not only are ports of varying value extremely numerous, but that they tend to lodge a large part of the usually dense population. From one point of view this illustrates a peculiarly Mediterranean feature, greatly accentuated here, the tendency for the people, mainly agriculturists though they are, to live in dense agglomerations rather than in scattered dwellings. The concentration within the coastal towns is due both to the natural difficulty of communication overland—a Mediterranean feature— and to what might almost be called a Greek imperfection of existing routes, which is in striking contrast to the dense railway net and the good roads of northern Italy. The latter condition, especially as regards the roads, was much improved under the Fascist *régime*.

Finally, and in some ways most important of all, we have the fact that the bulk of the population is engaged in primary occupations, either making a living directly by utilizing the resources of the soil by means of intensive cultivation, or by the relatively simple processes involved in working up the agricultural raw material obtained. In a broad sense, outside some of the larger ports, large-scale factory industry hardly exists, and the resources of the subsoil are limited. Further, though certain areas are remarkably productive, the birth-rate is so high, the density of population almost everywhere so great, often absolutely and always in relation to the available resources, that a large part of the inhabitants is living on the margin of subsistence. Judged from ordinary European standards a chronic problem of over-population appears to exist, which has been relieved in the immediate past by extensive emigration. These correlated phenomena of intensive and yet often primitive agriculture, and an extraordinarily dense population whose rapid multiplication seems to be subject to no check save natural calamities, such as pestilence and earthquakes, are sometimes regarded as characteristically Italian; they are in point of fact essentially features of the south. With them are associated a generally low level of education and a lack of local capital for development.

Before attempting to elaborate any of these points, something must be added to what has been already said in Chapter VI as to structure and relief, with special reference to their effects on human life. Of the scenery, particularly of the volcanic areas, so important to the physical geographer in that, apart from somewhat inaccessible areas in Iceland, they form the only parts of Europe in which active vulcanism can be observed, little can be said. It is the less necessary in that all the text-books give the essential facts and general descriptions are numerous.

As already stated, southern peninsular Italy shows three outstanding contrasts with Central Italy. In the first place, the tectonic forces which have led to the increase of the land surface to the west and are quiescent in the centre, are here still active. This is shown not only by the active vulcanism, the frequency of devastating earthquakes (note the Calabrian one of 1908, with the subsequent shocks), but also by the persistence and nature of the island areas. Examples of the latter are the still active Lipari Islands to the south; the Pontine group to the north, which are extinct volcanic masses; Ischia and Procida, which are island continuations of the Phlegraean Fields of the peninsula; and Capri, which is an isolated fragment of the Sorrento peninsula. It seems, therefore, that in the south the deeper forces are still modifying the actual framework and breaking the continuity of the processes of erosion and deposition, while in the centre the slow-acting surface agents are smoothing out a formerly more accentuated relief and concealing the heterogeneity of the elements.

Secondly, to the east the Monte Gargano peninsula—the spur of the Italian boot—the Murge tableland and its southern continuation, represent the addition of an alien element, believed to be of transadriatic origin. This is separated from the western or Apennine section by a lowland, including the Tavoliere di Puglia and eastern Lucania, which, with its cover of young deposits, has to be regarded as an elevated part of what was once the floor of the Adriatic (see Fig. 40, p. 131).

Finally, and again in sharp contrast with Central Italy, widespread calcareous rocks appear in the western Apennines. Limestones form the inner (eastern) girdle of the Terra di Lavoro, part of the plain of Campania; they extend out to the sea in the Sorrento peninsula and Capri; south of the Salerno plain they project seawards in the rectangular block of the Lucanian Apennines between the Gulfs of Salerno and Policastro. Farther south, the Calabrian peninsula, with its granitic masses of Sila and Aspromonte, is definitely mountainous, with but minor coastal plains and valleys. In other words, in this part of the peninsula the main Apennine chain is western, not eastern or central, and has a large calcareous element in addition to the crystalline rocks of the far south.

The effects of these conditions on human life and settlement are striking. The plain of Campania (Fig. 59), with soils derived in

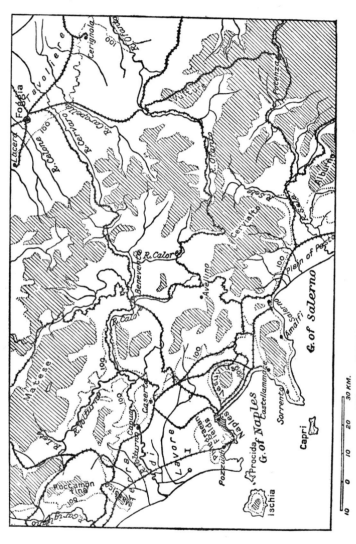

FIG. 59. ENVIRONS OF NAPLES, WITH CHIEF RAILWAYS

Heights above 600 m. are shaded.

1. Continuation of direct line (cf. Fig. 57) from Rome to Naples.

part from its calcareous inner border and in part of volcanic origin, with an abundant water-supply due to the rivers, particularly the Volturno, fed by the heavy rainfall of the mountainous interior, to the karstic springs of the limestone border, and to wells, is extremely productive. It carries a population (Fig. 65) which attains extraordinary densities in view of its absorption in agriculture. Further, lying as it does between the Apennines and the volcanic belt, it forms the continuation of the lowlands of the centre, which, as we saw, lie between the high Apennines and the western volcanic belt. The lowlands are continued into the Sacco-Liri (Garigliano) furrow, which, no less than the more difficult coastal route (p. 189), permits of the construction of effective lines of communication. The Naples area, indeed, is one of the few parts of the south which has at once a somewhat dense railway net of its own, and really efficient connexion with the general railway system of Italy.

The next point is that the western position of the main Apennine mass south of the Naples area, and the moderate elevation of the eastern area, which is continued into the peninsula of Otranto, results in a very marked shift of centres of population from the Tyrrhenian to the Adriatic shore. South-eastern Apulia (Puglia) is the second great area with a high density of population. Despite, however, the existence of the main east coast railway line it preserves a certain aloofness, and retains some curiously primitive features on the economic side. This densely-peopled area is separated from the west by the Tavoliere-Lucania lowland, which, particularly in the latter, is scantily peopled, mainly on account of the aridity. With the southward extension of the Calabrian peninsula, the modification of the relief due to the appearance of the crystalline rocks, and the proximity of Sicily in the Strait of Messina, we have another area suitable for dense settlement. The 'toe' of Calabria (Fig. 60), especially south of the Catanzaro gap, has indeed a notably high density, repeated on the opposite shore in Sicily.

To this general summary a few notes on details may be added. Apart from Roccamonfina to the north, and the Phlegraean Fields and Vesuvius to the south, the Naples area is girdled by limestone hills, through which the Volturno breaks at Capua. North-west, beyond the middle valley of that river (Fig. 59), rises the limestone mass of Matese (1,050 m.), with its lake, the karstic springs at the base (now dammed for hydro-electricity) accounting for a considerable density of settlement. Southwards and eastwards, the hills, of only moderate elevation, are built not of limestones but of sandstones and clays (Flysch). The notable exception is Monte Vulture (p. 130), which at once introduces an alien note into the landscape, and owing to the greater fertility of its volcanic rocks increases the density of settlement. To the east the hills, drained eastwards by the Cervaro and Ofanto rivers (followed by the railways) are but little dissected and the land relatively infertile. Westward it is cut up by a multiplicity of intersecting valleys, occupied especially by the feeders of the Calore tributary of the Volturno, and communication is easier and more land available for settlement (note Benevento, p. 133, and Avellino, both minor converging points of routes).

Southwards the massive limestones, alternating with Flysch rocks, form forbidding mountain blocks, and give rise to the complicated topography of the Lucanian Apennines. Thus behind Salerno stands Cervialto (1,809 m.), from which spring feeders of the River Sele. After receiving the Tanagro from the Vallo di Diano, this river breaks through at an angle to the recently reclaimed coastal plain of Paestum, with the marvellous ruined Greek temples of Paestum near its southern end. The Diano valley is margined to the west by other limestone masses, notably Alburno (1,742 m.) and Cervati (1,899 m.), while others project seawards in such a fashion, notably in the case of Monte Bulgheria to the south, as to make the construction of the mainly coastal railway to Reggio difficult and costly. East of the valley rises Volturino (1,836 m.), and at its head Monte Serino (2,005 m.), while farther south the great wall of Dolcedorme (2,271 m.) overlooks the deep Crati depression. From this eastern mountain area a number of parallel streams—the Basento, Cavone, Agri, and Sinni—flow eastwards across Lucania to the Gulf of Taranto, and with the Bradano, which rises farther north, cut its surface into a series of shallow, waste-filled valleys and low ridges which offer a considerable obstacle to communication. The coastal strip on the Gulf of Taranto is sandy and swampy, and has few important settlements.

South of the Dolcedorme group begins the Calabrian sub-peninsula (Fig. 60), with its two mountain masses of Sila and Aspromonte, and its characteristic dissection by faults. Despite the height of the massifs (Botte Donato in the Sila group 1,929 m., Aspromonte, 1,958 m.), they have only moderate, rounded relief, and because of the abundant water-supply, the summer pastures, the height to which cultivation can be carried, and their woodlands (beech, deciduous oaks, pines, chestnuts) their slopes offer more favourable sites for settlements than the swampy lowlands. The two massifs, as already noted, are separated by the Catanzaro depression. Reggio di Calabria in the south is the chief coastal town, but large inland villages and towns are numerous.

Apulia shows many points of interest. The Gargano peninsula, bare and karstic, projects boldly eastward, rising to a height of 1,056 m. Steep on all sides, its eastern coast-line is uniform, but to the north and south (Gulf of Manfredonia) it is fringed by a lagoon coast, recalling that of the north Adriatic. Westwards (Fig. 40) it is linked to the Italian peninsula proper by the Tavoliere di Puglia, floored mainly by post-tertiary deposits. To the north the plain is separated from the Lago di Lesina and the sea by a low tertiary ridge, from which rise the headstreams of the River Candelaro. This river follows the western base of Monte Gargano, is fed on the one side by the karstic springs from its limestones, and gathers up on the other Apennine streams as right-bank tributaries. But both the Candelaro and some of the more southerly Apennine rivers, such as the Cervaro, fail to reach the sea and are lost in the swamps which fringe the Gulf of Manfredonia. As the lowland narrows southward, however, with the appearance of the Apulian tableland, the Ofanto is able to break through, and forms almost the only permanent river in the long stretch of coast-land which ends to the south in Cape S. Maria di Leuca. The Tavoliere, which has Foggia (57,234) as its chief centre, was for long a desolate waste, and shows a combination of aridity towards the interior and swamps towards the coast, though many of the latter have been drained and the salt pans at Margherita di Savoia constructed. The Tavoliere is continued, over a low tertiary hill-country, forming the parting between the Ofanto and the Bradano, into the lowlands of Lucania. Taranto lies well to the east of the mouth of the Bradano on a ridge between a rounded gulf and an inner, double lake.

Much more important from the human standpoint is the limestone tableland which extends from the south of the lower Ofanto to the extremity of the Otranto peninsula. It was, save for its highest portions, submerged during the pliocene depression, and owes to this fact local deposits of late tertiary and post-tertiary beds which give the lower levels a productiveness in striking contrast to the dry and bare uplands. The so-called *terra rossa*, or red earth, derived from the decomposition of the limestones, also occurs in many localities and is similarly productive. From the Ofanto mouth nearly to Brindisi the tableland descends in steep terraced slopes to the sea, and these, watered by the springs which issue from the limestone, are extremely productive and densely peopled. This statement is also true of the Otranto peninsula generally, which is mainly lowland.

The limestone plateau can be divided into three sections. The highest and barest is the Murge in the north-west, which rises to 686 m. in Torre Disperata. A relative depression, through which passes the railway from Bari to Taranto, separates this from a second, moderate upland, where the maximum heights do not exceed greatly 500 m. South of the railway between Brindisi and Taranto there follows a low-lying neck, not rising above 43 m., which demarcates the third or southern region, where the Serre

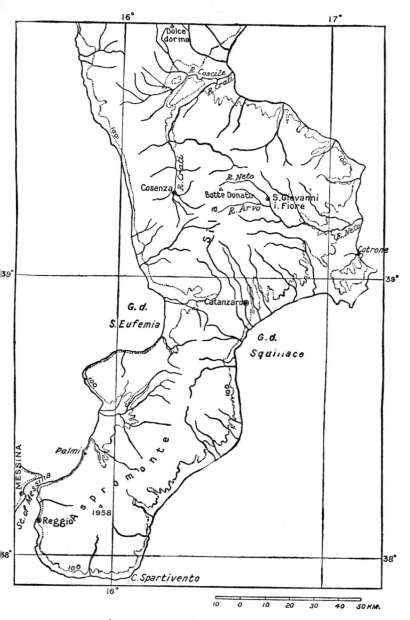

FIG. 60. CALABRIA AND THE STRAIT OF MESSINA
(*From the 1/1000000 map.*)

behind Cape S. Maria di Leuca attain a maximum height of about 200 m. Lecce (42,622) is the chief centre of the densely-peopled sub-peninsula.

SICILY

The triangular form of this island (Fig. 61), with the Egadi archipelago lying off its westward-pointing, truncated apex, and the great mass of Etna (3,274 m.; contrast Vesuvius 1,193 m.) occupying a large part of the base, reflects the presence of its three main elements. Though exceedingly complicated in detail, it consists essentially of a prolongation of the folded Apennines to the north; of the tertiary hill country which makes up much of the island, and is itself a continuation of the belt which borders the folded area throughout its extension (p. 125); and of the eastern volcanic element, here external to the range.

As already seen, the crystalline rocks of the Calabrian Apennines are represented in the Peloritani Mountains (1,374 m.) of the north-east corner, and the range is continued westwards in the Nebrodi Mountains (1,846 m.), where it consists mainly of sandstones and conglomerates. This hill belt, which slopes steeply down to the coast and has a dissected crest, may be said to end in the Madonie group (1,975 m.), where limestones make their appearance. This group lies to the east of the Torto valley, which forms a line of access to the interior (railway). West of this valley limestones predominate, forming block-like masses rather than a range, and there is also much shattering and dissection. Along the north coast these limestone masses reach no great height, and between them lie fertile lowlands, particularly the 'golden shell' (*conca d'oro*) round Palermo, the plain of Alcamo (with the ruins of Greek Segesta) bordering the Gulf of Castellammare, and the plain round Trapani. The Egadi islands are a continuation of these calcareous Apennines. Southwards the folded range is continued into the interior, and even approaches the south coast in the neighbourhood of Sciacca. In this section the heights are considerable in such peaks as Rocca Busambra (1,615 m.) and Monte Cammarata (1,579 m.).

The tertiary hill country is made of miocene beds, for the most part but slightly folded, and pliocene ones which have been extensively uplifted without disturbance. The uplifted surface has been so eroded by the multiplicity of southward-flowing streams as to present the appearance of a mountain country on a small scale, and except to the south-west, as round Marsala, there are few lowlands. With the miocene beds are associated deposits of salt, gypsum, and sulphur, the last worked on a considerable scale round Caltanissetta (37,463) and Agrigento (27,785). South-eastwards, where the land surface expands, it is occupied by the Hybla or Iblei Mountains

FIG. 61. THE ISLAND OF SICILY. (*From the* 1/1000000 *map*.)

The 100 m. contour has been inserted.

where the sedimentary beds are pierced by extinct volcanic cones, rising in Monte Lauro to 986 m., and forming the transition towards Etna farther north. The drainage here is markedly radial, and the lavas and tuffs of the volcanic hills are very productive. Siracusa (Syracuse), with its inner and outer havens, lies to the east of this volcanic area.

North of the Catanian plain rises the great circular mass of Etna, snowclad for most of the year, and always retaining some quasi-permanent snow-fields and patches, some of which are artificially protected for summer use. In addition to the main crater a number of subsidiary cones occur, and disastrous eruptions are frequent. The highly fertile slopes nevertheless support an extraordinarily dense population. Round the mountain, which is believed to have been piled up within a sea-gulf, runs a curious furrow, whose presence is marked both by a railway and by the courses of the Rivers Simeto and Alcantara. The former, together with a multitude of other streams (Dittaino, etc.) which join it, is responsible for the formation of the great plain of Catania, and the Dittaino valley forms the chief means of access for the railway into the interior from the east.

Of the seven volcanic masses which form the Lipari Islands it need only be said that Stromboli to the north-east and Vulcano to the south are technically active, the others being extinct. Stromboli shows a curious rhythmic activity, accompanied by a welling up of lava but not by its discharge, which is regarded as marking the dying stages of vulcanism. The islands are fertile and densely peopled, and, in addition to wine, etc., produce some minor mineral products, such as sulphur, pumice, alum, boracic acid, etc. They rise to a maximum height of just under 1,000 m. in Salina, the central island; Lipari, on the island of the same name, is the only considerable town and port.

Ustica is an isolated (extinct) volcanic island lying much farther west, and off the main traffic routes.

SARDINIA (FIG. 62)

If not notably in size (Sardinia 9,299 sq. miles or 24,090 sq. km.; Sicily, 9,929 sq. miles, or 25,738 sq. km.) yet in most other respects the two great islands are sharply contrasted. While triangular Sicily has its long axis lying east to west, in the direction of the Mediterranean, Sardinia is a quadrilateral extending north to south, its two shorter sides showing a south-west to north-east trend. If both include young volcanic rocks, the volcanoes of Sardinia are now extinct, and Mt. Ferru, the chief (1,050 m.) cannot be compared in height to Etna. In population the difference is enormous, for

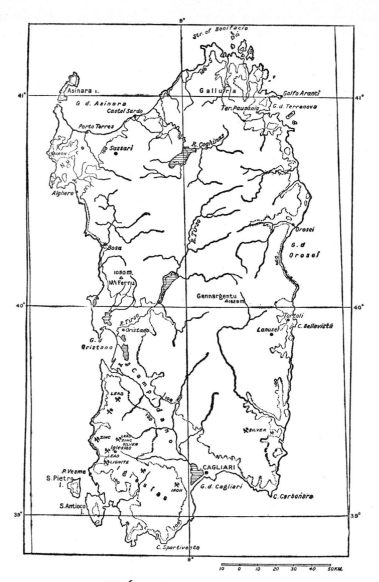

FIG. 62. THE ISLAND OF SARDINIA

The 100 m. contour has been inserted, and its relation to the Campidano lowland should be noted. The lakes on the course of the Tirso
and Coghinas rivers are artificial. (*From the 1/1000000 map, with
additions.*)

while Sicily has a mean density of about 172 per sq. km., or about 404 per sq. mile, Sardinia, with only 40 per sq. km. (111 per sq. mile), ranks as the most thinly-peopled part of Italy. With this is associated much more woodland (including both the holm oak, and especially in the north the economically important cork oak), while pastoral occupations are carried on on a notable scale, the flocks including great numbers of sheep as well as pigs, horses, and cattle, in addition to goats. One-third of the exports is derived from the mines, and the fact that nearly one-eighth of the total population lives in the single large town of Cagliari (78,632), and one-twentieth of the remainder in Sassari (44,130), the only other town of any size, suggests the thinly-peopled nature of much of the surface.

Without attempting any detailed account of the highly complex structure, we may note that the island falls naturally into an eastern and a western section. The former may be described as a typical crystalline massif, uplifted and fractured after a prolonged period of surface erosion. Granites form the main element in the centre and north, the great plateau of Gennargentu rising to the highest summit of the island. In the south the granite is mantled with palaeozoic schists, and in this area silver and antimony occur. The interior is forbidding, with difficult communications. A striking feature is the uniformity of the fractured coast-line, which, for the greater part of its length, offers no sites for ports of any value, so that Sardinia definitely turns its back to peninsular Italy. North of the upland within which the river Tirso rises there is, however, a marked change, which gives the Gallura, the north-eastern extremity of the island, special features of its own. It is separated from the remainder of the eastern upland by a well-marked depression, due to faulting, which begins at the Gulf of Terranova and is continued south-westwards, where it is occupied for a time by the upper Coghinas river. That river subsequently bends sharply to the north and enters the eastern end of the Gulf of Asinara. The Gulf of Terranova marks the beginning of the ria coast of north-eastern Sardinia, which closely resembles that of western Corsica, the islands of the Strait of Bonifacio forming a link between the two. On the shores of the gulf stands the small town and port of Terranova Pausania, which has steamer connexions with Civitavecchia and Leghorn. Since the depression affords passage to the railway to Cagliari with a branch to Sassari, the Terranova gulf forms a north-eastern gate to the island. Historically, however, it has never been important, the main entrances having always been in the western section, which is much more productive. This is demonstrated by the sequence of events, such as the foundation of the port of Cagliari by the Carthaginians and the later settlements on its gulf by the Romans, and also by the distribution of the curious megalithic monuments. These, particularly the Giants' Tombs and Nuraghi, or massive stone buildings, both dating from the late neolithic period, are widely spread in the west, and speak to a very early utilization of its mineral wealth by a people assumed to have been immigrant and warlike because of the strength of their fortresses and the skill with which they are placed at strategic points.

Apart from its minerals the great importance of the west results from the presence of the long (100 km.) but somewhat narrow (15 km.) Campidano rift valley, which extends from the Gulf of Cagliari in a north-westerly direction to the Gulf of Oristano, and was apparently once occupied by an arm of the sea. It contains a low and swampy water-parting separating the streams which flow to the two gulfs, the Oristano one also receiving the River Tirso, now, like the Coghinas in the north, dammed back in its middle course to supply power and irrigation water. Both the Cagliari and the Oristano gulfs have a lagoon coast, and the whole area is malarious, but nevertheless, with the bordering hill slopes, forms the main area of settlement and cultivation (grain, wine, olives, oranges).

To the south-west lies the hill-country of Iglesias, which, like eastern Sardinia, is largely built of granite, though other rocks also occur. The town stands in a region where faulting has given rise to a transverse furrow (railway). It lies inland, the railway being continued to the little haven of Porto Vesme, and is the centre of the important mining region. The chief minerals (Fig. 62) are lead and zinc; coal is also worked near Iglesias, being more important than the anthracitic coal which also occurs in Sardinia. Off the coast lie the large islands of S. Pietro and S. Antioco, the latter linked to the mainland by road and rail, which follow a sand-spit.

Immediately to the north of the north-western end of the Campidano rift valley rises the Monte Ferru volcanic area, active from pliocene to very early historic times, and now dissected by streams of the usual radial type. The slopes are fertile and hence fairly well peopled. The lava outflows extended both to the sea and also eastward, and it is through the latter area that the River Tirso has cut the deep and narrow valley which has facilitated the construction of the large artificial Lake Omodeo, which is said to be the largest artificial lake in Europe. Apart altogether from the question of water-power, the control of water supplies is a matter of great importance. It involves both the possibility of cheap and effective summer irrigation and of the prevention of cool season flooding, the latter not only dangerous because of direct flood damage, but, owing to the possible formation of stagnant pools, a menace to health.

A depression, traversed by the transverse railway to Bosa, separates the volcanic area proper from a northern one of more complex relief and rock composition. Here, in the central and lower section, the rocks are tertiary sedimentaries, and this region slopes north-wards to the alluvial plain fringing the Gulf of Asinara. East and west volcanic rocks appear, due to eruptions which occurred from oligocene to pleistocene times. Thus here, just as in peninsular Italy, vulcanism has developed in a north to south direction. The western and higher volcanic area is more thinly peopled than the lower eastern one, but settlement is concentrated in the central belt, where Sassari marks the northern gate of the island. In contrast to Cagliari it lies inland, and Porto Torres, its small port, is malarious. An alluvial depression, running from Porto Torres to Alghero on the west coast, cuts off the hilly Nurra country, with the curiously-shaped Asinara Island off its northern coast. The Nurra is of very complicated structure and contains a great variety of rocks; its chief human interest lies in its iron ore deposits.

CLIMATE, OCCUPATIONS, AND PRODUCTS

This summary account shows how much the peninsular and island areas have in common as regards surface features, and the resemblance is increased by the climatic conditions. January mean temperatures range roughly from 8° to 10°C. (46°–50°F.), Foggia 6·4°C., and Catania 10·8°C., showing relatively extreme conditions; and save in Campania frost is practically unknown in the low grounds, though snow lingers long on the heights. July means are of the order of 24°–26°C. (75°–79°F.), as, for example, Foggia 25·4°, Lecce 24·9°, Siracusa 25·2°, Cagliari 24·1°. Total precipitation is moderate, large areas in Sicily and the south of the peninsula having figures of about 500 mm. (20 in.), while except on the higher ground totals above 800 mm. (32 in.) occur only in restricted areas. Examples are Foggia, 470 mm.; Lecce, 628 mm.; Siracusa, 618 mm.; Sassari, 598 mm. Even more important, however, is the well-marked periodicity. Siracusa has but 3 per cent of its total in the summer months, Palermo 5 per cent, Sassari 7 per cent, Lecce 10 per cent. In Apulia especially the spring rise of temperature is followed rapidly by a diminution of rainfall. Throughout the whole region rivers, except where they head well within the mountains, tend to be seasonal, forming rapid torrents in the wet period and ceasing to flow in summer. This means great difficulty with the summer water-supply, especially marked in Apulia, where water used to be brought by train from the Naples area. There the problem has been solved by the construction of the great aqueduct, said to be the largest in the world, the headstreams of the River Sele (p. 130) having been tapped and the water carried through the Apennines in a tunnel 7½ miles long, the water being subsequently distributed to the Apulian towns in a multiplicity of channels. This is but an illustration of the general fact that the problems of the south require for their solution grandiose schemes for which, until recently, capital has not been available.

Again, the high summer temperatures and summer drought mean

FIG. 63. DISTRIBUTION OF MAJOR INDUSTRIAL CENTRES OF ITALY
■ Large centres with more than 10,000 persons employed in industry.
● Centres with 4,000–9,999 persons employed in industry.
● Minor centres with less than 4,000 persons employed in industry and generally with over 1,000 persons. (Based on industrial maps in *Atlante Fisico d'Italia, 1940*.)

that, for many crops, irrigation is essential. In the Terra di Lavoro and in Apulia large dependence is placed on wells; everywhere high density of population depends on access to irrigation water.

Fig. 63 emphasizes what has been already said as to the slight development of industry, and shows therefore by implication the importance of agriculture as the main support of the dense population. But the figure fails to make clear the full significance of the facts. The 'industrial' element is increased by those engaged in obtaining the rocks and minerals, particularly the metallic ores and coal of Sardinia, the sulphur of Sicily, the widely-spread but not very important lignites (Sardinia, peninsular provinces of Benevento, Potenza, Catanzaro, Reggio, etc.), and working in the numerous salt 'gardens'. Salt-works tend to occur wherever there are flat coastal stretches, as at Margherita di Savoia near Barletta in Apulia, and on the Gulf of Catania and near Trapani in Sicily. Apart from some of the ports, especially Naples and the surrounding towns, that type of industry, so well developed in the north, which consists in importing bulky raw materials and exporting manufactured goods scarcely exists. Naples, with Torre Annunziata and Bagnoli, has metallurgical and engineering industries, partly dependent on shipbuilding, and cotton, rayon, jute, leather, chemical, etc., industries. But most of its minor industries, such as rope-making, canning of tomatoes, coral working, making of macaroni, olive oil, and wine, depend in whole or in part (macaroni) on local products. Thus the chief imports, such as coal, mineral oil, phosphates, and chemical fertilizers, timber, grain, have only an indirect relation to the exports.

As regards modes of land utilization, wherever conditions permit cultivation is of the intensive type. The vine is widespread, though, with some exceptions, such as Marsala and the Lacrima Christi of the Vesuvian slopes, the wine is not of such a quality as to command a large external market. The olive is especially important on the coastal strip of Apulia near Bari, in Sicily, and in Calabria, and the region as a whole is responsible for the major part of the Italian production. Citrus fruits are produced especially in Sicily (where lemons are very important), in Calabria, to a lesser extent near Naples (Sorrento peninsula), where some winter protection is necessary, in Sardinia and on a smaller scale in parts of Apulia. Other fruit-trees include figs, almonds, pomegranates, walnuts, with chestnuts on the higher ground, carob, quince, peach, and so on. On the other hand, the mulberry for silkworm-rearing is not widely grown. It requires summer watering here, and this is costly, especially as the trees cast too heavy a shade for undercropping to be practised. Further, the silkworms require much labour at a time when field crops demand much attention. Cotton is grown in limited areas, and this is also true of sugar-cane, while sugar-beet has proved relatively unsuccessful in the Naples area. Very important are those minor crops which demand no great heat and can thus make their growth in the cooler part of the year. Examples are vegetables of all kinds, especially early potatoes, cauliflowers, and tomatoes; together with fodder crops, especially lupins and other leguminous plants. Tobacco is grown in Campania and parts of Apulia; liquorice root and castor oil plant are of some importance in Calabria. Generally, diversity is the keynote.

Grain, especially wheat, is widely produced, Mediterranean fashion, interspersed with other crops in the areas where this garden culture prevails, which, it should be noted, is especi- ally associated with slop- ing land, particularly where higher ground be- hind or karstic springs give an effective water- supply. Note as examples the slopes of Vesuvius and Etna, the borders of the Terra di Lavoro (cf. Fig. 64), the coastal strip of Apulia in the Bari region, the borders of the Campidano, and so on. But there are also large tracts of level or gently undulating land, often suffering alternately from an excess and a shortage of water, which, when devoid of facilities for summer irrigation, tend to become steppe - like wastes and are usually malarious and quite un- suited to the woody plants

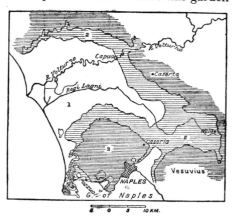

FIG. 64. RELIEF OF THE PLAIN OF CAMPANIA

1. 0–25 m. 2. 25–50 m. 3. over 50 m.

The plain is bounded to the north by Monte Massico and the last slopes of Roccamonfina, to the east by the slopes of the Campanian Apennines, and to the south by the cone of Vesuvius and the Phlegraean Fields. It is crossed by the R. Volturno, which carries a certain amount of silt and thus forms a low cone near its exit from the hills; the Regi Lagni is the chief collector of the system of drainage canals, by means of which the swampy parts of the plain are now drained and irrigated. (*After Dainelli, modified.*)

which form the basis of the intensive type of cultivation. Examples are the Tavoliere di Puglia, large parts of the interior of Sicily, the Campidano, and various coastal plains such as that of Paestum, that fringing the north and north-western shores of the Gulf of Taranto, the Catanian plain in Sicily, and so on. Whether these are used extensively for cool season grain production, or are mainly wastes furnishing only cool season pasturage, depends on a whole series of causes, social and economic, which have cumulative effects. Among the social causes the latifundia, or hereditary large estates favoured by the Bourbons, are assigned a high place. The tendency of the large owners, as in Spain, was to concentrate on pastoral industries, and the resultant neglect, as in the quite analogous case of the Roman Campagna, is said to have led to the degeneration of large tracts of once fertile land. A great number of sheep were, for example, formerly kept on the Tavoliere di Puglia in winter, but were driven along the broad drove tracks (*tratturi*) to the Apennine pastures in summer, whence they leisurely returned during the autumn. In recent years, however, the number of sheep has been greatly reduced owing to the decreasing amount of fodder and winter pasturage available on the plains. The practice of seasonal migration has considerably diminished since the middle of last century, and many of the *tratturi* have been converted into roads or ploughed up for cereal farming.

DISTRIBUTION OF POPULATION, TOWNS, AND COMMUNICATIONS

The general density of population and the main features of its distribution have been already emphasized, and the detailed description makes the causation clear. The area immediately round Naples (Fig. 65) ranks with that which centres on Milan as the most densely-peopled part of Italy, while considerable tracts in Apulia, particularly the coastal strip round Bari and the Otranto peninsula, as well as the extremity of the Calabrian peninsula, show densities of 200–500 per sq. km., or roughly 500–1,300 per sq. mile. The tendency towards concentration in towns or large villages is associated with the intensive type of cultivation, the areas with a scattered and thin population being those where this is impossible. In Apulia only 3 per cent of the total population live in scattered dwellings, but in more mountainous Campania and Calabria the figure rises to 17 per cent.

For reasons which have again been made obvious by the details given, the major ports are Naples (739,349), which ranks as the second port of the kingdom after Genoa; Palermo (339,497), Catania (241,462), and Messina (121,605) in Sicily, with Cagliari (78,632) in Sardinia. Of the other peninsular ports Bari (162,238), with a trade only one-sixth that of Naples, serves mainly the Adriatic area; Taranto (103,306) has re-acquired importance since, with Spezia and Naples, it became one of the three major naval stations; Reggio (60,342) carries on trade with Sicily and is the centre of a densely-peopled area, while Brindisi (35,984) is mainly a mail and to a less extent a passenger port. The numerous minor ports are due to the fact that each area of concentrated population tends to function as a more or less self-sufficing unit, with its own exit or exits to the sea. That decay of minor ports, and associated rise of a few great centres, so marked a feature of our own country since the development of its railway net, is here only in its early stages, because of the imperfect nature of the land-routes. Only Naples, especially since the completion of the direct route to Rome, can, as already stated, be said to have really effective railway connexions with the centre and north. With this is associated the enormous (over 1,000,000 persons per annum) passenger traffic of its port. Much of this is tourist traffic, the Naples area and parts of Sicily being the chief areas of the south visited by tourists. Much also is due to the importance of Naples both as a Mediterranean and as a world port; the shortening of the sea voyage, the scenic attractions and the effective connexions with all parts of Central Europe, making it a favourite stepping-off place, with some obvious advantages over either Genoa or Marseille.

On the other hand, the connexions between the Naples area and the densely peopled eastern strip of Apulia are far less satisfactory (cf. Fig. 40). As illustrations we may note that the distance between Naples and Brindisi in an air-line is 318 km., but 386 km. by rail; between Salerno and Bari the figures are 183 km. and 315 km. respectively; and between Salerno and Barletta 150 km. and 338 km.

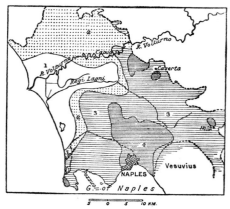

FIG. 65. DISTRIBUTION OF POPULATION IN THE PLAIN OF CAMPANIA

1. Below 50 per sq. km. (130 per sq. mile). 2. 50–250 per sq. km. (130–649 per sq. mile). 3. 250–1,000 per sq. km. (649–2,592 per sq. mile). 4. Over 1,000 per sq. km. (2,592 per sq. mile.)

The mean density is extremely high, and it reaches enormous figures, even in purely rural communes, near Naples. The low ground (Fig. 64) is relatively thinly peopled, especially near the coast and near the canal system of the Regi Lagni; this is a persistent effect of the unhealthy and swampy conditions of earlier days. The hill slopes are densely peopled, but a remarkable feature is the concentration in large villages, scattered dwellings being infrequent. The influences of the town of Naples, and of the lines of communication which pass near Capua, Caserta, and Nola and converge upon it are obvious. The northern hill slopes are less densely peopled and have fewer large villages because of the high ground behind and the relative distance from important lines of communication. (*After Dainelli, modified.*)

The railways are also costly to build and have high running costs. In Sicily conditions are even worse, and help to explain the curious fact that an island with three major ports yet maintains minor ports for special traffic, as Trapani, mainly for salt, Marsala mainly for wine, Porto Empedocle and Licata for sulphur.

Particularly curious are the conditions along the Apulian coast near Bari (Fig. 40) as illustrating the effects of the characteristic concentration in its extreme form. Between Barletta and Monopoli, a distance of under 100 km., there are eight or nine considerable coastal towns, while a corresponding row lies a short distance inland, each member of which is connected with its coastal counterpart by road and in some cases by rail; each serves as a minor road centre for its neighbourhood. The pairs may be given as Barletta—Andria; Trani—Corato; Molfetta—Terlizzi; Giovinazzo—Bitonto; Bari—Modugno; Mola di Bari—Rutigliano; Polignano a Mare—Conversano; Monopoli—Castellana. As already stated, the whole strip is remarkable for its intensive cultivation, the olive being particularly abundant, and while it is backed by the poor pasture of the karstic Murge tableland is itself fertile and well watered. The primitive 'Greek' simplicity of inner centre and coastal haven is disturbed, as it were, by the presence of the coastal railway and by the tendency of Bari, owing to its size and importance, to drag traffic routes towards itself. But that such obvious traces of an earlier condition should persist is evidence of the aloofness of Apulia, a region rarely visited by the tourist and very representative of the little-known south of Italy.

A few words may be added on what is being done to improve conditions generally in the south. Apart from road construction, drainage, and land reclamation schemes, effort was largely directed by the Fascists towards hydro-electric works, which, as already suggested in the case of Sardinia, often combined the production of power with irrigation by means of the discharged water. The power is used to electrify the railways, for pumping water from wells, etc., for irrigation, for light, and also for industrial purposes. A few examples may be noted. Naples obtains power from the mountain tributaries of the Luri and Volturno, especially the Lete, which heads in the Matese Massif (Fig. 59). The karstic lake of the massif is also being used to generate power which is transmitted over a distance of 70 km. to Naples, as well as to Benevento. A very ambitious scheme has been completed in Calabria in the Sila Massif near S. Giovanni in Fiore (Fig. 60). Here the convergent head streams of the River Neto (Neto, Garga, Arvo, Ampollino) have been dammed back to form reservoirs capable of producing a large amount of power. This is generated in three large power-stations and fed into the main transmission lines serving southern Italy and the electrified railways. In addition, large quantities are consumed locally at Crotone in the electro-chemical works and in the zinc refinery which is mainly dependent on imported Sardinian ores.

STATISTICAL SUMMARY (*See also* p. 304)

LAND UTILIZATION

Of the total surface of 310,140 sq. km., or 119,710 sq. miles, 41 per cent is arable, 19·4 per cent meadows and pasture, 7·4 per cent tree-crops, 17·9 per cent forest (though not the whole of this is productive), 6·2 per cent productive but uncultivated, and only 8 per cent unproductive. Wheat is the most important of the seed crops, occupying 39 per cent of the arable land. The acreage of wheat before 1939 was about 12,500,000 acres. Emilia, Sicily, Venezia Euganea, and Lombardy, in order of importance, are the largest producers. Maize is the second most important cereal and occupies 11 per cent of the arable land, with about 3,500,000 acres.

Italy is the only considerable raw silk producer in Europe and is the third world producer. She is also one of the largest manufacturers of artificial silk (rayon) in Europe, producing 291 million lb. of rayon and staple fibre in 1939. This manufacture is almost confined to the northern area, and apart from a limited use of native beech wood and reed pulp is dependent on imported wood-pulp. It has also the largest world area of vineyards. In 1939, 2·4 million acres were classified as specialized production and 7·3 million as mixed production, the vine sharing the ground with other crops. But the quantity of wine produced is less than in France, although the ratio of wine produced to area under the vine is increasing. In 1938, 2 million acres were planted only with olives, as contrasted with 3·3 million acres of mixed production. Italy is the second largest producer of olives after Spain. Apulia, Sicily, Calabria, Tuscany, and Liguria are, in order of importance, the chief areas.

The pastoral industry is relatively unimportant. In 1939 there were 7·9 million head of cattle, just over 2 million horses, asses, and mules, 9·9 million sheep, 1·9 million goats, and 3·3 million pigs.

POPULATION

At the 1936 census the population was 42,993,602, giving a mean density of about 139 per sq. km., or 360 per sq. mile. About 48·2 per cent are engaged in agriculture and fishing and 33·1 per cent in industry, mining, and transport. The birth-rate in 1938 was 23 per thousand and the excess of births over deaths about 12 per thousand. Some 9,000,000 Italians live outside the country. There are 15 towns with over 100,000 inhabitants, of which two have over a million. The population figure of the Italian commune is generally greater than the true size of the town, since the commune often includes large tracts of agricultural country. Foreigners frequently mistake the population of the commune for that of the town itself.

EXTERNAL TRADE

On a five years' average the value of the pre-war imports was about 9,871,000,000 lire and of the exports 7,389,000,000. Tourists and remittances of Italians abroad helped to redress the balance. The chief imports are minerals including coal, raw cotton, mineral oils, machinery, etc.; hence the desire to diminish coal imports by developing hydro-electric power. The chief exports are silk and artificial silk, vegetables and fruit, cotton, woollen, and silk goods. In 1938 70 per cent of the imports were raw or semi-manufactured goods, 13 per cent food products and 17 per cent manufactured products. Of the exports 42 per cent were manufactured goods, 32 per cent food products, and 26 per cent raw and semi-manufactured materials. The chief countries from which imports were derived in 1938 were Germany, U.S.A., Great Britain, Switzerland, Poland, India, and Argentine. Exports went to Italian colonies, Germany, U.S.A., Great Britain, Switzerland, and Argentine in that order.

REFERENCES

MAPS

For general purposes the sheets of the 1/1000000 international map suffice. For details the following may be consulted: *Nuova Carta Stradale d'Italia*, G. Marieni, thirty-five sheets, 1/250000, Bergamo; *Carta d'Italia del Touring Club Italiano*, L. V. Bertarelli, sixty-two sheets, 1/250000, Novara. The Istituto Geografica publishes survey maps to the scales of 1/100,000, 50,000, and 25,000. A large portfolio of annotated maps showing typical land forms in Italy and its colonies, somewhat difficult to handle but of much value, is in O. Marinelli, *Atlante dei Tipi Geografici* (Florence, 1922). For Roman roads, etc., *Italia* in Murray's *Handy Classical Maps*, edited by G. B. Grundy, two sheets, 1/1200000 (London), is convenient.

GENERAL GEOGRAPHY AND TOPOGRAPHY

Of the general books mention may be made of T. Fischer, *La Penisola Italiana* (Turin, 1902), the basis of most detailed descriptions of the country and of the volume on *La Méditerranée, Péninsules Méditer-ranéennes*, by J. Sion and Y. Châtaigneau, Tome VII of the *Géographie Universelle* (Paris, 1934). An excellent concise account will be found in A. Philippson's volume on Europe in the 3rd edition of Sievers' *Allge-meine Länderkunde* (Leipzig, 1928). Particularly good both for general and regional geography is the *Enciclopedia Italiana* (Rome, 1929–37). See also St. Grande, *La Patria: Geografia d'Italia*, in many parts. (Turin, 1925 onwards.)

Topographical detail is discussed in a number of guide-books, as: L. Bertarelli, *Guida d'Italia del Touring Club Italiano* (Milan, 1914 onwards); a part of this material is available in English in the Italian volumes of the *Blue Guides*. Baedeker's Italian guide-books have been brought up to date, and though this is not true of Murray's *Handbooks*, they remain invaluable for their classical information.

GEOLOGY AND MORPHOLOGY

For Kober's book see p. 45; G. Rovereto, *Trattato di Geologia Morfo-logica* (Genoa, 1923); du Riche Preller, *Italian Mountain Geology*, 3 parts (London, 1917–23).

STATISTICAL, ECONOMIC, AND TECHNICAL MATERIAL

Annuario Statistico Italiano; L'Annuario Generale d'Italia (Rome); G. Mortara, *Prospettivi Economiche* (Milan, from 1921 onwards); L. Visentino, *Calendario-Atlante De Agostini* (Novara); a small annual publication, with maps, giving a good deal of information for Italy as well as for other countries; *Le Irrigazioni in Italia*, Vol. I (Ministerio dei Lavori Publici, Rome, 1926), contains much useful climatological material. F. Milone, *La Localizzazione delle Industrie in Italia* (Rome, 1937) is excellent for industry, and for hydro-electric power in Italy see *Nel Cinquantenario della Societa Edison* (Milan, 1934).

REGIONAL STUDIES, ETC.

The proceedings of the successive Italian Geographical Congresses usually include local studies. Note in particular, for the southern part of the peninsula, *Atti d. XI Congresso Geografico Italiano tenuto a Napoli* (1930), 4 vols., especially papers by E. De Cillis, G. Alfieri, R. Almagia, D. Albani, G. Algranati, G. Albi, C. D'Alfonso, and the guides to the excursions (Phlegraean Fields, Sorrento Peninsula, Matese, and Vesuvius) by G. Dainelli and A. Malledra; part of the description in the text is based on these volumes. Notable regional studies include H. Kanter, *Kalabrien* (Hamburg, 1930), with lengthy bibliography; N. Krebs, *Die Ostalpen und has heutige Österreich* (Stuttgart, 1928), and A. Philippson, 'Apulien' in *Tijdschrift van het koninkligke Nederlandsch aardrijkskundig genootschappij Amsterdam* (Vol. LIV, 1937), p. 34, and 'Die Landschaften Siziliens' in *Zeitschrift der Gesellschaft für Erdkunde zu Berlin* (1934), p. 321. Notable in Italian are the 19 volumes of *Geografia d'Italia La Patria, Monografie regionali illustrate* (Turin, 1925–9).

Some of the problems of the newer Italian lands are dealt with in I. Bowman, *The New World* (Yonkers-on-Hudson), 4th edition, 1928. A full study of the eastern frontier problem is that by A. E. Moodie, *The Italo-Yugoslav Boundary*, 1945. See also the *Geographical Review*, January 1947. For the other frontier changes, see R. J. Harison Church, 'The New Franco-Italian Frontier,' *Geographical Journal*, Vol. CXI, pp. 143–6 and 293–4. On Land Reclamation see C. Longobardi, *Land Reclamation in Italy*, 1936. For current research see the issues of the *Rivista Geografica Italiana* and the *Bollettino d. Societa Geografica Italiana*. General books on the country are named in the annual issues of the *Statesman's Year-book*.

PART IV
THE IBERIAN PENINSULA

CHAPTER X

STRUCTURE AND RELIEF OF THE IBERIAN PENINSULA

General Survey: the Geography and the Human Response—
Relief and Geological Composition—Conceptions of Structure—
The Betic Cordillera—Summary of Structure

GENERAL SURVEY

THE Iberian peninsula, with a total area of some 580,000 sq. km., or 224,000 sq. miles, is at once much larger than the Italian one, and markedly different from it in shape, relief, structure, and products. The physical contrasts are reflected in the history of the two areas, and though the troubled and complex story of Spain and Portugal cannot be considered here, a few outstanding historical facts may be noted as throwing light on the geographical conditions.

As preliminary general points we have to notice first that within the peninsula, throughout the ages, unification has proved impossible to attain save for short periods, while that rise of indigenous cultures of high standard which is as characteristic of Italy as of the Greek lands is scarcely represented here. Both facts may be readily related to the geography. Thus we have to note the rectangular, massive shape, the high mean elevation, the aridity and barrenness of much of the surface, the outstanding contrasts between the constituent elements, and the difficulty of communication between them. The parallelism of the great rivers Douro, Tagus, Guadiana, and Guadalquivir during a part of their courses, and the divergence of their lower sections, is noteworthy as making clear the absence of converging lines of communication. The presence of coastal mountain belts, cutting off much of the interior from the surrounding seas, also largely nullifies the significance of the peninsular form. Throughout much of its history, indeed, the whole peninsula has stood aloof both from the Mediterranean and from the modern world, and there has been an absence of those vivifying contacts with the outside which are so important in promoting the rise of a high culture within a region.

This isolation of the peninsula is due both to the nature of the land frontier and to the position. As regards the latter point it may be noted that, at Tarifa, Spain practically reaches lat. 36°N., and thus forms quite definitely the most southerly point of the European mainland—of the European lands only the island of Crete has a more southerly position. In Cape da Roca the Iberian peninsula all but reaches long. 9° 30′ W. It thus stretches farther west than any other part of the mainland, and has an extension towards the ocean comparable to that of Ireland. Thus, in relation to Europe as a whole it is definitely marginal, while Italy is central alike as regards the Mediterranean Sea and the lands of mid-Europe, and Greece occupies a central position in the Eastern Mediterranean, and through both Crete and Asia Minor is linked to the more easterly lands. Again, paradoxical though the statement may appear, on the landward side the Pyrenees, if narrow, short, and low from alpine standpoints, form a barrier towards the continental interior far more serious than do the Alps to Italy. Effective lines of communication, like the water-lines on which they are so often based, depend less upon the actual physical obstacles to be overcome than upon the force of the current along them. From this point of view, as Philippson has pointed out, the contrast between the straight Pyrenean chain and the alpine arc is enormous. In the latter case there is a very great difference between the lands on the outer side of the chain—which are also highly diverse in themselves—and the inner plains. No such series of contrasts exists in the case of the Pyrenees. Further, routes across the alpine arc converge to a centre in the plains, which have themselves ready access to the sea-routes. No such point of convergence exists on the Spanish side of the Pyrenees, nor has Barcelona any such advantage of position as Genoa or Venice. Again, the easiest landways from the Mediterranean to the outer seas pass not through north-eastern Spain but through France, thus emphasizing once more the marginal position of the peninsula. Thus, even if, according to the phrase used at the time, the Pyrenees have been 'abolished' by the construction of the Somport tunnel, the fact remains that the east-to-west Pyrenean belt, combined with the Cantabrians, is an obstacle which tends to cut off the productive areas of the peninsula from the economic life of Europe. The forces which at all periods of history have drawn men to and fro across the Alps do not act here with similar strength. The persistence of the Basque people and of the Basque speech on both sides of the present Franco-Spanish frontier to the west is evidence enough that no great ancient highway has existed here, for it is not along thoroughfares that one expects to find archaisms. Eastward the tiny State of Andorra may be said to symbolize similarly the fact that man has had little motive for attempting to break down the barrier set by nature.

Just because the peninsula was neither a natural unit nor contained areas particularly fitted for local developments, early impacts upon it were of the nature of attempts by other peoples to exploit its more obvious resources. Among these its wealth of minerals was the most important. In this respect, as a result of the geological structure, it offers a marked contrast to the Mediterranean Lands in general and to Italy in particular. Without attempting to consider details we may state summarily that its mineral resources attracted prospectors from the dawn of history. In early days gold, silver, and copper were especially important, and the intervention of Carthage was determined primarily by the ores available. But the wide tracts of rough pasture, particularly suited to sheep, gave another motive for external exploitation, and Carthage obtained much wool in addition to minerals. Certain of the steppe-lands are suitable also to cereal production, and especially when Rome succeeded Carthage corn was added to the other products. Broadly then, there was a prolonged period during which the peninsula was essentially a borderland to the ancient world, its significance resting on its mineral wealth, the sheep pastures conditioned by the relief and the general aridity of the climate, and the possibility of cereal production, the last hampered, as in some other borderland areas, by the risk of crop failure owing to drought.

The next stage opens with the Moorish invasion, resulting in a far completer utilization of the natural resources than had previously been attempted. The Moors brought in a great number of new crop-plants, including the date palm, sugar-cane, cotton, almond, pomegranate, carob, orange, many kinds of vegetables, and a number of dye-producing and medicinal plants. They introduced silkworm-rearing, improved the breeds of sheep, and engaged in extensive stock-rearing, especially of horses, mules, and camels. Mining was reorganized and the variety of raw material available led to a great development of manufactures, including weapons, textiles, leather goods, all branches of pottery, and so on. Above all, however, and forming the basis of their high civilization, was their irrigation system, which rendered the cultivator independent of the small and uncertain rainfall. The Moorish achievement was enormous, but the basal weakness of their culture, from the geographical standpoint, was that it could only flourish within a strictly limited area. Those climatic and relief features upon which their system of agriculture depended exist only in a small part of the peninsula, and no military strength could maintain it beyond this area. The full meaning of this statement will appear later, when we consider details of structure, relief, and climate, but one or two points may be noted here. The date palm, the most characteristic of the Arab crops, can be grown along a coastal strip from the Ebro delta to Cape

St. Vincent, but its extension towards the interior is very limited save in the lower Guadalquivir valley, where it can thrive as far as the vicinity of Córdoba. Further, the conditions for the production of its fruits are completely favourable only between Almería and Alicante, and at the present time extensive date plantations exist only between Alicante and Murcia (Elche). The limit of the orange is generally similar to that of the date, with the notable exception that it extends up the coast of Portugal. Towards the north and north-west the conditions exclude even the hardier of the crops associated with Moorish agriculture, and the economic basis of their agriculture ceased to exist. The prolonged struggle against the invaders, if sharpened by the conflict between two religions, rested essentially upon the fact that a diversified agriculture based on irrigation and sub-tropical crops could exist only within a limited part of the peninsula, and the small size of the area available determined the final result of the struggle.

If the Moors were the first to realize the significance and potential value of the climate and relief of southern Spain, the next stage came when the significance of the world position was realized. The great discoveries due to the navigators who set out from the shores of Spain and Portugal depended on two sets of facts. In the first place, the genius of Columbus enabled him to make practical use of the effects of position on the wind *régime*. He launched out into the unknown with the help of the summer trades and came back with the westerlies, thus changing the history of Spain and of the world. Again, the proximity of the African coast as the result of the southern latitude, equally of course rendered possible that other great series of discoveries which forged a new link between east and west and helped to make the habitable world a unit.

It is, however, a commonplace that the very success of the navigators and conquerors brought a speedy nemesis, and that expansion, after a temporary period of greatness, was followed by collapse and renewed isolation. Again the course of history emphasizes the geographical conditions. The prolonged struggle and final expulsion of the Moors meant a great drop in population, not only because of war wastage but because of lowered production and the decay of the economic basis. Maull gives a figure of twenty-five to thirty millions for the total peninsular population in Moorish times, as contrasted with 5,000,000 in 1550, and increase at home was very slow, in part because of the drain to the new lands. In other words, the great Spanish Empire had too limited a basis in the homeland for persistence. Further, the type of mind produced in the Christian conquerors by the prolonged struggle at home, if well fitted to lead to the extension of the national territories, unfitted the Spaniard to develop these as against exploiting them by short-sighted methods.

More than all, however, the nature of the relation to the rest of Europe, and that south-westward extension which made the great discoveries possible, made it impossible for the inhabitants of the peninsula to utilize fully the new avenues of trade opened up by the navigators who went out from it. World trade passed into other hands and the peninsula fell back into an even more complete isolation than before. In Maull's words, it became, particularly in the eighteenth and part of the nineteenth century, more of a stranger to the European world than was the Balkan peninsula under the Turks. French travellers became the main interpreters of Spain to the outside world, and such phrases as that 'Africa begins at the Pyrenees' became widely current, and still find a place in some geographical text-books.

This conception of the African affinities of the peninsula, however, has at best but doubtful validity, and handicaps rather than helps a real grasp of its characteristics. At first sight, it is true, such features as the aridity, the wide esparto-covered steppes, the general absence of the articulated coast-line characteristic of Europe in general, the narrowness of the water gap at the Strait of Gibraltar, and, from the human standpoint, the prolonged Moslem domination, seem to justify the comparison. Even so, however, the comparison is less with Africa as a whole than with that northern strip which some German geographers regard as forming part of a wide west-to-east Orient belt which is unrelated to continental divisions. In other words, part of Spain is 'African' only in the sense that part of Africa, together with a considerable part of Asia, is 'Oriental' in its climate, relief, land-forms, and in the human response. It is interesting to note, however, that despite the narrowness of the sea intervening between southern Spain and Africa, human connexions here have not been reciprocal, as they have been in the case of the Balkan peninsula and the Asiatic margin. The two great attempts to penetrate the Atlas Lands from the north, represented by the movements of the Vandals and by latter-day Spanish efforts in Morocco, must be regarded as experiments that failed. The reason is obvious enough, for access to the interior of North Africa here, as contrasted with that by the north–south coast-line of what is now Tunisia, is difficult; southern Spain and the Atlas Lands in reality turn their backs on each other.

Further, a fuller knowledge of the peninsula has sapped the base of the old conception that there is a close structural analogy between Spain and North Africa. The older view that the Betic Cordillera (Sierra Nevada, etc.) is continued into the Atlas across the sunken Strait of Gibraltar has been abandoned by many geologists, while Staub, in the recent article upon which the description which follows is mainly based, emphasizes repeatedly the *Asiatic* as distinct from the African analogies of the peninsula. He rejects entirely the view that the Pyrenees and the Cantabrians can be regarded as in any true sense a part of the alpine folding. For him the chain of the Betic Cordillera represents the only truly alpine element in Spain. Thus we reach the curiously novel conception that, far from being African, the peninsula lies almost wholly to the north of the alpine fold-lines, and represents the south-western extension of Hercynian Europe, not without analogies with its north-western extension in Brittany and the south-western part of the British Isles. Staub believes that the greater part of the peninsula was affected only by repercussions of the alpine folding, which gave rise to secondary crumplings represented in the Pyrenees and elsewhere, and regards it as for the most part a rigid and ancient block, which owing to its rigidity was able to persist while some other parts of Hercynian Europe sank beneath the sea. Before, however, we attempt to outline his interpretation, it is necessary to consider the main surface features and the distribution of the constituent rocks.

In passing it may be noted that Staub's conception that the peninsula is in the main a south-western extension of the ancient Europe does appear to give a better explanation of the human response throughout the ages than any over-emphasis of the resemblances to the Atlas Lands, and also a clearer picture of the actual relief than the usual view that it consists mainly of a stable tableland (the meseta) with Alpine fold-mountains abutting on it to north and south. The existing complexity of the relief is explained by Staub as largely due to the secondary effects of the alpine storm, the great earth movements, save on the southern margin, being fended off by the rigidity of the ancient core. Much of Europe, on the other hand, was remodelled by those movements, and the effect is to leave the peninsula aloof and isolated, comparable to a fragment of Central Asia on the border of the European continent, of an older world on the margin of a newer one. From the human side the effect has been that the great traffic routes swing round it, leaving it as isolated economically as it is structurally.

RELIEF AND GEOLOGICAL COMPOSITION

Fig. 66 indicates, in generalized fashion, the main types of rock represented in the peninsula. In the north-west lies the Archaean granitic core, giving rise to the Galician upland, continued into northern Portugal. This is drained by the Minho and lower Douro (called Duero in Spain), and its ocean border displays the same ria type of coast as that present in south-western Ireland. In addition to the two rivers named, a number of smaller streams dissect the area, which has been worn down by prolonged erosion, so that it includes minor lowlands and nowhere attains great heights. The granitic rocks are continued eastwards in the Central Sierras of Gata (1,794 m.), Gredos (2,692 m.), and Guadarrama (2,405 m.), and to a less notable extent in the mountains of Toledo (1,392 m.) farther south. Abutting on this granitic core in the north, in Asturias and western León, and developed over a much more extensive area to

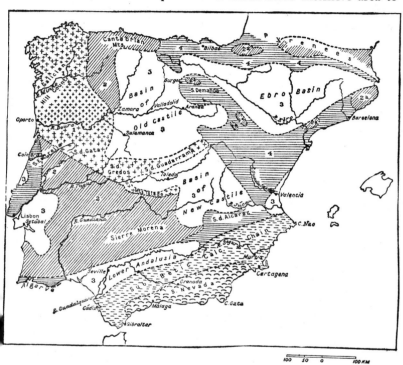

FIG. 66. THE MAIN STRUCTURAL ELEMENTS OF THE IBERIAN
PENINSULA

1. Archaean granites. 2. Palaeozoic sedimentary and crystalline rocks, mainly developed in the west, but occurring also (2a) in the border ranges (S. de la Demanda, etc.), the Catalonian coast ranges, and the Pyrenees. 3. The tertiary basins. 4. The areas floored by secondary rocks.

the south of the Central Sierras, in southern Portugal and Estremadura, etc., in southern Spain, is a great mass of folded palaeozoic sedimentaries and crystalline rocks, rising in western León to 1,200 m. and in the Peñas de Europa on the border of Asturias to 2,642 m. In the southern area the belt extends to the Atlantic shore near Cape St. Vincent. Farther east its wall-like border forms the Sierra Morena overlooking the Guadalquivir valley of Andalusia, which rises to 1,800 m. in the Sierra de Alcaráz towards its eastern extremity, as against 1,100 m. in the centre. Northwards the palaeozoic rocks combine with the granitic belt already noted to form the mountains of Toledo. Similar palaeozoic rocks occur in the Pyrenees, where granites are also present, as well as, to a minor extent, in the section of the peninsula intervening between them and the Sierra Nevada, as notably in the coastal mountains of Catalonia, and in the upland belt which abuts obliquely on the Central Sierras. Palaeozoic rocks are also present in the Sierra Nevada.

In striking contrast to these old rocks, developed, as this description makes clear, mainly in the western area of the peninsula, but forming an interrupted framework in its eastern half, is the large area floored by tertiary beds. These fall into two main groups: (1) Those of oligo-miocene age and fluvio-lacustrine origin which occur in inner basins, and (2) the marine pliocene beds found on the periphery of the peninsula. The first group covers much the greater area, and the beds occur in large basins separated from each other and from the sea by ridges of older rocks.

There are three of these basins, forming respectively the Ebro basin and those of Old and New Castile. The first, which includes considerable lowland areas, is roughly triangular, its broad base being separated from the Mediterranean by the coastal mountains of Catalonia, through which the River Ebro cuts its way. The Pyrenees, continued into the Cantabrians, form the northern border of the basin, while its south-western edge is constituted by that mass of high ground already noted which is usually called the Iberic Mountains, and includes in the Sierra de la Demanda (2,305 m.) and the conspicuous mass of Moncayo (2,349 m.) considerable elevations. This upland trends towards the Cantabrians, but is separated from them by an important though narrow gap at Burgos; south-eastwards it extends towards the Mediterranean coast north of the small coastal plain of Valencia. Through the Burgos gap the tertiary beds of the Ebro basin are continuous with those underlying the great basin of Old Castile, which is traversed throughout its length by the Douro. This basin again has a higher border, consisting of the upland already described to the east, the Cantabrians to the north, part of the Galician upland, mountains of León, etc., to the west and the Central Sierras to the south. But it is not itself, as might be assumed, a lowland. At Aranda on the Douro near its eastern border the height is 800 m. above sea-level, at Valladolid it is 700 m., dropping to 400–300 m. as the Portuguese frontier is approached.

Because of its height and more or less level surface the basin of Old Castile is usually included in the meseta or tableland; but it should be noted that this term, especially as often used, is not devoid of ambiguity. If, as by origin it should be, it is merely applied to the plateau areas of Spain, it carries no reference to the nature of the constituent rocks. There is, however, some tendency to imply that the meseta owes its plateau nature to the presence of old and hard rocks, and thus to ignore the fact that much of the basin of Old Castile, which is based on tertiaries, has a greater elevation than much of Galicia, which is based on granitic rocks. It is true that according to the geologists there is reason to believe that the tertiaries of Old Castile are overlying continuations of the primary rocks of Asturias, but the fact remains that the exposed beds are geologically young. Any general statement to the effect that the tableland as a whole is developed on the old rocks of the western part of the peninsula should thus be carefully avoided.

Owing to the heavy rainfall of the north-west, which feeds a number of Douro tributaries, the northern part of the basin is cut up by valleys which largely destroy the plateau-like nature of the surface. To the south it is much more uniform.

From the third basin, that of New Castile, Old Castile is, as already suggested, separated by the Central Sierras. This basin, which lies at a somewhat lower level than that of Old Castile, is incompletely divided into two parts by the belt of old rocks already described as forming the mountains of Toledo. The more northerly of the two is drained by the upper Tagus, the more southerly by the upper Guadiana. The latter shows a general parallelism to the Tagus and the Douro, before turning sharply as it approaches the Portuguese frontier to enter the north-to-south course which brings it into the Gulf of Cádiz. The eastern part of the basin particularly has again a very uniform surface, and like southern Old Castile is typically 'Spanish' in the sense of being arid, monotonous, and steppe-like in character. Both basins, indeed, may be said broadly to be steppes; in parts, particularly in Old Castile, the natural vegetation has been replaced by cereal cultivation, but large areas carry the original plant cover, and serve mainly as sheep pastures. On the other hand, the Ebro basin, with much greater possibilities of irrigation, is much more productive and carries a large variety of crops. Owing to the presence of the Catalonian coastal chain, however, it shares, if to a less extent, the isolation of the other two.

Very different, though unfortunately of a smaller total area and markedly separated from one another, are the peripheral or truly lowland tertiary basins. Largest and most important is the valley of lower Andalusia, watered by the Guadalquivir. The river, in contrast with the plateau sections of the Douro, Tagus, and Guadiana, is of some use as a waterway; the plain, as contrasted with the Ebro basin, opens directly seawards without an intervening mountain belt; the streams, particularly those from the Sierra Nevada, give great possibilities of irrigation; in contrast with the red soils or steppe soils which cover so much of Spain save in the damp north-west, a large tract of fertile, humus-containing black earth occurs. Generally, the natural conditions appear to be much more favour-able to human effort. The other chief areas floored by marine pliocene beds are the region round Valencia, between the lower courses of the rivers Júcar and Guadalaviar, and an extensive but interrupted tract in west-central Portugal, including a coastal strip south-west of Coimbra, the lower Tagus valley, and, virtually con-tinuous with this, the area which margins the Bay of Setúbal.

Two elements shown in the diagram remain to be considered. One is the great belt of the Betic Cordillera, including the secondary rocks on its northern border, and the other is constituted by the secondary rocks throughout the remainder of the peninsula. Taking the latter first we find that secondary rocks occur in west-central Portugal, interrupting the continuity of the marine tertiary beds there; on the coastal strip of Algarve in southern Portugal; in the belt which extends seawards from the eastern end of the primary rocks of the Sierra Morena, and separates the tertiary basin of Valencia from the Betic Cordillera. Finally, they cover large areas in the north-east, underlying a large part of the Pyrenees and eastern Cantabrians, extending along much of the east coast as far as the basin of Valencia, and trending north-west in the upland which separates the tertiary Ebro basin from those of the two Castiles. All these include areas of considerable elevation.

For the moment the Betic Cordillera may be briefly dismissed. Along the northern border, and forming the subsidiary ranges, lies a broad belt of secondary rocks, mainly jurassic limestones. This abuts on the sea to the east between Cape Nao and Cartagena, and to the south-west from a point north-east of Gibraltar to the mouth of the Guadalquivir; but is separated from it in the intervening area by the great mass of older, intensely disturbed and metamorphosed rocks which underlies the Sierra Nevada and adjacent mountains, the former rising in Mulhacén (3,481 m.) to the culminating point of the peninsula. To the north of the high chain the Calcareous Zone just described overlooks the tertiary valley of the Guadalquivir.

From this summary account it is clear that, despite the high mean elevation and the uniformity which prevails in unit areas, the peninsula is highly complex alike in its geological composition and in its relief elements. From the human standpoint the outstanding feature is the contrast between the central and the peripheral areas. The former are 'continental' in character, and have relatively difficult access to the marginal seas, while the Pyrenees, as already seen, form a barrier on the short landward border. The latter, including those on the ocean border of Portugal are 'Mediterranean' in climate and products, but are isolated from each other and have difficult access to the interior.

CONCEPTIONS OF STRUCTURE

We may begin with a brief note on Kober's views as indicated in Fig. 67. The previous description has given a basis for the interpretation of this. Thus we need merely point out that the diagram shows the old rocks as exposed in the meseta, using the term in the geological sense, with an indication of the Hercynian folding round

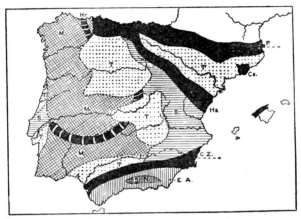

FIG. 67. KOBER'S CONCEPTION OF THE STRUCTURE OF THE IBERIAN PENINSULA

M. = rocks of core, the Hercynian folding (Hr.) being indicated diagrammatically. C.Z. = the outer or Calcareous Zone of the Betic Cordillera. E.A. = East Alpine nappes. S.N. = the Sierra Nevada, where Pennine nappes are exposed in a window. Hs. = the Iberian ranges, supposed by Kober to form the link between the Betic Cordillera and the Cantabro-Pyrenean chain. Cs. = Coastal Ranges of Catalonia. P. = Pyrenees. The tertiary basins (cf. Fig. 66) are marked with the letter T and secondary rocks with the letter S. (*After Kober, modified.*)

the granitic core; the large central and peripheral areas floored by tertiary deposits; the distribution of the secondary beds; and, finally, what Kober regards as folded alpine belts. Of the last only the Betic Cordillera is shown in any detail, and since both Kober and Staub agree as to the essential features of this, its characteristics may be noted. Both, as well as a number of other geologists, agree in abandoning Suess' view that the folds swing round across what is now the Strait of Gibraltar into the Atlas Lands. Instead, they believe that the chain ends on the ocean border, and is without direct relation to the Atlas chains. Both, also—and this is a point of much interest—regard the Sierra Nevada as a 'window' in which Pennine nappes are exposed, that is, as the precise analogue of the Hohe Tauern (p. 42) window. Around this window, again as in the Eastern Alps, lie upper, that is, East Alpine, nappes. The greater part of the northern Calcareous Zone is regarded by Kober as the equivalent of the outer zone of the Alps. It is indeed generally accepted that the Betic Cordillera as a whole is alpine in all its features, and is a direct continuation of the alpine folding, the tertiaries of the Guadalquivir valley being the equivalent of the molasse belt of the Alps.

Where Kober differs from Staub, and agrees with many other geologists, is that he regards the Pyrenees and the Cantabrians also as truly alpine. This makes it necessary to suggest some connexion between them and the Betic Cordillera. This is obtained, doubt-fully, as Kober himself states, through that upland belt known as the Iberic Mountains, which bounds the Ebro basin to the south-west, forms the parting between Mediterranean and Atlantic drainage, and includes the Sierra de la Demanda, etc. The name of Iberian ranges is sometimes applied to this belt. The conception of its former connexion with the Betic Cordillera involves, as the diagram shows, a peculiarly acute bend, and further leaves the Catalonian coastal mountains, which include similar elements, in a very isolated position.

Staub boldly solves the problem by maintaining that the Betic Cordillera forms the only truly alpine element in the peninsula, and that the other areas of young folding, including the Pyrenees, are not alpine, not the result of the crumpling and elevation of the floor of the Tethys, but are epicontinental in character, the result of repercussive movements (*contrecoups*) in the Foreland of the alpine chain. The full meaning of the contrast cannot be discussed here. But it may be noted broadly that this Foreland folding was a method of relieving pressure locally, rather than a widespread response to world forces. Further, affecting, as it did, not primarily the deposit of a deep sea, but a pre-existent, highly varied land surface, its action was upon a variety of rocks which responded differently according to their measure of rigidity or plasticity. Thus the secondary rocks which were subjected to the strain tended to be crumpled into folds of the simple Jura type, while the older and harder rocks responded by fracture, uplift, and minor displacement analogous to nappe formation in the alpine chains. Again, and this is a marked feature of the relief of the peninsula, the Foreland ranges do not show that continuity which is characteristic of the alpine chains. Rather do they tend to consist of a series of short overlapping ranges of what is called the *coulisse* type, that is, resembling the overlap of the side-scenes of a theatre.

Staub's thesis is elaborated in much detail in his recent (1926) paper, and has wide bearings on the interpretation of the structure of Western Europe and of North Africa. Much of this aspect seems beyond our scope, but so far as the peninsula is concerned his survey is of much value to the geographer. It does make clear its great complexity as opposed to the common assumption that it is uniform, monotonous, 'African'. It gives also a firmer basis for those outstanding contrasts between the regions—between Catalonia and Aragón, between Andalusia and the Castiles, between Galicia and northern Portugal on the one hand and central Portugal on the other—than can be obtained from the usual generalizations, such as that the greater part of the peninsula consists of the meseta whose fractured edge overlooks the fertile Guadalquivir valley.

In giving some account of his views it seems convenient to begin with the oldest elements and work forward in geological time. The archaean granitic mass in the north-west he compares to the Baltic Shield or to the Hebridean gneiss. Round it, he states, traces of Caledonian folding can be recognized, thus increasing the resemblance to north-western Europe. More obvious, however, are the Hercynian fold-lines which curve round it (cf. Fig. 67). In Asturias these have a north-east to south-west direction, their north-eastern extremity being interpenetrated by the Foreland folding. In the vicinity of Lugo on the upper Minho the old folds change in direction, sweeping round in a knee-like bend, till they trend from north-west to south-east, and finally disappear, west of León, under the tertiaries of Old Castile. They reappear, however, at the north-eastern extremity of the Central Sierras, where for a short time the direction is almost north-to-south. After again disappearing beneath the tertiaries of the basin of New Castile, they can be recognized anew in the region of the mountains of Toledo, now with a nearly east-to-west direction, turning finally towards the north-west, to disappear in the region where the archaean core approaches the Atlantic. In other words, the Hercynian folds are lost to sight at the western border of the peninsula, in a fashion analogous to the disappearance of the young folds of the Betic Cordillera farther south.

Within the peninsula the interrupted, fragmentary nature of these palaeozoic fold-mountains is associated with the development of the Foreland folding. To the former (Caledonian plus Hercynian) Staub gives the general name of Hispanides, and to the latter Iberides. The latter constitute the special feature of the peninsula. They often abut upon the Hispanides at a right angle, and interpenetrate and obscure the margin of the latter. Thus while in the diagram (Fig. 68) the border of the Hispanides towards the archaean core is indicated, their other border has not been shown.

The importance of the Iberides or Foreland folds here, as contrasted with their general absence in Central Europe, is associated with the fact that the block of the meseta (i.e. archaean core plus Hispanides) was, owing to the western narrowing of the Tethys, close to Africa, the area from which the Alpine push came, and offered great resistance to the pressure from that continent. Thus, in addition to the rise of the true alpine folds of the Betic Cordillera, a series of considerable chains rose in the Foreland, broadly parallel to each other and to the arc of the Cordillera. The intensity of the movement and the height of the resultant chains diminish from north to south, from the Pyrenees to the Sierra Morena, that is, increase with distance from the area of greatest resistance.

Four great chains can be recognized as constituting these Iberides, and these may be named in the first instance after their most conspicuous elements, the details being often complicated. They are: (I) The Pyrenees-Cantabrians; (II) the Central Chain; (III) the mountains of Toledo; (IV) the Sierra Morena. All are broadly transversal to the peninsula, but show minor curves in conformity with the arcuate nature of the alpine folding in the south, regarded by Staub as quite definitely linked to the Alps proper through the Balearic Isles.

In the diagram the somewhat complicated direction of the folds in these islands is indicated, and Staub's explanation of the 'fending-off' of the folds from the north-eastern part of the peninsula is as follows. He believes that the crystalline rocks present in the coastal mountains of Catalonia (themselves possibly continuous under the surface beds with the core of Galicia) represent a continuation of the Corsardinian block, the intervening section being sunk beneath the north-western Mediterranean Sea. The alpine chains in the Balearic Isles swing round this sunken massif, in a fashion comparable to the relation of the Betic Cordillera to the Spanish meseta. The southerly trend of the alpine folds, again, from Minorca to the vicinity of Cádiz, means that within the peninsula the chains of the Iberides are widely separated from each other in the centre, where the broad tertiary basins lie between them; but are pressed together, with a corresponding flattening out, in the east, where the basins disappear, and the width of the Foreland between the Betic Cordillera and the presumed, sunken, Catalonian Massif diminishes notably.

Another conception of Staub's which has a considerable bearing on the geography of the peninsula is that the line indicating the position of its culminating axis runs from Corunna across the archaean core and the Hispanides to Andújar on the Guadalquivir, whence it may be regarded as continued across the highest part of the Sierra Nevada. All the Iberid elements, with the intervening tertiary basins, rise in the north over the archaean core towards this

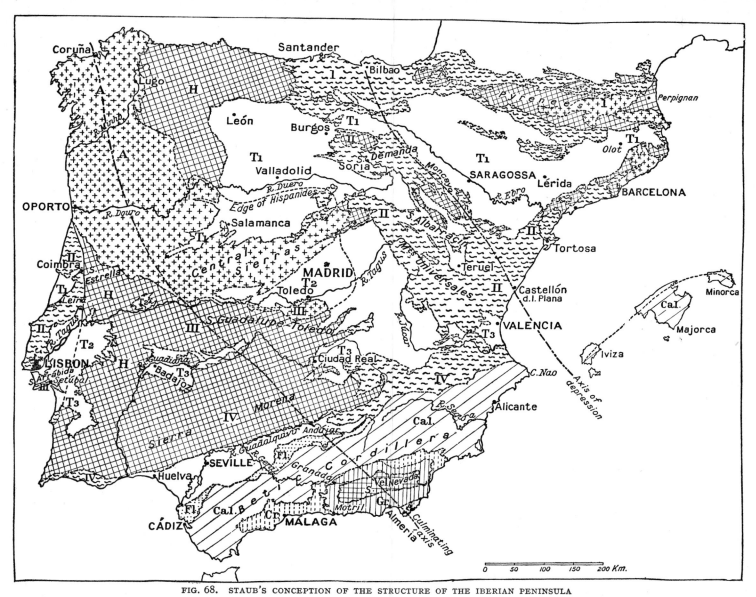

FIG. 68. STAUB'S CONCEPTION OF THE STRUCTURE OF THE IBERIAN PENINSULA

A = the Archaean granitic core. H = the Folded Palaeozoics (Hispanides), regarded as folded round the core, and as continuous beneath the Tertiaries of Old and New Castile. I, II, III, IV, the Foreland Ranges (Iberides), separated by the troughs T1, T2, T3. For the explanation of the lettering in the region of the Betic Cordillera see text. (*Reduced and generalized from Staub's Coloured Map.*)

axial culmination, disappearing 'in the air' to the west. But, farther south, with the disappearance of the core, the rise of the Iberides on the eastern side of the axis has its counterpart in an equivalent downward slope to the west. Thus central Portugal forms, as it were, a miniature replica of central Spain, its minor tertiary basins being the equivalent of the greater ones of Spain.

A few details may be added as to the individual Iberid ranges, beginning in the north. In Asturias the area which was involved in the Hercynian folding is deeply interpenetrated by the younger folds. In this region of intensely complicated structure the highest summits of the Cantabrians occur. To the Pyrenees, which similarly contain Hercynian elements greatly modified by the subsequent folding, the Asturias chains are linked through the lower area in the vicinity of Bilbao and Santander. This is floored by secondary rocks, also involved in the folding, and forming a kind of bridge between the older rocks to east and west. The more southerly part of the folded belt in Asturias is, however, regarded, not as directly continuous with the Pyrenees, but as continued, partly concealed beneath the sediments of the Ebro basin, into the Sierras lying to the north of Lérida.

The Central Iberid belt is much more complicated. It includes to the east the coastal mountains of Catalonia, which again have Hercynian elements, and what we have already called the Iberian ranges. The latter fall into two groups, separated by a trough which extends from the upper Douro across the Tagus-Ebro watershed to Teruel in the upper Guadalaviar basin. The northern group includes the Sierra de la Demanda, Moncayo, and the lower Sierras south of Saragossa. Near Burgos this belt disappears beneath the sediments of the basin of Old Castile, but eastwards it is continued into the Catalonian coastal ranges. The southern group includes the Sierra Albarracín and the Montes Universales. It is continued coastwards to Castellón de la Plana, where the folds flatten out to form the plateau-like area between the tertiary basin of Valencia and the Ebro mouth. Westwards this belt abuts at a right angle upon the Hispanid (Hercynian) chains of the Central Sierras, just as the Cantabrian folds farther north abut upon the Hispanid chains at a somewhat similar angle in Asturias. But while the folds of this Central Belt seem to disappear as the archaean core is approached, Staub regards them as reappearing on its hither side in the Serra da Estrella and the belt of folded secondary rocks extending from Coimbra through Leiria to Lisbon.

The two remaining Iberid ranges are much less complicated. The more northerly is formed by the mountains of Toledo continued into the Sierra de Guadalupe and the Sierras near Portalegre. After a notable gap it reappears in the Serra da Arrábida between the Tagus mouth and the Bay of Setúbal. The more southerly is formed by the Sierra Morena, continued westwards into the folded secondary rocks of Algarve, and eastwards, again through folded secondary rocks, to the Mediterranean south of Valencia.

Finally we have to note that this conception of four great folded chains crossing the peninsula transversely to the earlier Hispanid structure lines, but parallel to the young alpine chains of Andalusia and Murcia, involves also the notion that corresponding troughs separate them. This gives us a novel view of the tertiary basins already described (p. 222). Thus between the Cantabro-Pyrenean range and the central one there lies a great trough zone (T_1 of Fig. 68) of varying dimensions. It is narrow in the Olot region, expands into the wide Ebro basin, narrows once again at Burgos, expands once again in the basin of Old Castile, is prolonged into the archaean core, to the south-west of Salamanca, in the form of a narrowed inlet, and then disappears. But its prolongation can be recognized on the coast of Portugal to the south-west of Coimbra. Between the Central Belt and the short Toledo-Arrábida range lies the northern part of the basin of New Castile (T_2), continued along the line of the Tagus, where again it seems to disappear 'in the air' on the surface of the core, but reappears once more on its hither side, widening out along the line of the lower Tagus to the east and north-east of Lisbon. Between the Toledo-Arrábida belt and the Sierra Morena is the third and last trough zone (T_3) of the Foreland. This may be said to begin at the coastal plain of Valencia, where it is narrow. This section is virtually cut off from its continuation in the wide southern section of the basin of New Castile. The latter, through the basin of Ciudad Real, is continued, after a gap, into that of Badajoz, and then, after another interruption, appears once again in the Setúbal basin south of the Serra da Arrábida.

THE BETIC CORDILLERA

Something may be added to what has been already said as to Staub's interpretation of this important element. The folded belt (Fig. 68) extends over a distance of some 600 km., with a breadth in places of 160 km., from Cape Nao, between Valencia and Alicante, to the Gulf of Cádiz. It is of typical alpine structure and is alpine also in its details. Thus there is in the first place a Central Zone, which here abuts on the Mediterranean, built mainly of ancient crystalline and palaeozoic rocks, and containing the greatest elevations, as distinct from a northern Calcareous Zone (Cal.), the latter bordered as in the Alps by a slightly-developed Flysch (Fl.) zone. Beyond lies the tertiary basin of the Guadalquivir valley, above which rises the edge of the meseta in the Sierra Morena.

Staub's interpretation is as follows. The crystalline rocks of the Sierra Nevada and de los Filabres (cf. Fig. 81, p. 271) form the Veleta zone (Vel.), in which deep-lying Pennine nappes are exposed in a window, making the region, as already stated, the analogue of the crystalline dome of the Hohe Tauern. Surrounding this Veleta zone, and reaching the shore of the Mediterranean between Motril and Almería, is the Granada nappe (Gr.), built of triassic, palaeozoic and crystalline rocks, forming the equivalent of the Grisonid nappes of the Eastern Alps, and thus of the rim of the Hohe Tauern window. The Granada nappe has an incomplete border of crystalline rocks (Cr.) which form the Sierra de las Estancias and the mountains near Málaga. This interrupted crystalline border, together with the Calcareous Zone to the north, constitutes the Betic nappe, regarded as representing the upper or Tirolid East Alpine nappes, the crystallines having the same relation to the overthrust Calcareous or Sub-Betic belt, as e.g. the crystalline Oetztaler Alps to the Eastern Calcareous Alps. That is, the crystallines form the root-zone of the Calcareous Sub-Betic belt. As the figure shows, the Veleta and Granada nappes have but a limited extension, so that the greater part of the Cordillera is made up of the Betic nappe, and particularly of its calcareous section, which alone is present in the Balearic Isles. Westward the whole chain is regarded as thinning out towards the ocean, and Staub compares the Strait of Gibraltar to an enlarged *Drauzug* (p. 148).

SUMMARY OF STRUCTURE

The essential points of this somewhat lengthy description may be briefly summarized. The massive, quadrilateral Iberian peninsula is to be regarded as the south-western extension of Hercynian Europe, displaying the wealth of minerals characteristic generally of the Hercynian Lands. It includes an archaean granitic core, exposed at the surface mainly in the north-western section, but reappearing in the north-east, within the Pyrenees and in Catalonia. Round this core were developed first Caledonian and later Hercynian chains, now represented by shattered fragments, particularly to the north-east of the granitic core, in Asturias, and to the south of it. Against the old block made up of archaean core and palaeozoic mountains were folded the sediments of the narrowed Tethys, leading to the rise of the alpine chain of the Betic Cordillera, continued north-eastwards into the Balearic Isles, but separated from the old block to the north-west by the fertile Guadalquivir valley. The pressure from the south which led to the rise of the Cordillera induced secondary folding in the varied rocks of the Foreland, producing four belts of folding, transverse to the peninsula and to the swing of the earlier chains. Between these four belts, represented by the

Pyrenees-Cantabrian, the Catalonian-Lisbon, the Toledo-Cáceres-Arrábida, and the Valencia—Sierra-Morena—Algarve ridges, lie troughs which reach their greatest development in Spain but reappear in central Portugal.

In order from north to south these trough zones are as follows:

1. This begins in the Olot basin of Catalonia, and is prolonged into the Ebro basin which is continued through the Burgos gap into the basin of Old Castile. It disappears on the surface of the core to the south-west of Salamanca, but reappears on the coast of Portugal between Coimbra and Leiria.

2. This is made of the northern part of the basin of New Castile, and reappears in Portugal in the basin of the lower Tagus.

3. The plain of Valencia, continued into the southern part of the basin of New Castile, and linked through the small basins of Ciudad Real and Badajoz to the Setúbal basin of Portugal, forms the third trough zone.

It has to be noted, however, that this conception of an alternation of folds and troughs crossing the peninsula transversely, is a structural one, and takes little account of the actual geographical relations of the elements. Thus the Ebro basin is far more isolated, from the geographical standpoint, than the statement that it is a part of a great trough zone would suggest. Similarly, while the suggestion that the lowland areas of central Portugal are narrowed continuations of the great basins of the interior of Spain is of much interest, we have yet to remember that geographically the two are at once very different from each other and not readily linked because of the intervening core area.

It may be added that, in marked contrast to Italy, there are no extensive tracts floored by recent volcanic rocks within the peninsula. Nevertheless such rocks do occur over small areas, and form an important part of the evidence upon which Staub's view of the structure is based. Thus they are present in Catalonia between Olot and Gerona; round the lower Segura river and near Cartagena (Fig. 78, p. 264) in Murcia; in the vicinity of Ciudad Real; near Lisbon in Portugal; as well as elsewhere.

CHAPTER XI

CLIMATE, VEGETATION, AND THE HUMAN RESPONSE
TO THE NATURAL CONDITIONS

Climate—Natural Vegetation and Plant Limits—Spain and
Portugal—Distribution of Population—Lines of Communication
—Natural Divisions

I T is perhaps already clear that the Iberian Peninsula resembles
a miniature continent rather than merely forming a part of
Europe. This 'continentality' is particularly noticeable as regards
the prevailing climatic conditions and their effects. Again, the
account given of the structure and relief indicates that even the
smaller State of Portugal is not a natural unit, while Spain is obviously complex and consists of extremely diverse elements. Thus it
does not appear as if, despite the obvious convenience of such a
course, we can first separate the two political entities and then proceed to subdivide the larger into natural regions. Some general
treatment of the geography of the whole appears essential before a
sound basis for a subdivision can emerge.

CLIMATE

Here the fundamental factors are the position in latitude, with
the relation to the surrounding seas and adjacent or contiguous
land-masses; the breadth and massive nature of the whole peninsula;
and the distribution of the relief features. The result is to emphasize
once again the contrast between the central and the peripheral
elements. Broadly speaking, the interior tableland is cold in winter,
with resultant high pressures and a general tendency, often modified
by cyclonic movements, for outflowing winds to develop. In
summer, on the other hand, owing to the high temperatures prevailing, it becomes an area of low pressure, with inflowing winds.
There is thus, more especially in the east, a seasonal (monsoonal)
reversal of wind direction, accompanied by atmospheric disturbances
at the period of change. Owing to the nature of the relief, however,
as well as to the shape of the peninsula and its relation to the great
pressure systems, rainfall conditions have not the simplicity which
this generalized statement might appear to suggest. As a whole the
central area has a low total rainfall, the maximum fall tending to
come in spring, with a secondary one in autumn, and a summer
minimum, without total drought then, some 5 per cent to 9 per cent
of the total tending to fall within the two months of July and August.
As contrasted with this *régime*, which prevails over wide tracts of

the tableland, as well as in the Ebro basin, the peripheral areas show much diversity, alike in temperature range and in the amount and distribution of the rainfall. Before proceeding to consider the various climatic types which can be recognized, we may note one effect of their presence. It means that, in addition to making its own weather to a large extent, the peninsula shows, if faintly, the continental feature of displaying sharp contrasts, especially as regards mean and minimum winter temperatures, in similar latitudes. Thus the whole of the tableland has not only low mean winter temperatures, but is liable to spells of exceptional cold which have an important effect on the distribution of perennial plants, especially the more delicate fruit-bearing trees, which are economically so important. Though it is true that here—as elsewhere—the Mediterranean feature of a summer rainfall minimum is present, yet in essence the climate is neither Mediterranean nor peninsular but recalls that of continental interiors. Again, the north-west, with a heavy total rainfall, fairly well distributed throughout the year but showing a pronounced winter maximum, and a small temperature range, is not in any sense Mediterranean, and differs alike from the tableland and from the north-eastern area. This Western European type passes gradually into the Oceanic Mediterranean climate prevailing throughout most of Portugal, which, with lower total rainfall and accentuated summer drought, yet preserves the same feature of a moderate temperature gradient, though the actual temperatures are higher throughout the year. To the south and south-east a more extreme Mediterranean climate occurs, summer temperatures being high, winters very mild, total rainfall small, and the summer months virtually rainless. This again passes into the modified Mediterranean climate of the more northerly part of the east coast, where the temperature gradient is again steep, though mean winter and mean minima temperatures are higher than on the tableland. The result is that any traverse of the peninsula from west to east would show great contrasts both in climate and vegetation, while a north-to-south traverse would display a more gradual transition, alike in the climatic factors and in the human response.

The accompanying tables giving figures for representative stations help to make these points clear.

In the Table V note the low winter means and mean minima of the central stations (including the Ebro basin), the contrasts between Santiago and Saragossa being particularly striking, and the high winter means on the western seaboard (Coimbra and Lisbon), which rise still higher in the south-east and south (Murcia and Málaga). The table shows also the high summer temperatures on the plateau and in the south (particularly the Guadalquivir valley), and their moderate height in relation to latitude on the west coast.

TABLE V

Temperature Conditions at Selected Stations

Station	Lat.	Ht. above Sea-level. Metres	Mean Temp. Coldest Month. Degrees C.	Mean Minimum Temp. Degrees C.	Mean Temp. Hottest Month. Degrees C.	Position
Santiago . .	42° 53′	270	7·3	—2·2	18·9	North-west
Burgos . .	42° 20′	890	1·4	—10·8	18·0	Tableland
Saragossa .	41° 38′	205	4·8	—7·6	24·2	Ebro basin
Barcelona .	41° 22′	40	8·0	—0·8	23·3	North-east
Coimbra . .	40° 12′	140	8·8	—0·6	20·6	West coastal
Madrid . .	40° 24′	655	4·3	—7·6	24·3	Tableland
Valencia . .	39° 28′	20	9·2	—0·4	23·8	East coastal
Lisbon . .	38° 42′	95	9·6	2·9	21·2	West coastal
Ciudad Real .	38° 59′	635	5·2	—7·7	25·3	Tableland
Murcia . .	37° 59′	60	10·1	—1·8	26·0	East coastal
Seville . .	37° 23′	20	11·2	0·2	29·4	Guadalquivir Valley
Málaga . .	36° 43′	25	12·0	3·0	25·1	South coastal

From Table VI it is obvious that at least relative summer drought is universal, while there is much variation in the period of maximum fall. The combination of a relatively low total and a tendency to a spring maximum throughout the central area, combined with the steep temperature gradient, gives rise to a steppe type of climate there, rapid growth due to spring rains being followed by a marked drought check as temperature increases. This type tends to reappear in the south-east. Apart from the Pyrenean frontier region precipitation is heaviest in the north-west, where a considerable area has a fall of over 1,600 mm. (63 in.). A small area in the Serra da Estrella has, however, the maximum fall of over 2,900 mm. (113 in.).

The graphs which form Figs. 69, 70, 71, and 72, together with the Tables, make the contrasts between the various climatic regions clear. These may be classified as follows:

1. The widely prevalent Tableland type (Fig. 69). The essential points are the steep temperature gradient, the low total rainfall, with maxima in spring and autumn, the former usually the more marked.

2. The Western (Oceanic) European type (Fig. 70, Santiago), where the total rainfall is very heavy, with a marked winter maximum, and the differences between winter and summer temperatures

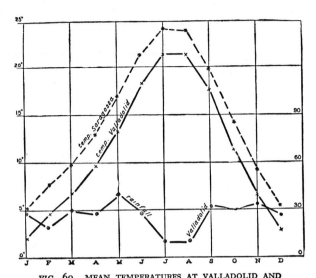

FIG. 69. MEAN TEMPERATURES AT VALLADOLID AND
SARAGOSSA AND MEAN RAINFALL AT VALLADOLID

In this and the three following figures temperatures are
in degrees C. and rainfall in mm.

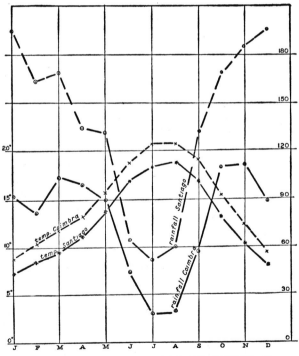

FIG. 70. MEAN TEMPERATURES AND RAINFALL AT
SANTIAGO AND COIMBRA

TABLE VI
Rainfall Conditions

Station	Total Rainfall. Millimetres	Mean Fall of Wettest Month		Mean Fall of Driest Month	
Santiago . .	1,652	Jan.	197	July	52
Burgos . .	563	May	70	Aug.	19
Saragossa .	314	May	48	Aug.	13
Barcelona .	537	Sept.	86	July	22
Coimbra . .	914	Nov.	111	July	18
Madrid . .	419	Apr. & Nov.	47	July & Aug.	12
Valencia . .	486	Oct.	84	Aug.	9
Lisbon . .	726	Dec.	101	July	4
Albacete . .	401	May	58	July	12
Murcia . .	380	Sept.	48	Aug.	5
Seville . .	471	Dec.	69	July	1
Jaén . .	719	Mar.	104	July	4

Note.—Albacete is in lat. 39°, height above sea-level 686 m., on the tableland; Jaén is in lat. 37° 47′, height 575 m., on the edge of the Guadalquivir valley. For other stations see previous table.

small. This type extends, with a drop in the total rainfall, along the north coast, and in the vicinity of Oporto passes into

3. The Oceanic Mediterranean type, which extends southwards throughout the remainder of Portugal, and is continued into south-western Spain to the region round the Gulf of Cádiz. The curves for Coimbra on Fig. 70 illustrate this type in its less extreme form. It should be noted that the maximum rainfall here is generally in late autumn, with a secondary maximum in spring. The total rainfall is considerable. To the south and east this type passes into

4. The Extreme Mediterranean climate of south-eastern Spain, which extends north-eastwards to Alicante, and is illustrated by the curve for Murcia on Fig. 71 and by Table VI. Note here the relatively steep temperature gradient, due to the high summer temperatures, the low total precipitation, the accentuated summer drought, the autumn rainfall maximum, with a secondary one in spring (April, 41 mm.). To the north-east this passes into

5. The Modified Mediterranean climate of the north-east, as represented by Barcelona on Fig. 71. The temperature curve is similar in shape to that of Murcia, with lower temperatures throughout, the increased divergence in the summer months reflecting the

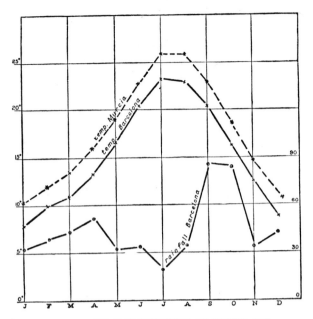

FIG. 71. MEAN TEMPERATURES AT MURCIA AND
BARCELONA AND MEAN RAINFALL AT BARCELONA

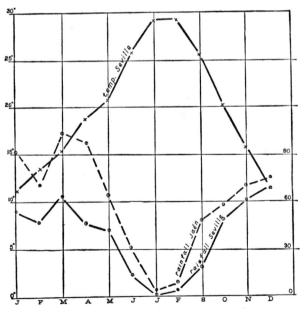

FIG. 72. MEAN RAINFALL AT SEVILLE AND JAÉN AND
MEAN TEMPERATURE AT SEVILLE

exceptionally high temperatures in the south then. Rainfall is heavier, summer drought less accentuated, and the autumn maximum is much more marked than the secondary spring one.

Finally, Fig. 72 has been drawn to indicate the curious conditions in the Guadalquivir valley, where the climate is transitional in character between those of the tableland and of the south. As the temperature curve for Seville shows, the area shares with the plateau a steep temperature gradient; but here this is due to the extremely high summer temperatures, the winters being very mild. With the south-east it shares accentuated summer drought, but the total rainfall is higher. At Jaén, as on the plateau, the maximum fall comes in spring, while at Seville the spring rains are not quite so heavy as those of late autumn and early winter. Both stations show the plateau feature of a drier period intervening between the early and the latter rains. This Andalusian type is sometimes regarded merely as a variant of the Tableland type, but the differences in temperature are very obvious.

NATURAL VEGETATION AND PLANT LIMITS

From this account of the climate it is apparent that the most outstanding contrast within the peninsula is that between the mild, damp north-west and the hot and arid south-east, the two being separated by the dry Tableland region with its extreme temperatures. The other diagonal, that from north-east to south-west, displays less difference between its extremities, since these lie respectively in the areas of Modified Mediterranean and Oceanic Mediterranean climate. The plant cover reflects these conditions.

In the north-west, with an extension along the north coast towards the Pyrenean area, the natural vegetation is of the Deciduous Forest and Meadowland type. As Fig. 73 shows, the beech is excluded from the extreme north-west, presumably because of the combination of acidic soils and a very heavy rainfall, but deciduous oaks, ash, birch, sweet chestnut, with the hardier conifers, all occur. The woods have a rich undergrowth, ivy and ferns are abundant and meadow grasses grow freely in the clearings. The 'European' character of the climate is further emphasized by such cool-temperate fruit-trees as apple, pear, and cherry, crops like rye and potatoes, as well as maize, and by the considerable live-stock industry (with dairying). This, then, is the least 'Spanish' part of the peninsula.

In sharp contrast with this vegetation type are the so-called steppe areas, including salt steppe, so characteristic of parts of Spain, and so un-European in aspect. Their distribution is interesting, though it may be noted that the limits are differently defined by various authorities. This is mainly because natural steppes have fluctuating boundaries owing to the spread of cultivation, especially of wheat, while some have almost ceased to exist owing to the possibility of irrigation and reclamation. Three major steppe areas may be recognized (Fig. 73). The Littoral steppe stretches along the coast from the vicinity of Cape Nao to beyond Cape Gata (Almería), and in the neighbourhood of Murcia extends inland along the Segura valley. With this the steppe of New Castile (La Mancha) is all but continuous, while it covers a wide tract towards the north-west. The third great steppe area is that of the Ebro basin, which extends from the lower valley north-westwards to the junction of the Aragón with the main stream. The small Catalonian or Lérida steppe, developed within the lower Segre valley, is almost continuous with this. Other minor steppes are that of Old Castile round Valladolid, and those of Andalusia, e.g., that lying north-east of Granada, that on the upper Guadalquivir north of Jaén, and that on the lower Genil (Betic steppe).

Apart from these steppe areas and from the north-western region already mentioned, the remainder of the peninsula may be said broadly to carry some variant of the Mediterranean evergreen vegetation type, not without an intermixture of deciduous trees, especially towards the north. High forest is scantily developed save on some of the mountains, but this is probably due to man's action. On the other hand, evergreen trees, such as evergreen oaks, including the economically important cork oak, and the more delicate conifers, are widespread. Large tracts are covered with scrub of the usual maquis type—here called *monte bajo*. This includes in places such shrubs as cistus, tree-heaths, and so forth, while elsewhere aromatic labiates like thyme, rosemary, lavender, etc., predominate, forming the so-called *tomillare*.

It will be noted that this summary description affords no support to a hasty deduction that the interior tableland, *qua* tableland, is mainly a steppe area, while conversely it shows that typical steppe occurs outside its limits, as on the south-eastern littoral and in Andalusia. Thus, apart from the distinctiveness of the north-west and north, it does not appear at first sight as if the distribution of vegetation confirmed the division already suggested between central and peripheral elements. It is necessary to look deeper to find an explanation of this apparent anomaly.

The distribution of steppe in the ecological sense is mainly a response to rainfall conditions. Thus the Littoral steppe reflects the hot, dry climate of the south-east, and the similarity between the total precipitation of Murcia and Albacete (p. 237) accounts for its practical continuity with that of New Castile. But the higher precipitation over the Central Sierras results in the complete separation of the latter from the much smaller steppe round Valladolid (rainfall 313 mm.). The extensive steppe within the Ebro basin is the result of the hill girdle already described, which shuts off rain-bearing winds. Finally, the minor steppes of Andalusia are a response to the high mean temperatures and local variations in rainfall due to relief. But these various steppes are not wholly comparable. Fig. 73 shows the distribution of esparto grass, which is sometimes regarded as the typical steppe plant. It will be noted

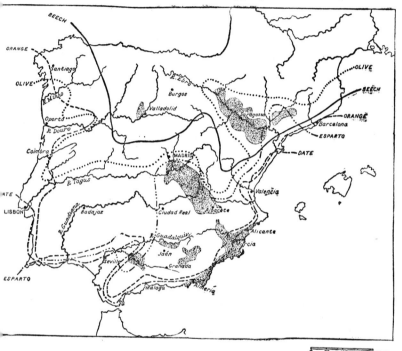

FIG. 73. STEPPE AREAS AND PLANT LIMITS IN THE IBERIAN PENINSULA

The steppe areas are stippled; the lines show the limits of the beech, the orange, the olive, the date palm, and esparto grass. (*After Willkomm.*)

that it is excluded from most of the Ebro basin as well as from Old Castile, a fact which emphasizes the contrast between the south-eastern and north-western sections of the peninsula. Further, though the North African—and Asiatic—feature of the appearance of patches of salt steppe is well marked throughout, in the Ebro basin and in Old Castile, as well as in the Littoral steppe, it does not appear that it is everywhere a response to present-day climatic conditions. In the tertiary basins the efflorescence of salt at the surface, the saline pools, the scanty cover of halophytic plants, and similar phenomena have a localized distribution which suggests that they are a result rather of the salt content of the underlying beds than of existing aridity.

As a whole, then, the central region, despite a general similarity of climatic *type* throughout, has a somewhat varied natural plant cover. North of the Central Sierras (note the distribution of the beech) the vegetation is more or less transitional between Western European and typical Mediterranean, diminishing to steppe in the Ebro basin and, less notably, in the heart of Old Castile. South of the Central Sierras peculiarly arid steppe is well developed in New Castile, but elsewhere drought-resistant scrub is widespread.

A variety of causes, however, combine to render this natural distribution a very imperfect guide to the actual use made of the land. In the peripheral areas we have a highly diversified surface, giving rise to many local variations of climate and relief. The high or moderate winter temperatures permit the more delicate fruit-bearing trees to penetrate far to the north (note orange and olive in Fig. 73). On the west coast the total rainfall is sufficiently great to make irrigation generally unnecessary while on the east and south-eastern coasts it is practised in a very elaborate fashion. The result is that cultivation is intensive and highly diversified, cropping may be nearly continuous throughout the year, and land-utilization is definitely labour-absorbing and of Mediterranean type.

With these conditions those present in the central area are markedly contrasted. Over large tracts, as already seen, the surface is very uniform; the low winter temperatures exclude citrus fruits, while the line indicating the northern limit of the olive gives a somewhat inadequate picture of the actual extent of cultivation of that fruit; finally, save over limited areas of the plateau and in the Ebro basin, irrigation water is difficult to obtain in summer. As against the diversified cultivation of the margins, therefore, there is a tendency here to concentrate either upon cereal production or upon sheep-rearing, with the usual seasonal transhumance, though the movements are now mainly carried out by train. Clouds of dust from the loose tertiary deposits, windmills because running water for power is not available, a spring greenness of scrub or corn-field rapidly fading to a summer grey: these are the prevailing notes. One must, however, be careful not to exaggerate the uniformity. The vine extends up the great river-valleys, with some olives in the case of Ebro and Tagus. Locally also there are oases of fertility, as for example, at Aranjuez on the Tagus, in central Spain, famous for its parks and gardens.

It may be noted that, as appears from this description, so far as Spain is concerned there is a certain balance between the constituent elements. The north-west retains more wood than elsewhere, yields cool-temperate crops and rears cattle. The other coastal belts especially where irrigated, yield so great a variety of sub-tropical crops as both to reduce the need for luxury imports—with such exceptions as coffee and cocoa—and to give a large surplus of fruit-products for export. Finally, if the central area is mainly important for its cereals and the products of its flocks, yet its limited and occasional production of wine, olive oil, fruits and vegetables, and generally the existence of transitional areas, ensure that the contrast between centre and periphery is not excessive. For reasons which have yet to be considered, indeed the tendency to separatism in the recent past has been more marked between Catalonia and the remainder than between those areas which show a more obvious contrast in the natural conditions. The acceptance of the peripheral areas—apart from Catalonia—of domination from the centre has, however, been due in large part to the collapse of the 'Moorish' type of culture as the result of the overthrow of the Moslem element.

It may be added that the account indicates the basis of that usual comparison between Spain and the Atlas Lands, whose inadequacy has been already discussed. The resemblance lies in the co-existence of arid grassland areas, suitable in part for wheat and barley and in part only for pasturage, and of those where intensive cultivation of sub-tropical crops can be carried on with irrigation. But even from this human standpoint the analogy is incomplete. The steppe areas of Spain are small, are surrounded and interpenetrated by lands of other and varied types, have a highly complex distribution. A comparison between the country as a whole and, e.g., Algeria and Tunisia, where there is a fertile fringe and an inner steppe, passing rapidly into true desert, is deceptive rather than useful.

SPAIN AND PORTUGAL

So far we have been mainly concerned with Spain, and some further consideration of Portugal is necessary. That it falls almost wholly into the peripheral zone is already clear, but its existence as an independent State proves that it is more highly individualized than the other marginal elements. The problem has therefore two aspects. On the one hand we have the actual details of the frontier separating the two States, and on the other we must note those characteristics of the lands included within Portugal which enable it to form an entity as against Spain. The latter point may be considered first, for it is naturally the more important; without some measure of self-sufficiency and distinctiveness the Portuguese State could not have maintained itself.

The essential feature is the oceanic outlook, with all its implications. The coast is rich in havens, and if the fine harbour of Lisbon and the poorer one of Oporto (with its artificial outport of Leixões) predominate over all others, this is chiefly because of their better hinterlands. Historically the presence of a number of ports on the Atlantic coast led in the first place to the acquisition of a wide overseas empire, while secondly it makes Portugal to-day a link on important ocean routes, especially that to South America. It is true that in the era of the great discoveries Genoese and other navigators played as—if not more—important a part as the Portuguese themselves, while to-day it is largely English ships which frequent the ports. Nevertheless this easy and direct access to the ocean is of much significance to the State. That significance is increased by the fact that not only, as already stated, have Lisbon and Oporto at least a considerable hinterland, i.e. the productive belt behind them is wide, but the rivers on which they stand have some value as waterways. In the first respect there is a marked contrast with northern and western Spain, where such harbours as exist have restricted hinterlands, cut off from the main productive areas of the country. As regards the second point, Spain is handicapped relatively to the smaller State by having, in proportion to its size, fewer stretches of navigable inland water with an effective connexion with the coast.

It may be noted here that of the rivers of the peninsula as a whole only five can be said to have any importance as waterways. The Ebro is available for small vessels to Tortosa, and for barges right to Tudela; but it has no important port at its deltaic mouth, and easy sea access has to be obtained by means of a canal. The Guadalquivir can be navigated by ships with a draught of 20 ft. up to Seville, and by barges to Córdoba; but though a very useful river it has again no important port at its mouth. The Guadiana is a frontier river for the last part of its course, and is navigable for only a short distance above Pomarão, the point where it begins to form the frontier. Douro and Tagus, on the other hand, are navigable to the frontier in the former case (for very small craft) and almost to it in the case of the latter.

But the influence of the ocean on Portugal is not limited to these factors. As has been already indicated the rainfall throughout is relatively high, the winter temperatures mild, points of course associated with the westerly position and the winter wind régime. But the extension in latitude from 37° to over 42° produces considerable variation in total rainfall, in the distribution throughout the year, and in the mean temperatures of the winter and summer months. The country indeed forms an area of transition between climatic types (cf. p. 235). Two consequences result. In the first place, the chief economic crops of the peninsula have here a wide distribution, both from north to south and from coast towards the interior. Secondly, there is a considerable diversity of production within the country. Thus, save for the higher belts, practically the whole of Portugal falls within the zone where the olive thrives. Again, the line marking the limit of the orange is deeply embayed in Portugal in the region of the Douro and Tagus valleys, while on the east of Spain it is much more nearly parallel to the coast, and in the more northerly area lies but a short distance from it. It will be noted also that the steppes of Spain are not represented in Portugal, and that the heavier precipitation renders elaborate irrigation works unnecessary.

As regards the second point, the diversity of production, we find that there is a fairly marked contrast between the climate and natural vegetation of the cooler, damper north and the hotter, drier south, which is reflected in the modes of land utilization practised. In this connexion the limit of the date palm, as shown on Fig. 73, is of interest, not because the plant has any economic importance in Portugal, but because its distribution is an index of climatic conditions. As a result of these minor variations in climate we find that, for example, the vine for wine is especially important in the north, as near Viana do Castelo, Braga, and especially in the Douro valley (Oporto, Vila Real), while cork oak is particularly exploited in the south and centre (Santarem, Portalegre). Similarly cattle predominate in the north as against sheep and goats, with many pigs in the region of oak woods, in the south. But such contrasts are not extreme. Thus the vine for wine-making is extensively cultivated in the Tagus valley, and reappears in the far south in the province of Algarve (Faro). Wheat also is widespread and forms the chief cereal grown, except in the north-west where maize predominates.

The net result is that within its limited area Portugal yields crops similar to those of Spain, without such excess or deficiency of any major product as to render exchange essential or even possible on any scale. It has its own ocean outlets, and need neither employ those of Spain, nor does it serve as an outlet for the exports of the larger country, which has its own ocean ports. There is indeed but little trade between the two States. It is true, as we have still to show, that the actual frontier runs through areas where intercommunication is difficult, and which are characterized also for the most part by infertility, especially on the Spanish side. This, however, seems less important than that, as has been indicated in the chapter on structure and relief, Portugal itself is a miniature (and modified) replica of Spain, containing within itself the main elements of the latter. Spain, despite the tendency to separatism of its elements, must retain at all costs some measure of union because the parts have need of each other. Catalonia, in many ways the most distinctive unit and that which shows the strongest separatist tendency, is yet the most strongly bound to the remainder by economic ties. That it has naturally difficult communication with the Castiles reminds us how unwise it is to over-emphasize the importance of the physical difficulties offered by the Spanish-Portuguese frontier. Trade currents, when powerful enough, can overcome far more serious obstacles than these.

The actual frontier can be followed readily enough on an atlas map, so that the description can be limited to the special features. For some half of its course it follows river-valleys, while the other half traverses hilly, scantily-peopled country. But the valley sections form barriers almost as complete as the mountains, owing to their gorge-like nature. They are narrow, deeply-cut—that of the Douro 200–400 and occasionally 500 m. deep—and contain rapid-infested, unnavigable rivers. More than this, the actual gorge section which forms the frontier marks a change in the character of the river, so that the Duero of the Spanish plateau appears like a different river from the navigable Douro of Portugal, and so with the Spanish Tajo and the Portuguese Tejo.

In detail we may note that the river sections of the frontier are formed by the lower Minho, unnavigable except in the lowest part of its course; by the Douro in the region where it cuts its way through the granitic mass of Sayago, together with a part of its Agueda tributary; by the Erjas tributary of the Tagus, followed by a section of the main river and by a short stretch along a tributary flowing from the S. de S. Mamede; finally come two sections of the Guadiana river. The first of these is downstream from the elbow bend at Badajoz; then follows a region where the frontier cuts across the western end of the Sierra Morena before following the Chança tributary and then the main river to the coast.

Three regions show points of special interest. Where the Douro begins to saw its way through the granites, downstream from Zamora, the barrier of the gorge is not only notable, but the contrasts between the areas separated are great. On the Portuguese side we are in the region of olive and vine; on the Spanish side is arid steppe or 'breadland' (*Tierra del pan*), though vineyards reappear near Zamora. That the frontier section of the Tagus valley is not a natural line of communication is indicated by the wide loop to the south of the river made by the railway from Madrid to Lisbon. The railway does not approach the river until it is well within Portuguese territory. On the other hand, the upper (Spanish) section of the Guadiana valley does quite definitely form a line of approach from Spain towards Portugal, as is shown by the railway line. This is the (naturally) weakest part of the frontier—it is in point of fact heavily fortified—and the physical contrasts between the two countries are not well marked here. On both sides the population is thin, and the occupations are broadly similar in both cases. With this may be associated the desire, sometimes expressed, of the inhabitants of Spanish Estremadura to separate from Spain and unite with Portugal. For somewhat similar reasons, Galicia, linked by an area of transition to northern Portugal, and resembling it in many ways, is credited with a similar desire. The essential Portugal, however, is the somewhat densely-peopled coastal belt which is at once most sharply contrasted with the interior of Spain and has the most difficult communication with it.

DISTRIBUTION OF POPULATION (FIG. 74)

Something must be said on this subject, which throws much light on the general geography of the peninsula. As one would expect, conditions are relatively simple in Portugal and much more complex in Spain. In the former country density decreases from north to south and as a rule even more markedly from coast to interior. Thus the highest density, not only for Portugal but for any administrative unit within the peninsula, occurs in the district of Oporto, where it reaches 411 per sq. km. (1,064 per sq. mile). As contrasted with this Algarve (Faro) has but 63 per sq. km. (163 per sq. mile). The contrast between coast and interior in similar latitudes is indicated by such figures as Braga 177 per sq. km. and Bragança 33 per sq. km.; Lisbon 389 and Evora 28. It may be added that while the two large cities of Portugal (Lisbon over 700,000, Oporto over 260,000) are coastal, the only other towns, coastal or interior, which approach to the 40,000 limit, are Setúbal and Coimbra.

The contrast between coast and interior is readily explained by such factors as more favourable climate, lower mean elevation, greater productivity and better means of communication in the former. But the significance of a coastal position must not in itself be pressed too far, for in the province of Alemtejo the district of Beja, which extends to the coast, has a density of but 27 per sq. km. as against 28 in purely inland Evora. Even if the causation of the varying density from north to south is complex, it seems justifiable to say that in Portugal the areas of higher latitude and therefore less accentuated Mediterranean climate are more favourable to settlement than the lower latitudes of more extreme climatic type. This is generally true of the peninsula, though in Spain the effect is partly masked by the rise in production associated with intensive irrigation in some southerly areas. It may be said that the influence is not one of climate but of increasing remoteness from the economically important parts of Europe. One has to note, however, that the great diversity of production characteristic of lands of extreme Mediterranean climate, whatever its apparent advantage to the cultivator, is not that which appears to bring most prosperity in the modern world, adapted as it is to large-scale methods.

In the forty-seven mainland provinces of Spain the highest density is found in the province of Barcelona where it now reaches 252 per sq. km. (652 per sq. mile). Barcelona is followed closely by Vizcaya (611 per sq. mile). The figure for Vizcaya is an expression of the fact that the whole oceanic coast of Spain in the north and north-west is relatively densely peopled. Thus Guipúzcoa, the contiguous province to the east, has a figure of 172, and Santander

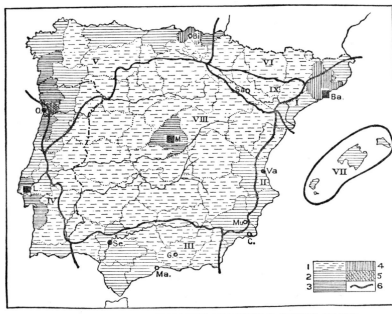

FIG. 74. DENSITY OF POPULATION AND NATURAL REGIONS IN THE
IBERIAN PENINSULA (1940)

1. Under 60 persons per sq. km. 2. Under 120. 3. Under 200. 4. Under 300. 5. Over 400. 6. Limits of natural regions: I. Catalonian coastlands. II. South-eastern coastland. III. Southern Spain. IV. Central and Southern Portugal. V. North-western region. VI. Pyrenean region. VII. Balearic Isles. VIII. Castilian Tableland. IX. Ebro Basin.

Bi.=Bilbao. Sa.=Saragossa. Ba.=Barcelona. Va.=Valencia. Mu.= Murcia. C.=Cartagena. G.=Granada. Ma.=Malaga. Se.=Seville. L.=Lisbon. O.=Oporto. For the populations of these towns see text.

to the west one of 74. Farther west the density diminishes to under 60 in Lugo, but rises again through Corunna (116) to the high figure of 156 in Pontevedra. The figures are readily explained when one remembers that this coastal stretch contains Spain's main outlets to the great seaways of the world, and that locally mineral wealth (especially iron) is not only very important but within easy access of the sea.

The province of Barcelona includes lands of considerable agricultural productivity, while the actual port has a favourable position both as regards Mediterranean trade generally and the coasting trade of the country, including that with the Balearic Isles in particular. But the main explanation of the high density lies in the considerable development of manufactures, based partly on imported coal and partly on local water-power, and finding a protected market within the motherland.

The only other province with a density nearly reaching 200 per sq. km. is Madrid (199), which shows a surprisingly high figure in view of the extreme climate, the elevation, and the somewhat low productivity of the land. The extent to which the provincial density is due to the presence of the great city of Madrid is shown by the fact that over 1,000,000 of the total of under 1,650,000 dwell within its confines. Madrid is indeed the successor of a series of interior capital towns, tried out, as it were, experimentally; it is essential that there should be somewhere on the plateau a centralized link between the separate units of the country.

To the south of Barcelona the provinces which have a frontage on the Mediterranean Sea tend to show decreasing densities, save where wide-watered lands (*huertas* and *vegas*) increase productivity. The following sequence is interesting: Tarragona 53, Castellón 50, show the drop as the Catalonian manufacturing area is left; the figures for Valencia (118) and Alicante (108) reflect the presence of coastal plains where irrigation is easy. The drop in Murcia (63) is due to the limited amount of land which can be watered in relation to the total area, for the province has a considerable extension inland. Almería (43) has again but a small amount of land under irrigation, and the watered parts of Granada (58) are small in relation to the large tracts of mountainous land. The density rises to 94 in Málaga, with its fairly wide, irrigated coastal plains, and maintains a similar level in Cádiz, which is largely lowland. Farther to the west, in Huelva, it drops to 37 in spite of the presence of the mines. The three provinces which abut on the inner course of the Guadalquivir, Jaén, Córdoba, and Seville, have all moderate densities of 50–70.

As regards the inner provinces apart from Madrid, it is noteworthy that Saragossa, the most important province of the Ebro basin, despite the possibilities of irrigation and local intensity of cultivation, has a mean density of only 33, and the contiguous provinces of Huesca (16), Soria (15 per sq. km., or 39 per sq. mile), Guadalajara (17), Teruel (17), with Cuenca (20) to the south, show the lowest figures for the peninsula. Albacete (25) is in little better case, while Valladolid (44), with the surrounding provinces, shows the influence both of the corn-lands and of the relation to important

lines of communication. Generally, the inland provinces to the eas
and south-east of Madrid show densities below 30 per sq. km. an
those of the north-west of over 30.

In sum, then, densities are relatively high, over 150 per sq. km
at the eastern end of the north coast, and also on the north-wes
coast, as a continuation of the densely-peopled belt in north Portuga
on the north-eastern coast; in the interior round Madrid. They ar
moderate on the east and south coasts and in the Guadalquivi
valley, with a notable rise where extensive irrigation is possible
They are moderate also in the north-western part of the inne
tableland, but low in its eastern and south-eastern parts.

As regards the towns, Madrid and Barcelona are both of th
order of a million, Madrid being a little the larger. Valencia an
Seville both exceed the 300,000 limit and five others—Málaga
Saragossa, Murcia, Bilbao, and Granada—contain more than 150,00
inhabitants, while Córdoba approximates closely to this figure.

LINES OF COMMUNICATION

Within the peninsula these show three outstanding features. Th
inner tableland, especially the great basins, is at least relativel
suitable for railway construction, and the convergence of a numbe
of lines on Madrid is noteworthy. Great difficulties, however, ar
experienced during the rise from the margins to the interior, and a
ways tend to follow a few routes definitely marked out by the relie
Thirdly, as a whole the coastal belts display too varied a relief fo
the easy building of railways parallel to them, and, in marked con
trast with Italy, continuous coastal routes are little developed. I
Spain indeed the predominance of Madrid is largely assured by th
way in which railways radiate out from it to the chief centres c
population on the periphery, which have themselves but imperfec
connexions. The last point is well illustrated by the complicate
and lengthy route between the two large towns of Valencia an
Málaga. As a whole, also, the railway network is loose, the train
slow, the cost of transit high owing to the difficulties encountere
Motor traffic is important, and the roads are being improved, b
pack- and riding-animals retain some of their earlier importance i
the more remote districts, and help to give an air of primitivenes
to the country. Air traffic is developing, but the relief and th
meteorological conditions, together with Spanish poverty, are likel
to prove obstacles to its extensive use.

The effect of the Pyrenees in checking communication with th
European mainland has been already emphasized. The older route
which form the starting-points of the Spanish system, round th
two ends of the chain, the one from Bordeaux by Irún and Sa

Sebastián, the other from Toulouse by Port Bou to Barcelona. Two intermediate routes have been added. From Pau the Pyrenees are negotiated by the Somport tunnel, giving direct access via Jaca and Huesca to Saragossa. From Toulouse via Foix and Ax the eastern Pyrenees are traversed in French territory by the Puymorens tunnel, and thereafter the picturesque transpyrenean route leads from Puigcerdá via Ripoll direct to Barcelona. These are difficult routes with steep gradients and sharp curves and even in normal times could carry little traffic. For political reasons all lines have frequently been closed to international traffic.

From San Sebastián the main line has a difficult route by Vitoria and the Burgos gap to the basin of Old Castile. Once this is attained the development of a network becomes possible, and a multiplicity of routes goes off to the coast (to Santander, Oviedo, and Gijón, Corunna, Vigo) as well as to Portugal. The main line is continued by Valladolid and the important junction of Medina del Campo through the Central Sierras to Madrid. Here great divergence occurs. The southerly continuation is to the junction of Alcázar de San Juan, from which the Guadalquivir valley is reached via the Despeñaperros pass across the Sierra Morena. Again, after the traverse of that obstacle, divergence becomes possible. Thus while the main line is continued along the Guadalquivir valley by Córdoba and Seville, and diverges to the ports of Cádiz and Huelva, important branches find their way across the Betic Cordillera to the Mediterranean coast. The chief are that to Almería, with branches to Granada and to Murcia, and that from Córdoba to Málaga. In a similar way the easterly branch from Alcázar, after negotiating the drop from the plateau near Albacete, diverges to Valencia, to Alicante, and to Cartagena via Murcia. There is also a direct line from Madrid via Cuenca to Valencia.

From Madrid a westerly trunk line, with a number of branches, runs to Lisbon. To the north-east there diverges the line connecting Madrid with Saragossa and Barcelona, so that the first-named town forms a point of intersection between the routes which enter Spain at the western and eastern ends of the Pyrenees. The Madrid-Saragossa line is difficult, the crucial point being Medinaceli, near which the parting between Ebro and Tagus feeders is crossed.

Saragossa is also connected, both by Pamplona and by the upper Ebro valley, to the San Sebastián-Burgos-Madrid route. These routes form an important cross-connexion between the trunk lines, and also link Barcelona to the northern and north-western area and its ports. Further, as one of the exceptions to the statement already made that lines parallel to the coast are infrequent, we find that Barcelona is linked along the coast to Valencia, which has somewhat indirect connexions with Alicante, Murcia, and Cartagena.

NATURAL DIVISIONS

On the basis of this general description we may proceed to sub-divide the peninsula. The first division is necessarily into central and peripheral elements, the latter being numerous and diverse, while alike in the relief and the human response much uniformity prevails over large parts of the interior. It has been already shown that the interior lands, apart from the province of Madrid, fall into the area where the population density is below 50 per sq. km., while the marginal regions differ enormously both as regards actual figures and as to the factors leading to the appearance of relatively high densities.

Two major divisions occur within the central area. To the one, following Maull, the name of Castilian Tableland may conveniently be given, while the other is the Ebro basin. The boundaries of the latter are clear enough. To the north lie the Pyrenees, to the south-west that mountain belt which has no common geographical name though, as stated on p. 226, that of Iberian Ranges has been applied to it, while other geographers use the term Iberic Mountains. The third border is constituted by the coastal ranges of Catalonia, to whose presence its interior character is due.

The Castilian tableland is bounded on the north by the hills of the Basque provinces and by the higher area in Asturias which forms the Cantabrian Mountains proper, and on the north-west by the hill country of Galicia. Southwards it ends in the Sierra Morena and north-eastwards in the Iberian ranges. Its boundary toward central and southern Portugal is determined by the drop in height of Staub's three southerly Iberid ranges in the region, beyond the culminating axis, where the Iberid folding affects younger, softer rocks in place of the harder ones of the core (Fig. 68). Thus the Central Sierras formed by the Guadarrama, Gredos, Gata, Estrella etc., mountains, which traverse it centrally, diminish notably in height in the region of Leiria, so that the regional boundary between the Castilian tableland and the peripheral belt of mid-Portugal transgresses the political frontier. In the more southerly range formed by the mountains of Toledo, Guadalupe, and their western continuations (Mamede, etc.), the regional boundary corresponds more closely to the political one, and this is also true in the case of the Sierra Morena. There the theoretical continuity of the Iberid folding into the hills on the northern border of Algarve is not accompanied by such an elevation as to affect notably the character of the landscape, even though, as has been shown, the western coast of Portugal displays here the plateau feature of a thin population (Fig. 74).

Generally, then, the Castilian tableland is characterized by a thin population, except round Madrid, by a notable hill girdle to north, north-east, and south, and by transverse mountain belts, which, especially in the centre, prolong it across the frontier into Portugal. Geologically also it shows a marked contrast between the great tertiary basins, with their minor continuations (Fig. 68), and the old, hard rocks of the core.

The peripheral belt has been variously divided, but for our purpose the following seems the most suitable arrangement:

(1) The Catalonian coastal strip is so distinctive that it must be regarded as a separate entity, extending southwards to the area of the Ebro delta, but not including all the lands of the old province.

(2) The south-eastern coastal strip, with its limited areas of intensive cultivation, may be taken as extending from the delta area to Cape Gata.

(3) Southern Spain includes not only the lower Guadalquivir valley, with the lowland extending westward to the Portuguese frontier, but also the Cordilleran mountain belt and the minor lowlands of the coast.

Portugal, as already suggested, does not form as a whole a single natural region. Apart from the interpenetration of the mountain belts of the tableland, particularly in the Serra da Estrella, the area north of the Douro, developed on the rocks of the core, shows a much closer resemblance to Galicia than to the remainder of Portugal. We must therefore separate (4) central and south Portugal, with their alternation of hill country and lowland, from this northern section.

This leaves us with (5) the north-western region (including north Portugal, Galicia, Asturias, and the coastal Basque provinces) as distinct from (6) the Pyrenean area.

Finally, (7) the Balearic Isles form a separate unit.

CHAPTER XII

THE PERIPHERAL NATURAL REGIONS

Catalonia and the Catalonian Coastlands—The South-eastern
Coastal Belt—Southern Spain—Central and Southern Portugal—
The North-western Region—The Pyrenean Area—The Balearic
Isles

CATALONIA AND THE CATALONIAN COASTLANDS

CATALONIA, in the historic sense, may be regarded as one
of the most individualized parts of Spain. Its inhabitants
have their own speech, distinct from Castilian Spanish; the
presence of notable ports on the Mediterranean Sea, varying in
position throughout the ages but always relatively important, has
given them a wider outlook, a larger share in the life of the extra-
peninsular world than most of its other peoples. Finally, the
present-day development of large-scale industry is scarcely represented elsewhere within the peninsula.

But meantime, whatever may happen in the immediate future,
Catalonia is only a name, and the four Catalonian provinces of
Tarragona, Lérida, Barcelona, and Gerona form neither a natural
nor an economic unit. On the other hand, what we have called the
Catalonian Coastlands are well defined both by structure and relief,
and to a considerable extent by climate, natural vegetation, and
cultivated crops. At the same time the great development of industry, especially since the latter part of the nineteenth century, with
Barcelona as its centre, has brought great changes, superimposing
new modes of life on parts of the area. But in spite of the physio-
graphic unity the whole coastland has not become industrialized
parts of it retain their own economy, independent of that of Barcelona
based on their own agricultural products, and served by their own
ports. On the other hand, the industries of Barcelona, instead of
spreading mainly coastwards, within the limits of the region, have
on account of their dependence on water-power, tended to follow
the valleys towards the interior. Thus while industrial development
is not characteristic of the whole coastland, it yet transcends its
limits.

In itself there is perhaps nothing particularly remarkable in this
In the case of Liguria we have seen that the influence of Genoa
extends over a part only of the Riviera strip, leaving other area
untouched. But the contrasts between Barcelona and Genoa are
outstanding. Genoa, owing to the skill of the modern engineer, is
but an annex of the industrial area of the Italian plains, which are

254

themselves closely linked to industrialized Central Europe. At Barcelona industries appeared late, relatively to the rest of the continent, and, save to a certain extent during the war, especially as regards the chemical industries, production has been mainly for the protected home market, not for an external one. That market, if assured, is yet easily saturated, and an intense local nationalism, apt to resent equally Castilian and foreign intervention, whether in the form of capital, technical help, or in any other way, has checked

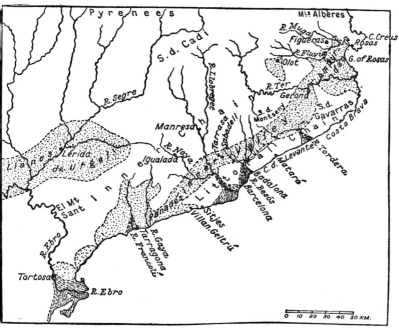

FIG. 75. THE CATALONIAN COASTLANDS
The alluvial plains are indicated by dots and the deltaic areas by broken lines.

expansion and exerted much influence both on the nature of the industries and on their localization. Industrialized Catalonia as a result is curiously aloof and isolated, alike so far as the rest of the peninsula and the industrialized world at large is concerned.

It might seem as if either historic Catalonia, or that part of it which is distinguished by large-scale industry, might form a better unit on which to base a description than the natural region of the coastland. Neither area, however, shows the kind of unity which is so characteristic of the coastland, and gives its recognition as a separate entity advantages which outweigh the apparent disadvantages.

Fig. 75, combined with those showing the structural elements of the peninsula, indicates clearly enough its limits and characteristics. From the seaward slopes of the Pyrenees in the Albères chain to the lower Ebro upstream from Tortosa, there extends a belt, including a great variety of rocks, which appears to have been involved both in the earlier Hispanid and in the later Iberid folding. Within the belt the granites of the core are exposed in places, as in the Montseny Massif (1,700 m.). Elsewhere the folded rocks are of palaeozoic age, as in the Gavarras Mountains, Tibidabo (531 m.) behind Barcelona, and El Mont Sant (1,071 m.) near the Ebro; or are secondaries, including especially limestones, as in the Altos de Garraf (595 m.), south-west of Barcelona (Fig. 76). The Iberid folding has in places also involved tertiary rocks, as in the remarkable Montserrat region (1,238 m.), where sandstones and conglomerates build up a ridge which has been dissected into strange forms.

More important, however, than the actual rocks are the topographical features suggested in Figs. 75 and 76. A longitudinal valley, floored by alluvial deposits resting on tertiary beds, extends in a south-westerly direction from the neighbourhood of Gerona on the Ter, and separates an inner hill belt from a shorter, lower, and less continuous littoral chain. The latter begins to the south of the Ter mouth and dies away to the south of that of the Llobregat in the neighbourhood of Villanueva y Geltrú. Thus beyond that town the longitudinal valley may be said to reach the coast, along which it extends to the Ebro delta. The origin of the valley is somewhat uncertain, but it has been regarded as of the nature of a rift valley, and the numerous extinct volcanoes near Olot and in the vicinity of Gerona (19,000) suggest that tectonic causes have been active here. To the north-east, across the Ter river, the valley is continued into the large Ampurdán basin, believed to be a faulted depression. It is largely floored by the deposits brought down by the Ter, Fluvia, and Muga rivers, and there have been considerable changes in the coast-line during the historic period. It should be noted that the position of Gerona on the Ter, and thus between the Ampurdán basin and the longitudinal valley, makes that town an obvious route-centre, for the valley forms the main line of communication.

The whole folded belt, inner chain, longitudinal valley, and littoral chain, is cut through transversely by a series of rivers. The most important of these, all having valleys wider than their present size seems to justify, are the Ter, the Llobregat, and the Ebro. Their importance is due to their Pyrenean feeders, while the Tordera, the Besós, the Gaya, and the Francolí take their origin within the folded belt. It should be noted that the Llobregat, with its tributary the Cardoner, the Ter, and the Segre tributary of the Ebro traverse in their middle course the north-easterly prolongation of the Ebro basin, the steppe region of the Llanos de Urgel round Lérida (cf. Fig. 73) being shown on the map. This part of historic Catalonia will be discussed in connexion with the Ebro basin of Aragón.

Two further points should be noted before proceeding to details. The rivers, particularly the Llobregat and of course the Ebro, both with feeders from the Pyrenees, which were heavily glaciated during

FIG. 76. BARCELONA AND THE NEIGHBOURING TOWNS

the Ice Age, bring down much alluvium and tend to build out deltas. That of the Llobregat, practically confluent with the smaller fan of the Besós, is particularly important because of the hill backing. Again, the Llobregat, with an almost north-to-south direction, apparently little influenced by the presence of the longitudinal valley which, like the inner and littoral hill belts, it crosses transversely, and fed copiously by water from the Pyrenees, not only supplies much water-power in its lower course, but can also be utilized in its upper reaches. This is true also of the head-waters of the Ter. It is on this power that the industries of Catalonia mainly depend. Thus the influence of Barcelona extends beyond the inner hill belt in the sense that factories and factory towns are strong along the rivers outside the physiographical limit of the coastland. There they form an alien element in the landscape, illustrating the statement already made that the economic region of Barcelona extends beyond the natural one of the coastland.

It will be noted also that this summary description makes clear the fact that within the coastland three areas offer particularly favourable sites for settlements. The first is the Ampurdán basin, with much productive land and a considerable variety of resources; here, on the shore of the Gulf of Rosas, stood the Greek Emporion (cf. p. 19). The second is the alluvial fan formed by the Llobregat and Besós, which has the great advantage of easy access to the longitudinal valley; this is the site of medieval and modern Barcelona. Finally, in the area where the littoral chain disappears so that the longitudinal valley abuts on the coast, the fan of the Francolí river offers an advantageous position, occupied by Roman Tarraco and modern Tarragona (28,000). The advantages of Gerona, where the transverse route indicated by the Ter valley crosses that from the basin of Ampurdán to the longitudinal valley, have been already indicated. On the other hand, the Ebro is too powerful a stream for its great delta to afford a suitable site for a large settlement.

The coastal strip as a whole shows considerable variety in scenery and products. In the Sierra de Rosas old folded rocks run out seawards, giving rise to a precipitous shore-line, much dissected by the sea (cf. Cape Creus). Miniature rias occur between the promontories, and here minor ports occur, serving as fishing havens. Fruit-trees thrive near the shore, and the inner slopes are clothed with cork oak and other trees. With the Gulf of Rosas a change occurs. Here the shore is low and sandy, and the gulf itself forms a gently-rounded arc. Considerable changes have occurred during the historic period, so that the old port of Emporion is silted up. The lands near the sea show indeed a certain resemblance to the deltaic lands of the Rhone. Thus rice is grown and the saltings afford pasturage for cattle, horses, and transhumant sheep, the last ascending to the mountain pastures of the Pyrenees in summer. Further inland the Ampurdán basin displays a certain alternation of alluvial deposits and tertiary hillocks, the former being occupied especially by market gardens and fields of cereals, and the latter by such fruit-trees as olives, carobs, and vines.

Beyond the mouth of the Ter the scene changes once again. Though the littoral hill belt is low (400–600 m.), yet it rises steeply from the sea, leaving little land available for cultivation, save that the slopes are planted with olives, carobs, and vines, as in the region generally. This Costa Brava, as it is called, recalls that of part of Provence, and is of the Riviera type. The small ports are fishing havens for the most part, though S. Feliú de Guixols serves as the outlet for the cork industry of Gerona. Considerable settlements are few, but the tourist industry supplements the somewhat meagre natural resources.

This fretted coast-line continues to the small delta of the Tordera, beyond which it gives place to the Costa del Levante, which extends south-westwards beyond the Llobregat mouth. Here there is a fairly wide alluvial fringe, becoming wider as the confluent deltas of the Llobregat and Besós are approached, which are fertile and productive. But the special feature is that, much as happens in the case of Genoa, the influence of Barcelona expresses itself in the rise of a number of small manufacturing towns, which follow one another almost uninterruptedly along the densely-peopled coastal strip. Mataró and Badalona, both with a variety of textile industries (cotton, linen, silk, jute) and Badalona also with chemical industries, may be given as examples; but there are many others.

Beyond the Llobregat delta the Altos de Garraf continue a similar type of coast to Sitjes, but from Villanueva y Geltrú to the Ebro delta the shore becomes flat and alluvial, with occasional limestone hills. The climate also becomes milder, citrus fruits in number and variety being added to the usual fruit-trees, while the palms recall those of Valencia to the south. Tarragona is especially important for its wine, the vineyards of the Panadés region being noted for the value of their product. The fact that the monks expelled from the Grande Chartreuse of France manufacture their famous liqueur here is also interesting.

Farther inland the longitudinal valley is very productive, being noted for its market gardens and orchards. Northwards there are large cork oak woods on the hills round Gerona, forming the basis of its chief industry.

As contrasted with this development of natural features in a north-east to south-west direction, and the corresponding spread of the satellites of Barcelona along the Costa del Levante, we find that the other industrial towns tend to spread up the river-valleys, especially that of the Llobregat. There is, however, a certain distinction between the factories of the upper valleys outside the coastland region and those of the longitudinal rift and the river-valleys within it. The headstreams of the Llobregat, Ter, and Fluvia obtain from the Pyrenees an almost constant flow of water throughout the year; the valleys, in contradistinction to the Segre, afford direct lines of communication to the coastland area; the mountain folk furnish cheap labour. As a result we find the somewhat exceptional condition—in the modern world—of the frequent direct use of water-power for spinning yarns. These upland townships necessarily cling to the sides of the streams which supply the motive power. Ribas on the upper Ter, Baga on the upper Llobregat may be mentioned as examples; but Manresa, on the Cardoner tributary of the Llobregat and on the border of the coastland region, is also a spinning town.

In contrast to these hill towns those of the longitudinal valley and its slopes use hydro-electric power, and engage mainly in weaving. Tarrasa and Sabadell (48,000) manufacture woollen goods, Granollers chiefly cotton goods, Igualada adds leather industries to its cotton-weaving, and paper (including cigarette paper) is made in the towns on the Noya tributary of the Llobregat and along the course of the Besós. The power used for these varied industries is derived especially from the Segre headstreams. Thus the Pantano de Tremp, on the Noguera Pallaresa tributary, is a reservoir formed by means of a great barrage, formerly the fourth in size in the world. Together with subsidiary works it supplies most of the electricity used in the neighbourhood of Barcelona. Unfortunately the water-level may drop notably during the summer, and then coal must be used to supplement flowing water at the power stations. There is a little local coal in Catalonia, as at Calaf on the railway between Manresa and Lérida, but the quantity is small and the quality poor, most being lignite. The costs of transport from the coal-fields of Asturias are high, and the Asturias coal is inferior in steam-raising quality to that of South Wales, which can be imported at Barcelona at not dissimilar prices. The imports of English coal are of the order of 360,000 tons per annum in normal years.

In addition to the important textile industries, and the others which have been already mentioned, the Barcelona region manufactures a considerable amount of machinery for local use. There is but little local smelting, however, iron and steel being mostly imported either from the Basque provinces or from England, Belgium, etc. It is indeed generally true that the coastland has comparatively little in the shape of local raw material, though the Salina, or mountain of salt, at Cardona on the Cardoner, and the potassium deposits at Suria, farther down the same river, may be noted as interesting. Cotton has to be imported, chiefly from the U.S.A. Wool is largely supplied by other parts of Spain, but has to be supplemented by imports from the Argentine and Australia. It may be added that even where raw material can be obtained from other parts of the peninsula, the difficulty of communication makes transport charges high. Water-power and the energy of the inhabitants are thus the main advantages which Catalonia possesses, and it is not likely that this restless area will push its nationalism to the point where the command of the home market is threatened. This has always been the great hold of Castile upon it.

THE SOUTH-EASTERN COASTAL BELT

We have included here the area from the Ebro delta to Cape de Gata, that is, the provinces of Castellón, Valencia, Alicante, and Murcia. A part of the province of Almería is also within this belt, but the town is excluded. At first sight the region may appear unnatural in view of the fact that the folds of the Betic Cordillera run out seaward in Cape de la Nao, making this a structural limit. But there is so much general resemblance between the main areas of settlement to the north and south-west of the cape as to make it desirable to consider them together, rather than include the latter in the region of southern Spain. Population is concentrated on the two coastal lowlands round Valencia and Murcia respectively. Here, and here only, on any scale is that irrigation possible on which cultivation depends in this arid part of Spain; the cultivated plants are similar in the two lowlands, and they have both a definitely Mediterranean outlook. Both Valencia and Murcia also command routes from the plateau to the sea, and thus occupy analogous positions in relation to the interior. This is associated with the fact that the Cordilleran chains diminish in height and in extent as they approach Cape de la Nao, and are physiographically so incompletely separated from the slopes of the tableland that the Segura, which crosses them transversely, has a course broadly parallel to that of the Júcar, which is a tableland river. In other words, the provinces of Murcia and Alicante show, in essentials if not in detail, a direct seaward slope as contrasted with the tendency manifest in southern Spain for the valleys to run parallel to the Cordilleran folds.

From the Ebro mouth to the Cape de la Nao the coast swings round in a gentle curve, showing much uniformity of outline. From the vicinity of Oropesa, where the hills approach the coast, to Denia, that is, over a distance of some 160 km., or 100 miles, it is fringed by a coastal plain. This is widest behind Valencia and narrows towards both extremities. It is floored by alluvial deposits brought down by the rivers Mijares, Palancia, Guadalaviar (or Turia), and Júcar, with some smaller streams, and is remarkably level, the surface being broken only by a few isolated hills, such as that near Játiva. Behind the plain rises the edge of the tableland, through which the rivers tend to break in gorges. Of these the most noteworthy is the Salto de Chulilla on the Guadalaviar. Because of the presence of this gorge Valencia has no easy direct access to the surface of the plateau, a fact which gives particular interest to the two ancient town-sites of Sagunto and Játiva, placed respectively to the north and south of Valencia (Fig. 77). Játiva occupies a strategic position near the point where the Albaida tributary of the Júcar is joined by the Montesa or Cañotes, a stream flowing in an open valley between the tableland and the Sierra Grosa, the first of the Cordilleran ranges. The valley affords an easy route to the surface of the tableland, which is followed by the railway from Valencia to Madrid via Albacete. It will be noted that this means that that railway is compelled to take a considerable bend to the south before ascending the plateau. Sagunto occupies similarly a strategically

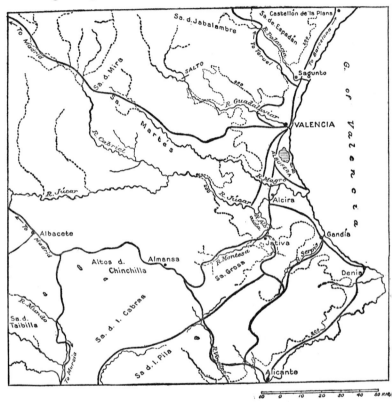

FIG. 77. VALENCIA AND ITS COASTAL PLAIN

important site on a hill near the mouth of the Palancia, the valley of which affords a means of reaching the northern part of the tableland. From the town a railway runs via Teruel to Calatayud on the main Saragossa-Madrid route.

Within the plain of Valencia all the rivers can be used for irrigation purposes, though the Júcar supplies most water. From it the *Acequia real* or main canal is taken off, and this ends in the freshwater lagoon called Albufera, near Valencia, and separated from the sea by a pine-clad ridge. On its inner border are many rice-fields.

All the towns of the region lie near the rivers, and thus serve as centres for the intensively-cultivated *huertas*, or garden-lands, this being the Spanish term, while *vega* is the Moorish equivalent used in Andalusia. Valencia on the Guadalaviar is of course much the largest town, but Castellón de la Plana (47,000), near the Mijares, Alcira in the Júcar valley, and Gandía, with a very productive huerta watered by the Serpis river, should also be noted. Valencia is now some 5 km. from the sea, its port being Villanueva del Grao. The surrounding huerta is watered both by the river and from springs, and an interesting relic of Moorish days is the Water Tribunal (*Tribunal de las Aguas*), which meets every week, eight peasants acting as judges and settling all disputes and difficulties over water rights. The cultivated crops are like those of Murcia, but the abundance of oranges and the vines, grown especially for Valencian raisins, are noteworthy. As would be expected from its size and position Valencia has a number of minor industries, such as silk, leather, pottery, and so on, and this is true generally of the larger towns of this productive belt.

South of the promontory which has Cape de la Nao at its extremity the coast trends away to the south-west. It is divided into two flattened bays by a prolongation which ends in Cape de Palos, has the large salt lagoon of Mar Menor to the north, and the sheltered haven of Cartagena to the south. This area is backed by the low (under 900 m.) Sierra de Almenara, which has a south-west to north-east trend, but gives off eastwards an offshoot—the Sierra de Cartagena—ending in the Palos cape. The lowland region lying between the Sierra de Almenara and the inner hill country is watered by the feeders of the Segura, which supplies water to the great huerta of Murcia (Fig. 78). Together with the much smaller Vinalpó, also, it opens up those routes to the interior which give the region much of its importance. These two rivers indeed, with some smaller streams, assisted by the iron and silver-lead ores of the Sierra de Almenara and their offshoot in the Sierra de Cartagena, may be said to have enabled a dense population to thrive in an area which away from the fertilizing streams is little more than a desert. Outside the watered area the land yields little save scattered and scanty tufts of esparto grass, offering poor feed even for thrifty Spanish sheep.

The Segura rises in the Sierra of the same name, not far from the sources of the Guadalquivir, and flows first north and then east until its emergence from the hill country upstream from Cieza. Here the Quipar tributary is dammed back in the great reservoir of the Pantano de Alfonso XIII, while the Mundo tributary from the north allows of the passage of the railway from Madrid via Albacete. At Cieza the main stream bends to the south-east, and just upstream from Murcia turns sharply on itself at a right angle to enter the wide valley between the inner hill country and the Sierra de Almenara.

That valley extends from Lorca (69,000) to Alicante (100,000), and between Lorca and Murcia is occupied by the Sangonera tributary. After the junction the united stream bends once more at Orihuela to run eastward to the Mediterranean. The valley just mentioned permits of an easy passage of the railway to Alicante, while south

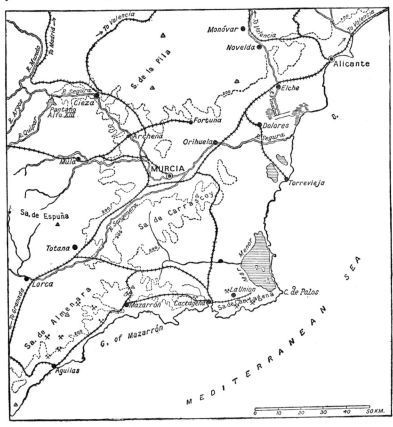

FIG. 78. MURCIA AND THE ADJACENT AREA
The chief mines (iron and silver-lead) are indicated by crossed picks.

of Orihuela (37,000) a branch goes off to Cartagena. Thus Murcia has a double outlet to the sea, at Alicante and at Cartagena (Fig. 78.) From Lorca also a continuation of the valley permits of the passage of the railway to Granada, with a branch to the small port of Aguilas. It is thus clear that Murcia is a point of convergence of a number of routes.

Short and apparently unimportant as the Vinalpó is compared with the Segura, yet its headstreams approach sufficiently near to those of the Montesa tributary of the Júcar to permit the passage of a railway connecting Alicante with the Albacete-Játiva-Valencia line, thus linking together the two important watered areas. There is now, in addition, a coastal railway to Alicante via Denía. The Vinalpó supplies water to the famous date plantations of Elche as well as to the neighbouring huertas.

The huerta of Murcia is supplied by a dense network of canals taken off from the Segura and Sangonera, and the watered area extends up the former river to Cieza and up the latter to Lorca (the Pantano de Puentes lies upstream from the latter town). The crops which can be produced cover an astounding range from temperate to sub-tropical and even tropical. It is noteworthy, however, that —a very exceptional feature in the Mediterranean lands of Europe— even wheat, olive, and vine need watering here. Among the crop plants may be mentioned lucerne, which yields many cuts in the year, tobacco, hemp, a great variety of vegetables such as tomatoes, peas, beans, onions, capsicums; mulberry for silkworm-rearing, and many fruit-bearing trees, such as oranges and lemons, carobs, figs, almonds, pomegranates, and so on; cotton, some sugar-cane, and even ground-nuts and bananas, as well as cereals, including maize; and olives and vines.

Cartagena is a naval station and has a fine position; with the adjacent town of La Union it has an iron industry based on the local ores, but dependent on imported coal. The town of Mazarrón, some little distance from the sea, on which it has a small port, exports iron ores. Archena, on the Segura between Cieza and Murcia, has thermal sulphur springs and ranks as one of the chief spas of Spain. Of the minor industries of Murcia mention may be made of silkworm gut for fishing tackle, though the silk industry generally is not very flourishing.

SOUTHERN SPAIN

The steep southern slope of the Sierra Morena forms a natural limit between Castile in the wide sense and that southern region where the Moorish *régime* lingered longest, and left its most marked effects, alike on the people and on the cities. This is the Spain of the tourist, the part which is most frequently visited and colours deeply current conceptions of the country. Despite modern developments, and despite the presence of three of the greater cities of Spain—Seville (312,000; compare Valencia, 451,000), Málaga 238,000), Granada (155,000)—it belongs rather to the past than to the present. Its two great periods of activity were in Moorish times and during the era of the great discoveries, and since the latter it has been more or less static. Such areas are at once more attractive to the visitor and lend themselves more easily to picturesque description than those in process of active evolution, where the really important lines of evolution are difficult to pick out. The sunny climate and the luxuriant vegetation of the better-watered lands are also very attractive, and the people have a lightheartedness and vivacity which distinguishes them from the Castilians.

Southern Spain, in the sense defined, may be said to fall into two nearly equal parts, the funnel-shaped Guadalquivir valley, opening westward and floored by tertiary or younger beds, still extending seawards (Fig. 79), and the hill and mountain country of the Betic Cordillera. Eight provinces are included. Of these Huelva and Cádiz face towards the open sea and extend over the widened swampy mouth of the funnel. Málaga, Granada, and Almería include much of the mountain country, with at best but narrow coastal plains to the south, though Almería has a double shore-line to south and east, and, as already indicated, is transitional to the south-eastern area. Sevilla, Córdoba, and Jaén are inland provinces within which lies the steadily-narrowing lowland, with a correlated eastward expansion of the bounding hill country.

It will be noted that the region generally offers a certain analogy to northern India, with the obvious difference—among many others —that the plateau lies here to the north and the young folded mountains to the south, instead of the reverse condition. Just as happens in India, therefore, the longer and more voluminous streams from the mountains force the main stream towards the plateau edge, so that it is not central within the wide valley floor. But just up-stream from Seville, as the Cordilleran chains diminish in height and turn southward, this factor ceases to act, and the river bends to the south-west. Here also the tertiary foundation is largely con-cealed beneath river-borne alluvium, and the river crosses the Marismas or extensive swampy area gained from the sea, and opens by a broad, winding estuary (Fig. 79). The coast is fringed by a low cliff against which the currents set up by the south-westerly wind have piled up sand-dunes (the Arenas Gordas). The same currents account for the spit which bounds the estuarine opening of the rivers Odiel and Tinto with Huelva (56,000) as the port of the former. West of Huelva the lagoon coast continues to the Portuguese frontier. The narrowing of the tertiary belt in this region (cf. Fig. 68), with the direct seaward slope, is of much im-portance in connexion with the working of the Rio Tinto and Tharsis copper-mines.

The Guadalquivir mouth has on it only the insignificant port of Sanlucar de Barrameda, but farther south a double bay, with the inner ports of Puerto de Santa María and S. Fernando on its arms, is partially closed by the long island spit which bears the port of Cádiz (88,000), at its northern extremity, on a very congested site. The low lagoon type of coast continues southwards, but at Tarifa the hills jut out seawards. Farther east the beautifully rounded bay of Algeciras (Fig. 80) is bounded to the east by the Gibraltar promontory, with its rocky, fortified slopes.

From this description certain points about the position of Seville emerge. It is virtually the highest point which can be reached by

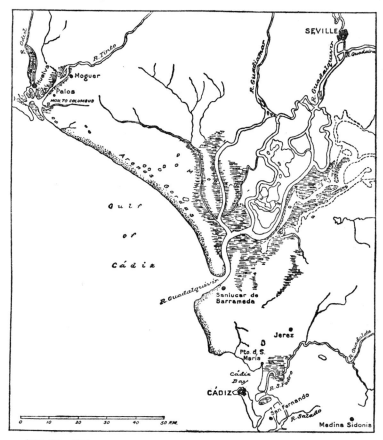

FIG. 79. THE MOUTH OF THE GUADALQUIVIR AND THE SITE OF CADIZ
(*From the 1/500000 map.*)

sea-going ships, marks the entrance of the Guadalquivir on its truly lowland track, where it becomes broad and sluggish, and is necessarily the lowest point at which the river can be conveniently bridged, and thus a converging point of routes. Roughly speaking it marks the junction between the inner lowland and the level and often swampy coastal one.

The inner lowland may be said to extend from the Guadalquivir between Seville and a point upstream from Andújar to the slopes of the sub-Betic chains. It is not level but gently undulating. Its existence, it may be recalled, is the result of the uplifting of tertiary beds lying between the Betic Cordillera and the meseta. But the left-bank tributaries from the mountains, especially the Guadajoz, Genil, and Guadairo (note that the prefix Guad=wady, and is one of the relics of Moorish influence) have dissected it into an alternation of vales and rolling uplands. This dissection of the tertiary surface is necessarily accentuated upstream, particularly where the right-bank Guadalimar tributary enters after a long course on the

FIG. 80. GIBRALTAR AND ALGECIRAS BAY

The railway from Ronda is shown terminating at the Spanish town of Algeciras. There is no railway to Gibraltar.

plateau. Thus the Loma de Ubeda (828 m.) and the Loma de Chiclana (981 m.), lying on either side of the river before it joins the Guadalquivir, present the appearance of mountain ranges though developed on unfolded miocene beds. Generally the undulating nature of the surface, combined with deficient supplies of water, exert much influence on the landscape. The vales are richly cultivated, producing rice, tobacco, cotton, sugar-cane, but much of the undissected surface presents the appearance of a steppe in summer, after the winter-sown wheat has been cut, though it yields a considerable amount of pasture. The bordering hills carry vines, olives, mulberry for silkworm-rearing, oranges (but note limit on Fig. 73) and other fruit-trees.

Córdoba (143,000) is a minor convergence point of routes, but has lost relative importance since the days when its great mosque, now the cathedral, was the centre of Moorish intellectual life. Like Seville, it has some minor manufactures, and also railway connexion with the interior across the Sierra Morena. The main railway from Madrid, however, crosses much farther east by the Puerto d

Despeñaperros (=overthrow of the dogs, or infidels, an allusion to the defeat of the Moors here in 1212).

As contrasted with the relative simplicity of lower Andalusia the hill country is highly complex. We may recall first the main structural features as shown in Fig. 68. From Estepona north-east of Gibraltar to the vicinity of Aguilas on the coast of Murcia province, the palaeozoic and crystalline rocks of the central area rise steeply from the coast, which trends parallel to the fold-lines. But between the mountains and the sea there occur at intervals basins of varying size floored by tertiary and post-tertiary beds. The largest and most productive is that in which Málaga lies. Then come in series along the south coast those of Velez-Málaga, Motril, Adra, and Almería (Fig. 81).

Fig. 68 shows another point which has been already emphasized. This is that the hard rocks of the inner nappes are fringed on their northern border by the secondary limestone rocks of the sub-Betic chains, extending from Cape de la Nao to the vicinity of Cádiz. The junction of the two rock types is indicated by a longitudinal valley which throughout the greater part of its course serves as a line of communication. The fact is the key to the geography of the area, and it is essential that the run of the valley should be realized. Even on an atlas map its general direction is obvious from the towns strung along it. Note particularly—Lorca on the Sangonera; Guadix on a feeder of the Fardes tributary of the Guadiana Menor; Loja on the Genil downstream from Granada; the small town of Bobadilla on the bend of the Guadalhorce, the river which waters the Málaga basin, or the larger adjacent town of Campillos to the west; Ronda on the Guadiaro. All these are stations on the Murcia-Algeciras railway, which traverses southern Spain from east to south-west, though the railway does not correspond in all its details to the longitudinal valley.

One other example may be given in order to justify the general statement that the longitudinal zoning of the structural elements of the Cordillera is reflected in the topography. It was explained on p. 231 that the Sierra Nevada forms part of the Veleta nappe, Veleta being the name of the peak west of Mulhacén and not greatly inferior to it in height (3,428 m., as against 3,481 m.). This nappe is surrounded by the Granada nappe. To the south the two nappes are separated by a longitudinal valley which can be traced on the map. Thus the Guadalfeo river, which waters the Motril basin, has on its course a right-angled bend similar to that on the Guadalhorce. Its upper section traverses the valley of Las Alpujarras and the valley is continued across a water-parting into those traversed by two feeders—right and left bank respectively—of the Almería river, and then to the east coast by the Rio de Aguas near Mojácar.

The next point is that, inevitably, in view of the height of the central chains, there is a tendency also for the development of transverse valleys, for the drainage of the heights is ultimately either to the Guadalquivir or by the shorter route to the southern sea. This leads to the gridiron arrangement of valleys common in folded mountains of complex structure, and always geographically important. But before noting examples we must first consider the general arrangement of the folds. As has been already shown, while this is broadly west to east in the centre, there is a change at both extremities.

To the east, particularly as regards the sub-Betic chains, there is a tendency for the folds to swing to the north-east. At the same time they become lower and diverge, so as to leave intervening valleys, thus opening out the country towards the east coast. Note, for example, the fact that the Sierra de los Filabres has a west-to-east direction, while the Sierra de las Estancias to the north trends from south-west to north-east, leaving a considerable lowland watered by the Almanzora river. This gives an easier route for the Lorca-Guadix section of the railway than that of the longitudinal valley already described, which runs to the north of the Sierra de las Estancias. Farther north the Sierra de Taibilla trends even more markedly northward, so that the Quipar tributary of the Segura (Fig. 78) follows a well-marked lowland. The human effects of this condition have been already suggested by our separation of the south-eastern region from southern Spain proper.

Westward the chains turn to the south-west and then nearly south, whence arose the older view that they were continued across the Strait of Gibraltar into northern Africa. The Sierra Abdalagis and Sierra Bermeja may be noted as illustrations, while the change of direction of the coast-line east and west of Málaga corresponds to that of the folds. Further, the southerly swing of the folds, combined with the disappearance of the crystallines of the Betic nappe (p. 231) near Ronda, accounts for the southward bend of the longitudinal valley, and thus for the course of the railway between Bobadilla junction and Algeciras, via the Ronda gorge.

Turning next to the transverse valleys we find that though Córdoba and Málaga are separated by the whole width of the Cordillera they are united by a railway which—for a Spanish railway—is remarkably direct and has on its course no major crest tunnel. The railway ascends the gentle northern slopes, crosses the longitudinal valley at Bobadilla junction, and descends the gorge of the Guadalhorce by the aid of many minor tunnels and much difficult engineering. Again, though here there is no railway, Granada is connected to Motril by a direct road which utilizes the lower Guadalfeo, the river whose upper section traverses the longitudinal Alpujarras valley.

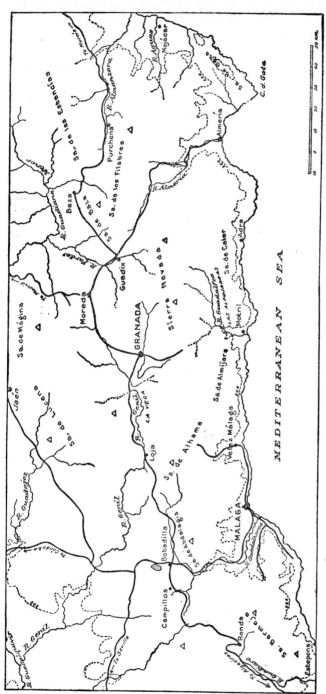

FIG. 81. THE RAILWAY SYSTEM OF PART OF SOUTHERN SPAIN IN RELATION TO DRAINAGE LINES

(*From the* 1/1000000 *map.*)

Similarly the Almería river opens up a transverse gap between the Sierra Nevada and the Sierra de los Filabres, which allows of the passage of a railway from Linares (and Madrid), via Guadix on the longitudinal valley, to the town of Almería.

Generally it is clear that the valley system of the Betic Cordillera proper is highly developed, and that the railway engineers have taken full advantage of the opportunities offered. The conditions suggest, even apart from the figures already given for the population of Málaga and Granada, that the sub-Betic chains, despite their lower height (few points surpass 2,000 m.), are less favourable to settlement than the area included within the belt of older and harder rocks. The former indeed tend generally to be dry and somewhat infertile. This is especially true of the area watered by the numerous feeders of the Guadiana Menor, which includes bare limestone hills. Jaén (55,000) is the key town to this area. Granada owes its importance to its fertile vega, watered by the Genil, and to the copious supplies of water from the quasi-permanent snow of the Sierra Nevada. The towns of the coastal basins are based upon the productivity of the surrounding land, and the possibility of communication with the interior. A great variety of crops can be grown, including all the usual fruit-trees, cotton, sugar-cane, custard apples, sweet potatoes, and so on. But the predominance of the vine is a notable feature. Thus Almería (80,000) exports largely fresh grapes, Málaga raisins, and sweet wine. The slopes of the south-western hills produce vintage grapes of high quality; note sherry which takes its name from Jérez de la Frontera (Fig. 79).

Within the region, or on its borders, a considerable variety of ores occurs, and in addition to the numerous pasture lands adds much to its resources. Iron occurs behind Málaga and Almería, with both lead and copper in the latter case. There are also extensive iron beds on the north slopes of the Sierra de los Filabres, as near Purchena. Lead is most extensively worked near Linares (40,000), on a loop of the main line from Madrid to the Guadalquivir valley. It will be remembered that Linares is also connected to Almería, which exports ores in addition to fruit. Coal occurs at Bélmez, north of Córdoba, in an area which also yields ores. The most important copper-mines are those already mentioned at Rio Tinto and Tharsis, which have been worked since very early times.

CENTRAL AND SOUTHERN PORTUGAL

The essential feature of this region is that although the Iberic ranges of central Spain are continued across it, they reach no great height, so that the landscape is one of lowlands and undulating hills. Thus the Central Sierras of Spain are continued through the Serra da Estrella into the lower hills, built of secondary rocks, which confront the sea between Cape Carvoeiro and Cape da Roca. Off the former cape lie the Berlengas and Farilhões islets, forming a seaward prolongation of the range. Behind Cape da Roca rise the hills of Cintra, while to the south the hill country descends steeply, its eastern section overlooking the estuarine mouth of the Tagus. South-eastwards of the hill belt the tertiary basin of the lower Tagus (p. 230), forming the counterpart of that of New Castile, abuts on the sea, and sand deposits derived from its soft beds constrict the lowest part of the estuary. Above it expands into the wide basin on which Lisbon stands.

Similarly, the Toledo-Guadalupe sierras of Spain are continued by the Serra d'Ossa into the low Serra da Arrábida, which overlooks the bay of Setúbal and the estuarine mouth of the little Sado river. Here, however, in contrast to the Tagus mouth, a marked sand-spit has developed, partially shutting off the wide Sado estuary. The land-forms here offer a curious resemblance to those near Cádiz, though the port of Setúbal is on the north shore of the bay, and not, like Cádiz, at the end of the sand-spit.

The third Iberid range is the western continuation of the Sierra Morena in the hills of Algarve, which, like those of Cintra, overlook a typical Riviera coast to the south. Between the Bay of Setúbal and Cape St. Vincent the east coast is divided into two parts by Cape Sines, the southern section being fringed by low cliffs, where the old rocks of Alemtejo reach the sea. To the north of the cape the tertiary beds of the Setúbal basin extend seawards and the coast is sandy.

North of Cape Carvoeiro, whether the actual coastal beds are of secondary or tertiary age, the shore tends to be of the sandy, lagoon-fringed type, this being particularly marked at the mouth of the Mondego river and near Aveiro. A notable change takes place near Oporto, where the granites of the core become coastal and we thus pass into the north-western region.

With this framework as a basis the details are readily grasped. Portuguese Estremadura, including the Lisbon, Santarém, and Leiria districts, is mainly fertile, producing especially oranges and wine. The two ports of Lisbon and Setúbal, despite the similarity of position, can scarcely be compared, for the latter, even though it ranks as the third town of Portugal, has but 37,000 inhabitants. In addition to the salt from the Sado marshes it produces sardines, and there are extensive orange groves and vineyards in the neighbourhood. The scenery along the coast to the west, from which the Serra da Arrábida rises, is beautiful, but much less frequented than the area to the west of Lisbon, where the rich vegetation and wonderful gardens of the Cintra region are renowned, while the coastal stations, such as Estoril, Mont Estoril, and Cascais, are much frequented in winter by the English on account of the mild climate. Lisbon, magnificently placed on hills above the right bank of the Tagus, where the river expands into the Mar de Palha, despite its ancient foundation presents the appearance of a modern city. This is due to the replanning after the disastrous earthquake of 1775. Santarém stands high above the Tagus, well upstream from Lisbon, and Leiria to the north-west on the banks of the Lis.

Farther north, where the province of Douro forms an artificial unit, we come to an interesting type of country. The swampy coastal strip is noted for its rice-fields, salt-pans, and fishing population, the latter especially concentrated by Aveiro and Ovar. Here there are no ports of any account, though Figuéira da Foz, at the mouth of the Mondego river, has some local importance. Pine woods cover large tracts of the coastal sands, and the population is thin and settlements few. As the land rises towards the interior, however, cultivation increases, and grain-fields, vineyards, and in places garden crops of southern type appear. The centre of this belt is Coimbra, picturesquely placed on a hill above the Mondego. It is a former capital of Portugal, and has an ancient university. Still farther inland lies the hill country of Beira, mainly devoted to sheep-rearing.

Of Oporto and the wine-producing region around it, something has been already said. The town is beautifully placed above the rocky gorge of the Douro, but the mouth of the river is partially blocked by a dangerous sand-bar, and the larger boats put in at the artificial harbour of Leixões, at the mouth of the small river Leça, some 5 miles distant.

East and south of Lisbon district is the province of Alemtejo, mainly rolling heath country, rearing sheep, with pigs in the oak woods, and producing cork. Formerly it yielded much grain, but the presence of large estates is unfavourable to intensive cultivation. The centres of the districts from north to south are Portalegre, Evora, and Beja, all small towns, though Evora has interesting relics of the great past of Portugal.

More important is the province of Algarve, the hill belt of which is fringed to the south by an extremely fertile strip of tertiary and alluvial deposits, where the climate is very mild in winter. Both the vegetation and the buildings are 'African' in character, and the name is indeed derived from 'el garb', the old Moorish kingdom of the west, which included Tangier. This is the most Moorish part of Portugal. The hills are mainly pasture land with some chestnut and cork oak woods, but the slopes are planted with olives and vines, and on the coastal strip, in part with the help of irrigation, oranges, almonds, figs, pomegranates, and carobs are grown. Palms and the ubiquitous prickly pear are abundant, increasing the resemblance to

Morocco. On the slopes stand the towns of Silves, the ancient capital, and Loulé (17,000), the largest settlement. Along the shore one little haven follows the other—Lagos, Portimão, Faro, Olhão, Tavira. The inhabitants, Mediterranean fashion, combine fishing, especially for tunny, with intensive garden cultivation. Vila Real de Santo Antonio, close to the frontier, has some importance because of the copper mines of São Domingos a few miles inland. Only the absence of suitable accommodation prevents this favoured coastal strip from becoming a winter tourist resort.

THE NORTH-WESTERN REGION

This is neither a structural nor strictly speaking a natural geographical unit. The inclusion of northern Portugal, north-western Spain, and the northern coastal strip of the latter country in a single region is indeed rather a matter of convenience than of strict logic. A reference to Fig. 68 will recall the highly diverse structural elements included. A line of latitude passing through the small town of Comillas, to the west of Santander, marks approximately the western limit of the secondary rocks of the eastern area. The rocks are mainly cretaceous, but the jurassic beds are particularly important because of the rich iron ores found within them near the port of Bilbao. Another line passing from Lugo on the upper Minho (Miño) to Vivero on the north coast marks similarly, if somewhat less accurately, the region where the complexly-folded rocks of the Hispanid ranges give place to the granites and schists of the core. This seems to afford a basis for a threefold division into the undulating granitic country of Spanish Galicia and northern Portugal; the high region of Asturias (province of Oviedo), with somewhat limited access both to the sea and to the interior; the lower eastern belt.

Such a broad division, however, involves many difficulties. Reference to an atlas map shows that the structural divisions as defined do not correspond in detail either to provincial boundaries or to the old historical divisions. Thus the palaeozoic Cantabrian mountains of Asturias, with their complex trend lines, extend into Santander province, while the latter province, which belongs to Old Castile, contains also a prolongation of the low mesozoic hills of the Basque provinces of Vizcaya and Guipúzcoa. More important perhaps is the fact that this summary account of structure and rock composition is highly generalized and omits much. Thus the old rocks of the Pyrenees are continued into the eastern area and are associated there with a tendency for hill belts to run parallel to the coast, with intervening well-peopled valleys. A good example is the valley in which lies the town of Tolosa, formerly the capital of

Guipúzcoa. Again, an extensive basin of cretaceous rocks occurs in Asturias round Oviedo, introducing an alien note into the landscape of that area. Tertiary basins occur in or on the borders of Galicia, as on the Sil tributary of the Minho in the productive Bierzo basin at Villafranca (in León), and near Monforte farther down the same river. The point is simply that the contrasts between the three areas are not quite so great, their characters not quite so definite, as a generalized statement might suggest. There is, moreover, a certain broad resemblance in the human geography throughout, despite much difference in detail. If Asturias as a whole has few good ports, yet the Oviedo basin has an important outlet at Gijón, and by means of the Nalón valley is connected to the interior. Conversely, despite the lower height of the eastern hill country, the topography is such that railway construction is difficult and costly. This is well exemplified by the routes leading from Bilbao and Santander to the interior. Spanish Galicia, with its wide rias, has some excellent ports, El Ferrol being said to be one of the best natural ports in the world, though again connexion with the interior is difficult, and this although Galicia reaches for the most part but moderate elevations. The result is that through the area generally, while there is quite definitely an ocean outlook, and the harbours are numerous and good, the whole is yet somewhat isolated from the rest of Spain, and tends to lead its own life. This distinctiveness is accentuated by the effect of the climatic conditions. The mild winters, the copious rainfall, the moderate summer temperatures produce a definitely West European note as different from that of Mediterranean Spain as from the arid interior.

The crops are generally similar throughout. Maize, with rye in the higher areas especially of Galicia, is the chief cereal, as compared with the wheat and barley of the plateau, and sweet chestnut is a notable accessory in the less productive parts. Cattle largely replace sheep, and with the absence of the olive butter becomes important, especially in Galicia, where cheese is also made on an extensive scale. Though the vine is grown in places the hardier fruit-trees are most in evidence, and the local production of cider to replace wine is particularly interesting. Curiously enough, however, the mildness of the winters permits citrus fruits to flourish where shelter from wind is obtainable. Thus Santander province has some 2,000 productive orange-trees, though the area is beyond the natural limit of the tree (cf. Fig. 73). Lemons also grow here as well as in Guipúzcoa; both are found in parts of Galicia. As we have seen, the trees include many deciduous types, and pigs are reared in the oak forests. The forests account for a considerable furniture-making industry in the Basque provinces.

It would be unprofitable to attempt to give a detailed account of the topography. The curious swing round of the Hispanid folds has been already emphasized, and the names of the individual ranges are of minor importance. On the north coast, as one would expect from the relief and rainfall, the rivers are numerous but mostly short, though in detail their courses are often complex. Apart from the fact that, particularly in Vizcaya and Guipúzcoa, they run in valleys which allow of considerable density of population, they have little general interest, save where their valleys serve as lines of communication. This is true also of the larger rivers which flow to the west coast, where the Minho and its tributary the Sil are important for both reasons. Thus the most convenient starting-point for a short description of the chief areas seems to be to note the course of the main railways.

The line from Paris to Madrid via Bordeaux and Bayonne reaches Spain at Irún, on the frontier river of the Bidassoa, and continues to San Sebastián (104,000), a fashionable bathing-resort and minor route centre. It is placed on the little river Urumea, and the complex course of the railway reflects the detailed complexity of the relief. Thus the line crosses a low parting from the Urumea valley to that of the Oria, passes Tolosa in the longitudinal valley already mentioned, and crosses another parting to the Urola valley to the west. This finally enables it to ascend (tunnels) to the main crest, crossed at about 600 m., whence a descent is made to Alsasua on an Ebro feeder. Alsasua lies in the Basque province of Alava in a longitudinal valley, traversed by two tributaries of the Ebro flowing in opposing directions, and having Vitoria at its western end. Thus while the Madrid line bends sharply west, there is also an eastward connexion via Pamplona to Saragossa and Barcelona. From Vitoria the Madrid line reaches Miranda de Ebro, whence the Pancorbo pass is crossed to reach Burgos. San Sebastián is also connected directly to Pamplona, and to Bilbao by a devious route. Generally, the routes which converge upon it are far from direct, and the services poor.

Miranda de Ebro is the junction for the direct line to Bilbao (195,000), placed where the Nervión river expands to form the ria of Bilbao. This is somewhat shallow and a dangerous bar made it necessary to use the outport of Portugalete. The bar has been dredged, the ria deepened, and navigation generally improved. Around the town lie the rich deposits of haematite, largely exported to England, etc., though not on the same scale as formerly. The best ores (55 per cent of iron) have been mostly worked out, and it is necessary to treat the poorer ones on the spot with the help of imported coal in order to diminish transport costs. Since coal comes in cheaply as a return cargo on boats taking away ores, a certain development of local industry has taken place. Metal industries, shipbuilding and repairing, the making of chemicals, and jute fabrics may be mentioned, and there is an important local fishing industry. The railway ascends the Nervión valley, and although the actual level of the Gújuli summit tunnel is only 625 metres, the engineering difficulties in the Concha de Orduña at the head of the Nervión are very great, and the course of the line circuitous. The descent to Miranda is rapid. The difficulties of the route, no less than the fact that Miranda itself is remote from the densely-peopled areas of Spain, make clear enough the reason why the rich ores of the Bilbao district have meant so little to the country as a whole, while they have played a not unimportant part in the development of the metal industries of north-western Europe. Spain produces about 3,750,000 tons of iron ore per annum, and of this nearly half comes from the Bilbao field.

West of Bilbao the routes from our region converge on Valladolid (Fig. 83), on the Pisuerga tributary of the Duero, and the exits over the rim of the basin of Old Castile become increasingly difficult. The fairly direct route between Santander and Valladolid accounts for the attachment of the former to Old Castile, of which it serves as the port. León, on the Bernesga, a tributary of the Esla, itself a Duero tributary, is the point of divergence of the lines to Oviedo and the western area, the trunk line taking off from the Santander route at Palencia.

The Palencia-Santander line shows several points of interest. In the first place, the parting between the Pisuerga and the Ebro has to be negotiated, at a height of nearly 1,000 m., in order to reach Reinosa on the Ebro headstream. Curiously enough, however, the parting (height 877 m.) between the Ebro and the Besaya, which enters the sea west of Santander, is almost imperceptible. It is not until the latter stream is fairly reached that the difficulties begin, for it plunges downwards in a steep and narrow gorge, above which the railway has to be carried by the aid of many tunnels and long curves. When it reaches the lower ground the line diverges eastward to end at Santander (102,000), placed near the western entrance of a sheltered bay. The entrance is somewhat shallow, but the bay is commodious and well protected from the strong northerly and north-westerly winds. To the south-west of the town, at Cabargo and Camargo, rich iron ores occur, and there are also lead and zinc ores within the province. Apart for some smelting there is comparatively little industry, and the province is chiefly noted for its farming, including much cattle-rearing. Torrelavega, on the lower Besaya, has an important cattle market. Near at hand are the famous caves of Altamira, with their wonderful prehistoric paintings. Local lines connect Santander on the one hand with Bilbao and on the other with Oviedo. Its suburb of Sardinero is a health resort.

Turning next to Asturias we find that the railway from León has a difficult passage over the lofty Cantabrians. The crossing is made by the Puerto de Pajares, where the road reaches a height of 1,364 m., while the railway penetrates by the La Perucca tunnel 3 km. (or nearly 2 miles) long, and attaining 1,280 m. The pass marks the limit between the dry wheat-lands of Old Castile and green Asturias with its numerous cattle, fields of maize, and apple orchards. The upper part of the railway is electrified, but the power, rather oddly, is derived from the tempestuous streams and not from the local coal-field. The difficult descent is made by a feeder of the Nalón river, a stream which, aided by the presence of the softer secondary rocks, drains with its numerous tributaries a large area, and has given rise to a somewhat complicated relief. The details may be studied in Scheu's paper (cf. p. 309). Here it is sufficient to note that Oviedo (83,000) is not on the Nalón but lies in the most southerly part of a curious longitudinal valley, separated from the Nalón by a low parting, not itself occupied by a single stream, and within easy reach of the sea. The eastern part of the valley is occupied by the Sella river, and is traversed by the railway from Bilbao to Oviedo via Santander. The railway turns inland along the valley at Ribadesella, after having been coastal. This means that there is no direct railway connexion between Santander and Gijón (100,000), despite the fact that such a connexion appears on some atlas maps. Gijón is connected directly to Oviedo and thus forms the terminus of the line from León, though there is also a cross-connexion to the smaller port of Avilés to the west.

South of Oviedo lies the coal-field (Fig. 82). The seams vary in thickness from 0·4 to 2 m. (1⅓ to 6½ ft.), but are very steeply inclined and difficult to work. They are mined in drifts extending upwards from the exposures in the deeply-dissected valleys of the Nalón basin. Mieres, on the main railway, is the most important centre, but the other mining towns are shown on the figure, which indicates also their relation to the Nalón. Coal production is of the order of 4,500,000 metric tons per annum, and the field yields by far the greatest part of the total Spanish production. As Fig. 82 shows, iron ore also occurs locally. Owing to its high silica content, however, it is little used, the better ores of Bilbao being imported for the local iron industry. Among other minerals are zinc ores near Avilés, and quicksilver near Mieres. Local resources of water-power are also considerable.

Gijón stands on a peninsula to the east of its bay, on a somewhat congested site. It is an important port, and a new harbour has been laid out to the west (Puerto del Musel). Like the other towns of the region it has a considerable development of industry. Cider and beer are local products, and Gijón makes the bottles; there is an important fishing industry, and Gijón preserves fish for export, especially to South America; ship-repairing is also carried on. In the area generally there is a considerable iron industry, and railway plant is made. The coal is extensively used on the Spanish railways and competes with Welsh coal at Barcelona (cf. p. 260).

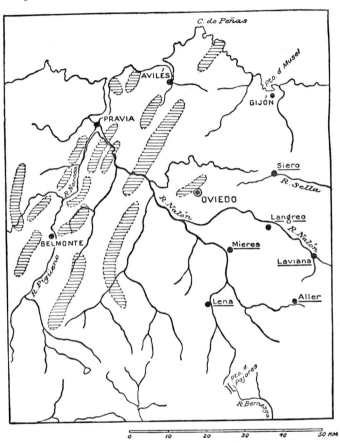

FIG. 82. THE COAL AND IRON FIELDS OF ASTURIAS

The chief coal-mining towns are underlined, the iron deposits are shaded. Railways are omitted, but the Puerto de Pajares and the Bernesga headstreams are shown. (*From Scheu and the 1/500000 map.*)

Galicia is economically less important than Asturias, but shows many points of interest alike as regards physical features and the human geography. From León the railway ascends past Astorga to the Puerta de Manzanal which is lower (about 1,100 m.) than the Pajares pass, and in contrast to the latter is negotiated by help of only a short tunnel. The descent to the Sil valley is, however, difficult, and the complicated relief, combined with the absence of extensive mineral resources, results in Galicia generally, as well as western León, having but an imperfect and devious railway system. Thus the main line only skirts the productive but high-lying Bierzo basin, giving off branches to Villafranca and Villablino. After its difficult descent it clings to the Sil valley till the Monforte basin gives greater freedom. At this town the line forks, the northern branch keeping to the east of the upper Minho until the expansion of the valley, downstream from Lugo (36,000), a market centre, permits it to approach the river. Thereafter it crosses the low water-parting of the Sierra de la Loba, and branches to the ports of El Ferrol (62,000) and Corunna (La Coruña, 104,000). Ferrol is a naval station, the Atlantic counterpart of the Mediterranean base of Cartagena, and derives its chief importance from this fact. Corunna (cf. Portsmouth and Southampton) is the commercial port, its harbour affording shelter on the stormy and dangerous coast between capes Ortegal and Finisterre. Its exports include some iron ore mined near Lugo, and the cattle, etc., of Galicia generally. As at Vigo, there is much fishing, especially of sardines, which are tinned for export.

From Monforte the other branch of the railway follows the Minho, keeping to the north or Spanish bank to Tuy, where the river is bridged and a connexion made through Valença with the Portuguese system. From Tuy the Spanish line runs northward to Santiago de Compostela (50,000) via Vigo (100,000), Pontevedra, and Padrón. Vigo, apart from its sardine fisheries, is a port of call on a sheltered ria, not, however, altogether easy of access (note the Cies Islands, sometimes regarded as the Cassiterides or tin islands, off the mouth of the bay), nor very well equipped. There is direct railway connexion between Santiago and Corunna (opened in 1943), but the very devious route by which the former town must be reached by rail from León should be noted in connexion with what has been said as to Galician railways.

Santiago is one of those pilgrimage centres which always constitute a challenge to the geographer, unable like the devout to assign their origin simply to miracle. According to the story the bishop of Iria Flavia, the Roman name for Padrón, saw in 813 a star above a wood on the present site, which guided him to the bones of St. James (Sant' Iago), which had landed at Padrón in a stone coffin. Hence the supposed derivation of Compostela from *Campus Stellae*. But nearly a hundred years earlier, in 718, the first great check to the Moorish invasion had occurred at Covadonga in Asturias, and St. James was a rallying cry of the Christians in their resistance to the Moors. Santiago is placed on a main road leading from Corunna via Padrón and Pontevedra to Vigo, in a green and not unproductive plain. The Romans at Padrón were almost certainly following in the steps of much earlier pioneers, and traces of both gold and tin exist in this part of Galicia, with some evidences of Bronze Age occupation. If the sanctity of the site of Santiago, especially during the Middle Ages, was associated with St. James, and thus with the successful resistance of the Christians to the Moslems, it is probable that the roots of the sanctity can be traced much farther back, and that the rise of the town had both geographical and historical causes.

As regards the area to the south of the Minho, falling into northern Portugal, we have to note that apart from the gorge section of the river, which forms the actual frontier, there is here a certain change in the topography, despite the southward extension of the granitic rocks. Hills such as the Serra do Gerez appear, with a general north-east to south-west direction, which sink down rapidly coastward, leaving a wider and more continuous coastal plain than in Spanish Galicia. The ria form of the coast-line is also less pronounced, and such ports as do occur, e.g., Viana do Castelo at the mouth of the river Limia, are of minor importance, traffic being concentrated on Oporto. Wine is largely produced from the local vineyards, Viana having been the first town to send port to England. Braga (30,000), an inland town on the slopes of the hill country, is of very ancient origin, now serving as a market centre, with small manufactures of silk and felt hats. It may be added that the genuine port wine grape is said to be limited to an area floored with mica schists which extends along the Douro above Régoa and up the small Corgo tributary. This is the Paiz do Vinho or wine country, and some of the wine is sent down the river in flat-bottomed barges to Oporto. The trade is largely in English hands.

THE PYRENEAN AREA

The whole range of the Pyrenees is described in some detail in Dr. Hilda Ormsby's *France* (pp. 200–28), so that the treatment here need only be summary and restricted to the distinctively Spanish features. In the first place, the chain may conveniently be divided into Western, Central, and Eastern sections, the division lines being taken as the Somport pass (1,640 m.) and the French Col de la Perche (1,577 m.). In the Western Pyrenees the peaks rarely exceed 2,000 m., the Pic d'Anie (2,504 m.) near the eastern extremity being the most notable exception. The passes are of low or moderate height, the most famous being the Puerto de Ibañeta (1,090 m.) better known as the Roncevalles pass, leading from St. Jean Pied de Port in France to Pamplona in Spain. In the central area many peaks rise to heights of over 3,000 m., the passes are all high, non being below 1,800 m. and most ranging from 2,200–2,500 m., so that cross-communication is difficult and intercourse slight. Finally, in the Eastern Pyrenees the peaks only occasionally reach notable heights, as in Puigmal (2,909 m.), and the run of the frontier is such that most of the higher area lies in France.

As a broad generalization it may be said that the Pyrenees consist of a central zone developed on crystallines or palaeozoic sedimentaries, bordered on either side by younger beds. But there is a notable contrast between the two sides, particularly marked in the central area. On the French side the slope is steep and short, the mountains rising wall-like from the lower ground, and the streams having a direct course. On the south side the topography is much more complex. In the first place we have to note that the border towards the Ebro basin is formed not by the high Pyrenees but by the sierras of Aragón, made of intensely-folded triassic and cretaceous rocks, eocene beds being also involved in the folding. Various names are given to parts of the ridge, but the Sierra de Guara between the Gállego and Cinca rivers and the Sierra de Montsech farther east may be noted. Between this sub-Pyrenean belt and the high Pyrenees lies a wide belt of upper and middle eocene beds, consisting of sandstones, clays, and limestones. Partly because of their softer nature, partly, it would seem, on account of recent disturbances, these beds have dissected out into an alternation of longitudinal valleys and ridges. Of the valleys the most striking is that of the upper Aragón, which is bounded to the south by the ridge of the Sierra de la Peña. At the eastern end of the east-to-west valley lies the little town of Jaca, on the Somport route, reached from Canfranc, the station at the Spanish side of the tunnel, by a direct descent of the Aragón valley. Jaca lies in an arid area, showing that curious type of surface dissection noticeable also in places in the tertiary Apennines, to which the American name of 'badland' is often given, because it is so marked a feature of parts of the western U.S.A., as in western Nebraska and Dakota. It is always associated with rocks of slight but varying resistance, the harder rocks sticking up in steep ridges, while the soft clays are washed out into gullies. A dry climate is necessary for its full development, for the presence of the ridges is due to the fact that heavy rains or floods are rare, and while sufficient to wear away the softer clays are unable to effect greatly the other rocks.

Apart from the Aragón the tendency to develop longitudinal valleys is shown on the Arga (note the position of Pamplona), on the Gállego (note the sharp bend on its course), and on the Ara tributary of the Cinca (in the Sobrarbe region). The effects of the presence of the valleys are both varied and interesting. From the human standpoint the area is isolated, for the courses of the streams, which break through the Sierra belt in gorges, make communication with the Ebro basin proper difficult, while to the north lie the high Pyrenees. In consequence, while to the west and the east respectively the Basques and the Catalans are found on both sides of the mountains and of the present political frontier, this central region is the homeland of the individualized and purely Spanish Aragonese. Jaca was taken by the Moors in 716, but was recaptured by the Aragonese, under the leadership of a king of Sobrarbe, in 760, and served as the first headquarters of the Christians in their re-conquest of Aragón. It was also the scene of the first mutterings of the revolutionary storm which was to cost Alfonso XIII his throne in 1931. Insignificant as the town is, therefore, it has played its part in history, and this is true of some of the other settlements in this narrow tertiary belt.

It has to be noted further that to the west of the Aragón river, that is, in the region lying to the south of Pamplona, the folded sierra belt disappears. Here, therefore, the unfolded tertiaries of the Ebro basin extend far to the north, without any intervening barrier ridge. Still farther west, however, folded secondary rocks (triassic and cretaceous) reappear. These form a continuation of the Pyrenean folds, and give rise to east-to-west ranges, such as the Sierra de Aralar and the Sierra de Andia. It is between these that there is developed the longitudinal valley, described on p. 277, in which lie the towns of Vitoria and Alsasua. The result is to make Pamplona an interesting if minor route centre. It is connected by rail with San Sebastián direct, with the San Sebastián-Virotia-Madrid line at Alsasua, and with the Ebro valley line by a route running south. North-eastwards it is connected with France by the road (no railway) over the Roncevalles pass, a route which was of great importance in pre-railway days. Pamplona is the capital of the province of Navarre (Navarra), which though it ranks as one of the Basque provinces has had a very different history from the others. Spanish Navarre is a part of the old kingdom which extended over the Pyrenees into France. For a prolonged period Pamplona was the main entrance-gate into Spain and ranked as one of the strongest fortresses of the country. Its fortifications have now been in part dismantled.

THE BALEARIC ISLES

These are essentially a continuation of the calcareous belt of the Sub-Betic Cordillera of southern Spain. The fact is most apparent in the belt of folded jurassic limestones which rises to a height of 1,445 m. on the north-west coast of Majorca.

The islands (5,014 sq. km.) fall into two groups, the north easterly including Majorca (Mallorca) and Minorca (Menorca), with the smaller islands of Cabrera and Conejera off the south coast of the former, and the south-westerly group formed by Iviza and Formentera, with some small islands and islets. The latter are sometimes called the Pityusae or Pine Islands, because of the abundant woods of Aleppo pine. The islands as a whole are of somewhat varied composition. Formentera is low and built of uplifted marine deposits; Minorca includes a considerable variety of rocks. In Majorca the jurassic folded rocks already mentioned bound a wide belt of unfolded marine miocene beds (limestones, clays, and conglomerates) which are remarkably fertile. This belt has at its north-eastern and south-western ends the two rounded bays of Alcudia and Palma. On the latter is placed the town of Palma (114,000), an important tourist resort, both on account of the mild climate and the beautiful scenery of the island.

As its name indicates Majorca[1] is the largest of the islands (area 3,390 sq. km., or 1,309 sq. miles); it produces the usual Mediterranean crops, such as olives, wine, oranges and lemons, almonds, cereals, and so on. The land is terraced for cultivation, and irrigation is practised. Cabrera or Goat Island is somewhat desolate, being covered with a scanty scrub on which goats feed. Minorca has a good natural port in Mahón, placed on a long inlet to the south-east. The island is famous for its wealth of ancient stone monuments (cf. Sardinia, p. 203), but is less fertile and not so picturesque as Majorca. The stone walls which divide the properties and the windmills are characteristic features. Iviza and Formentera produce cereals and fruit (figs, almonds, apricots, etc.), but are specially noted for their salt-pans, a large amount of salt being produced (about 65,000 tons per annum). Lead is also found in Iviza.

It may be added that the Columbretes are a group of small volcanic islands lying off Castellón.

[1] See E. W. Gilbert: 'The Human Geography of Mallorca', *Scottish Geographical Magazine*, 1934, pp. 129–47.

CHAPTER XIII

THE EBRO BASIN AND THE CASTILIAN TABLELAND

The Ebro Basin—Divisions of the Tableland—The Basin of Old
Castile—The Basin of New Castile—The Mountain Belts and
Intervening Valleys

THE EBRO BASIN

IT has already been made abundantly clear that the Ebro basin
as a structural unit consists of a great triangle, floored by little-
disturbed tertiary beds and surrounded by a rim of older, harder,
intensely-folded rocks. This rim must be surmounted before either
the sea or other parts of the interior can be reached, so that the
whole area has at once a considerable measure of natural isolation,
and is yet traversed by important through routes.

Since both the cold north-west and the warm south-east winds
must rise over mountains before reaching the basin, the latter is
remarkably arid, and largely steppe-like in character, with surface
encrustations of salt. The rains come mostly in spring and autumn
and summer is dry. Though hot on the average, sudden changes of
temperature are liable to occur during that season, associated with
storm rains, which constitute the greater part of the warm season
precipitation. The low average winter temperatures are influenced
by the fact that cold air tends then to stagnate over the valley, giving
spells of specially low temperatures.

Because of the aridity and the generally scanty cover of vegetation
much of the surface within the basin can only be used as winter
pasture for transhumant sheep, which are taken in summer to the
high Pyrenean pastures, or, to a somewhat less notable extent, to
the surface of the tableland, especially the higher areas of the
province of Teruel. But where irrigation water is available cultivation can be carried on very intensively. Vines and olives are the
chief fruit-bearing plants, with almonds, etc., and wine of good
quality is produced, especially in the upper basin near Logroño
Wheat is the chief cereal, with some barley. In the upper basin
especially round Haro, upstream from Logroño, the alluvial fans of
the hill streams are used for cereal cultivation. As one would expect
from the seasonal nature of the rainfall these rivers show great
variation in flow, coming down in flood with a heavy load of debris
during the wet periods, and shrinking to narrow rivulets within
their wide beds in summer. As the flood waters diminish at the end
of the spring rains, grain is sown on the land between the separate

286

rills, which has to be laboriously cleared of large stones, but gives good crops. This is a kind of natural irrigation, for the water-table is close to the surface. Where aridity is more accentuated, as in the more easterly parts of the basin, elaborate irrigation channels become essential. This is especially marked round Lérida, in an area naturally very dry. Here canals are taken off from the Segre, its Noguera Ribagorzana tributary, and from the Cinca. The conditions recall those which we have already noted in the Murcia area or in southern Spain. A similar but somewhat less elaborate canal system exists round Saragossa. On such watered lands, in addition to the crops already mentioned, many kinds of vegetables are grown, as well as sugar-beet, a recent crop now produced to an increasing extent.

Before proceeding to some points of detail it is well to be clear as to the north-west limit of the basin, which is not conterminous with that of the river. We have already learnt that the Ebro rises far to the north-west, in the neighbourhood of Reinosa (p. 278). Its source lies well within the Cantabrians, using the name in the wide sense, to include the hills formed by the secondary rocks of the Basque provinces and eastern Santander. The emergence of the river into the tertiary basin may be said to occur upstream from the little town of Haro, where it breaks through the secondary sierras in a gorge, and emerges into what is called the Rioja Alta, or upper basin. This is floored by miocene rocks, and is bounded to the south by the considerable (2,132 m.) heights of the Sierra de la Demanda. From this upper basin to the vicinity of Mont Sant (p. 256) in the province of Tarragona, extends the tertiary basin, floored by easily eroded sandstones, clays, and marls, with beds of salt and gypsum, and some lignites near the periphery. For the most part the beds lie flat and undisturbed as they were laid down, but there are traces of gentle anticlinal folding.

It is believed that the origin of the basin is to be sought in a great depression which occurred at the end of the eocene period, resulting in the formation of a large inland sea, within which, especially during lower oligocene time, copious sedimentation occurred. The basin was subsequently uplifted, but not, it would appear, in a single but in several successive movements, so that younger tertiary and post-tertiary beds are superimposed on the original oligocene filling The older tertiary surface has been extensively denuded, and is not on the whole a plain but highly diversified. In detail the relief is complex, but the general impression is one of monotony, owing to the constant repetition of the same types of landscape. There is considerable resemblance, though the area concerned is of course much more extensive, to the other tertiary belt near the Pyrenees already described (p. 283). Thus the sandstones tend to form terraces, while the softer clays and marls give rise to 'badland' relief. The rivers, both the main stream and the lateral tributaries, flow for the most part in narrow alluvial valleys, their bordering plains being interrupted by spurs of the more resistant rocks.

Bearing in mind what has been already said as to the climate and the need for irrigation water before any extensive cultivation can be carried on, it becomes easy enough to deduce from the above account what are the most suitable sites for large settlements. The tributaries, especially the powerful ones from the Pyrenees, necessarily bring down much silt, and give rise to alluvial fans, or even, where several converge, to considerable plains, like that round Lérida (cf. Fig. 75, p. 255). Such streams can also supply the water without which the surface is unproductive. Finally, from whatever side of the basin important streams enter they are likely to open up routes both within it and across the bounding rim. Thus we would expect to find towns rising in 'oasis' areas where irrigation is possible, and varying in size according both to the amount of watered land available in the vicinity, and to the extent to which both local and external lines of communication converge upon them. The three chief towns of the basin—Saragossa (Zaragoza, 238,000), Lérida (41,000), Logroño (46,000)—form interesting illustrations, alike as regards their individual sites and their relative sizes.

Logroño is the centre of the Rioja Alta, which gives its name (Rioja) to a wine of some local repute, also exported to England under the name of Spanish burgundy. The special feature of the region is that while the left-bank tributaries are short, those from the Sierra de la Demanda to the south are long and bring much water. The Tirón, which enters at Haro, and the Tregua, joining the Ebro just below Logroño, may be mentioned. The Tirón has itself a long tributary called the Oja, which gives its name to the region. On it stands the small town of Santo Domingo, the centre of that extensive production of cereals whose nature has been already noted. The extensive alluvial fans here are especially due to the fact that the hills of the Sierra de la Demanda were glaciated during the Ice Age. It is interesting to note also that remnants of miocene beds occur high up on their slopes, as well as on the Cantabrian Sierras through which the Ebro breaks in its gorge. That gorge doubtless owes its origin to the fact that the river was at first flowing over the miocene filling of the little basin. The erosion of the tertiaries, to a depth of some 400–500 m., enabled the Ebro to cut its way through the hills.

Logroño is a road centre for the Rioja Alta generally and the neighbouring district, including Pamplona. It has, however, only one broad-gauge railway passing through it, this being the line from Miranda de Ebro to Saragossa. Its relatively small size may thus be associated with the fact that it is only to a minor extent a converging point of routes.

Downstream from Logroño the valley narrows until a considerable change occurs near the small town of Tudela. The tertiary basin is now becoming wider between the bordering hills, while at the same time the parting between the Ebro and other river systems is much more remote. Further, we are reaching the area where the high Pyrenees (p. 284) constitute the source of the left-bank tributaries. Not far upstream from Tudela the Aragón enters after its junction with the Arga. The valley of the Zidaco tributary of the former river allows for the passage of the railway from Pamplona to the Ebro valley line, while at Tudela itself the valley of a small right-bank tributary carries a railway to Tarazona, from which a road (no railway) leads to Soria in the upper Duero valley, that town now being connected to Burgos direct as well as to the Saragossa-Madrid line. Still farther downstream the Jalón enters on the south bank. The importance of this river can scarcely be over-estimated. Its main valley carries the Barcelona-Saragossa line to Madrid, that of its tributary the Jiloca, which joins it at Calatayud, affords a passage to the line from Sagunto and Valencia (p. 261). Again, a little below Saragossa, the Gállego from the Pyrenees joins the Ebro, and down its valley comes the railway from Pau via the Somport tunnel and Jaca. This line has a cross-connexion via Lérida with Barcelona, while the other line from Barcelona comes via Tarragona and Reus, crosses the Ebro at Mora la Nueva, and ascends the right bank, avoiding the major bends of the river, particularly that which occurs at the Segre junction.

Such facts afford a very adequate explanation of the importance of Saragossa, especially when we add that there are in the neighbourhood large tracts of irrigable land. The town is indeed the main point of convergence not only of routes within the basin, but of those which traverse it to reach the two adjacent seas, the interior of the Spanish tableland, and France and thus continental Europe generally. It presents, on the whole, the appearance of a modern town, despite the two cathedrals, the one a former mosque and the other containing the famous shrine of the Virgin of the Pillar, associated with a vision said to have been vouchsafed to St. James (cf. p. 282) while he was preaching in Spain in A.D. 40. The town contains a university, is an important market centre, and carries on minor industries, including the making of machinery. The land in the neighbourhood is intensively cultivated and well watered. Among the canals mention may be made of the Imperial Canal which follows the right bank of the Ebro for a distance of over 100 km. It has some minor importance as a waterway in addition to supplying irrigation water to the undulating land there, for the level alluvial belt is necessarily widest on the north or left bank, owing to the waste brought down by the Pyrenean tributaries.

20

Other smaller canals have been constructed on this bank. Huesca (14,000), connected both with the Jaca and Lérida lines, stands within an area irrigated by the Isuela tributary of the Gállego.

 ⋆Lérida is in Catalonia (cf. Fig. 75, p. 255), not in Aragón, and lies within a wide plain formed by the Segre, with its two great tributaries, the Noguera Pallaresa and the Noguera Ribagorzana, and the Cinca. Apart from the watered area already noted, much of the plain is a dreary steppe. The town is a minor converging-point of routes, being connected to Tarragona as well as to Saragossa and Barcelona.

DIVISIONS OF THE TABLELAND

Separated from the Ebro basin by the broad belt of high land which extends from near Burgos to Sagunto, bounded on its other sides by the peripheral regions already considered, lies the inner tableland. Its centre is Madrid, upon which lines of communication converge from all the marginal areas; but it does not itself form a unit element. In endeavouring to systematize the impressions already gained as to its constituent parts we may note first the Central Sierras (Guadarrama, Gredos, Gata, Estrella) as the most obvious dividing line. This belt forms the southern limit of the basin of Old Castile, crossed by the Duero river, and bounded to the north and west by the curving ranges of Asturias. The heavy precipitation of these mountains enables them to give birth to powerful streams. Thus, as in all similar cases, the master stream of the Duero is not median to the basin, but lies nearer the sierra belt, which, on account of its lower rainfall, feeds rivers with a lesser water content.

The second of the three parallel ranges which cross the west-central part of the peninsula is made up of the Toledo-Guadalupe hills. Since these have but a limited extension to the east they form but a partial interruption of the basin of New Castile. This is separated from its north-western analogue by the Sierra de Guadarrama, which has a south-west to north-east direction, as contrasted with the nearly west-to-east one of the Sierra de Gredos. While the basin of Old Castile, as just indicated, is drained by the converging tributaries of the single river system of the Duero, that of New Castile includes parts of three. Its northern section is traversed by the Tagus headstream, which is joined by a number of tributaries. It may be conveniently called the upper Tagus basin. Farther south is the drier, more definitely steppe-like area of La Mancha, from which comparatively few streams drain towards the upper Guadiana, while the Júcar, after its emergence from the north-eastern hill belt, turns on itself and flows eastwards to the Mediterranean Sea.

If the boundaries of this double basin of New Castile are fairly obvious to north, east, and south (continuation of Sierra Morena), the conditions to the west demand a little consideration. Some distance west of Toledo the Tagus leaves the narrowed western continuation of the tertiary basin in which its upper course is developed, and begins to cut its way across the hard rocks of the meseta (cf. Fig. 68). In a quite analogous fashion the Guadiana, west of Ciudad Real, leaves the tertiary Mancha basin, and saws a course through hard and ancient rocks, making a great northern bend as it does so. Obviously, then, both sections of the basin of New Castile are continued westward in narrowed valley sections between the bounding hills. These valleys, though forming relative lowlands, differ notably from the great tertiary basin in that they are developed, at least largely, on old and hard rocks. Because of their gorge-like character they do not, as one might naturally suppose, form lines of communication. Rather do they act as notable barriers to transverse movement, while not on the whole facilitating movement in the direction of flow. It is indeed impossible to grasp the full significance of the site of Madrid unless one realizes that the middle Tagus, and part at least of the middle Guadiana, are much more definitely barrier belts than are the Central Sierras, especially towards their north-eastern extremity. The point may be brought out by some more detailed consideration of those railway routes whose general trend has been already considered.

The main line from Burgos, after passing Valladolid on the Pisuerga tributary of the Duero, and crossing that river, reaches the junction of Medina del Campo. Here one branch passes Segovia, tunnels through the Sierra de Guadarrama and descends upon Madrid. Another branch passes Ávila, takes advantage of the gap between the Sierra de Guadarrama and the Sierra de Gredos, and reaches the capital after passing Philip II's monastery-palace of the Escorial. We have already seen that the San Sebastián-Burgos-Valladolid line gathers up routes from the whole of northern Spain. From Madrid it is continued nearly due south, past the eastern end of the mountains of Toledo, till it is able to cross the Despeñaperros pass and so reach the Guadalquivir valley. En route it gives off at Alcázar de S. Juan the trunk line which branches to the south-eastern area.

From Medina del Campo a line, roughly parallel to the Central Sierras, but at some distance to the south of the Duero, runs past Salamanca and Ciudad Rodrigo, crosses the frontier, and finally connects with the Portuguese system generally at Coimbra. It gives off two important branches which cross the whole sierra belt, and thus emphasize once again that this is not a very serious barrier. The one takes off from Salamanca, utilizes for part of its journey the valley of the Tormes tributary of the Duero, passes Béjar, finds its way between the Sierra de Gredos and the Sierra de Gata, and so reaches Plasencia on the Madrid-Lisbon line. The other lies within Portugal, takes off from the town of Guarda, finds a winding path between the Sierra de Gata and the Serra da Estrella, passes Castelo Branco and descends to Abrantes on the lower Tagus, where it joins the Madrid-Lisbon line.

Turning next to that line we find that it follows a remarkable course. At first it runs along the southern base of the sierras, and save at the little town of Talavera de la Reina, on the northern bend of the river, nowhere approaches the Tagus till, after a south-westerly approach from Plasencia, it crosses by a great bridge (ruins of a Roman one near by) just to the east of the small town of Garro-villas. Thereafter the line runs southward, sends a branch to Cáceres, avoids completely the gorge section of the Tagus which forms the frontier (cf. p. 246), and does not again approach the river till Abrantes is reached. Upstream the nearest railway bridge is that to the east of Toledo. The distance between this and the bridge at Garrovillas is some 225 km. (140 miles) in a straight line. A line of similar length along the course of the sierras would include three transverse railway routes. The distance between Garrovillas bridge and Abrantes is some 150 km. (93 miles). Further, from Toledo to the Portuguese frontier along the Tagus valley there is no town of any importance save Talavera, which has under 14,000 inhabitants. In particular the absence of a considerable bridge-town at the Roman and modern river crossing is interesting. The significance of such a site is so often emphasized that it is well to be reminded that it is not the crossing in itself but the number of people likely to want to use it which is the important point. The conditions in the valley make clear enough why Madrid and not Toledo was chosen as the capital of a united Spain, the latter being in a pocket off the main routes. They show also what is meant by saying that the middle Tagus valley is a barrier belt, as unfavourable to close settlement as to that easy communication on which density of population depends.

The middle Guadiana valley is analogous in essentials but different in detail. The great northerly bend of the river, much more exten-sive than the corresponding one on the Tagus, is avoided alike by considerable towns and by lines of communication. On a railway map the area is indicated by one of those curious blanks which constitute such a challenge to the geographer. In this particular case the general absence of good roads greatly accentuates the isolation, so that this is once more a barrier belt. With the south-westward swing of the river, however, a change occurs. The stream is now leaving the surface of the meseta and finding its way into the small tertiary basin of Badajoz. With the change in the underlying rocks settlements increase in number and in size, converging railway lines appear, and generally the area attracts rather than repels man. The two notable towns are Mérida and Badajoz. The railway from Ciudad Real, after a devious course across the gentle northern slopes of the Sierra Morena, approaches and then crosses the river east of Mérida, follows its course to Badajoz, beyond which it crosses the frontier into Portugal. Mérida has a cross-connexion with the Madrid-Lisbon line via Cáceres, and there are also routes across the Sierra Morena to Huelva and Seville, the latter line branching via Bélmez (p. 272) to Córdoba. The Sierra Morena is not indeed a very serious barrier, and has mineral wealth enough to justify railway construction. Thus we must regard the middle Guadiana as composed of two sections, an eastern barrier area and the western basin of Badajoz.

We have still to consider the complex upland region which forms the north-eastern boundary of the Old and New Castile basins, separating both from the Ebro basin and the latter also from the Catalonian coastlands. This includes what Staub calls the Hesperian Ranges and some other authors the Iberian Ranges or Iberic Mountains, and constitutes the major water-parting of the peninsula (p. 252).

The ranges fall into two belts, the line of separation, by one of those anomalies in which the peninsula abounds, being far more obvious on a railway map than on one showing relief. It is indeed the justification of the detailed account already given of the structure and distribution of rocks that on the Spanish plateau the actual relief is often more a trap than a guide to the geography. The middle Tagus valley presents on the map the appearance of an attractive intersected by important lines of communication. To solve the lowland between forbidding hills, which is precisely what it is not. The Iberian Ranges seem to be a continuous barrier and are yet antinomy we have to keep in mind the fact that relief is less important than petrology. Both man and his routes tend to avoid the old resistant rocks and cling to the softer deposits. Thus the distribution of tertiary beds is often the key to problems otherwise puzzling.

The more northerly of the two hill belts sinks down to the basin of Old Castile in the vicinity of Burgos. Its main elements are the Sierra de la Demanda, the Sierra Cebollera, Moncayo, followed by the sierras of Virgen, Vicor, Cucalon, and San Just, beyond which the belt bends north-eastwards towards the Catalonian coastal ranges. We may regard the second belt as beginning in the Sierra Ministra, the water-parting between the Jalón tributary of the Ebro (p. 289) and the Henares tributary of the Tagus, which is crossed by the Saragossa-Madrid railway in the vicinity of Medinaceli. The belt is continued in the hills near Molina into the Sierra de Albarracín and the Montes Universales, and reaches the coast to the south of Castellón de la Plana through the sierras of Javalambre and Espadán. The increasing separation between the two belts towards the south-east allows for the development of a mass of intervening high ground, including the Sierra de Gudar, in the province of Teruel.

As regards the rivers we have to note that the Duero rises to the north-west between the two component belts. Ebro tributaries flow to the north-east. Minor streams find their way directly to the Mediterranean Sea on the south-east, but the Guadalaviar and Júcar, the most important of the Mediterranean rivers here, have a southerly or south-westerly course before swinging round eastwards to enter that sea. Finally the Tagus headstream flows north-west before it swings round to flow in a south-western direction. It is during this second part of its course that it receives the ramifying right-bank tributaries which water the northern part of the basin of New Castile, before this is narrowed westwards between the Central Sierras and the mountains of Toledo.

The Duero rises in the Sierra Cebollera, with another headstream from the imposing, often snow-crowned Moncayo range. Its source is thus far to the east, just as conversely that of the Ebro is far to the west. In the case of the Duero the cause is found in an eastern, narrowed prolongation of the tertiary beds underlying the basin of Old Castile, which have enabled the river to cut back easily. The tertiaries are also continued, after an interruption, into the little basin of Calatayud, where the Jiloca joins the Jalón (p. 289). The former river flows along a valley also floored by tertiary rocks which, beyond a low water-parting, is continued into the basin of Teruel, on the upper Guadalaviar. From Calatayud, as we have already seen, a railway passes up the Jiloca valley and over the parting to Teruel, where Sagunto and Valencia are reached by a route which is shorter than that followed by the Guadalaviar river. Calatayud is connected direct to Burgos via Soria, over wild country, and there is also a connexion to Valladolid along the Duero valley, which takes off from the Saragossa line east of Calatayud. The tertiary basin in which it lies thus gives the town an importance as a route centre which is unexpected. The Calatayud-Soria-Burgos-Santander line gives direct connexion to Valencia from the Biscayan coast. Though intended primarily for strategic purposes, the line is of considerable economic importance, especially as forests occur between Soria and Burgos.

It should perhaps be added, lest an erroneous impression is given, that while in western Europe generally the presence of a railway line is proof presumptive that trains run over it with fair frequency, the Spanish railway time-table discourages such a hasty assumption. Further, once off the main thoroughfares, the traveller is apt to find that even the official time-table may give an optimistic view of the services, the printed word having less sanctity than in countries where literacy is virtually universal. Some such caveat is necessary in case the detailed account of the railway system appears to contradict what has been said as to the inadequate communications in Spain.

If we now sum up this account of the elements included in the tableland area, it may be said that the most important are the basins of Old and New Castile. The latter is subdivided into a better-peopled northern section, watered by converging Tagus tributaries, and the drier Mancha region which is crossed by the low parting between the Júcar and the Guadiana. The middle Tagus and part of the middle Guadiana flow through barrier valley sections, but the former has an annex in the little Cáceres basin, and the latter in the much more important Badajoz basin. The three transverse ranges of the west, the Central Sierras, the Toledo-Guadalupe hills, and the Sierra Morena, with the north-eastern bordering ranges, form a final group of elements with at least their elevation as a common characteristic.

THE BASIN OF OLD CASTILE

Within the confines of this region, which are not the same as those of the former kingdom, may be included, in whole or in part, the seven provinces of Burgos, Palencia, León, Valladolid, Zamora, Segovia, and Salamanca, the capitals of which form the chief towns. The main interest of the basin lies in its combination of advantages and drawbacks, and in the effects of these on the human response, alike in the past and in the present. The advantages are obvious enough. Crossed transversely by the Duero, which is fed on both right and left banks by large mountain-born tributaries, the basin is naturally a converging point of routes from the bordering areas, while communication within is easy. Parts of its surface are well adapted for wheat, and since it is also the home of the merino sheep certain basal products are assured. That Castilian is the literary language of Spain as Tuscan is of Italy is itself a proof of a long tradition of culture. On the other hand, an average elevation of some 800 m., combined with the hill border, means a harsh climate, at once dry and suffering from cold winters. The olive is excluded, the vine has but a limited extension, and the range of possible crops is very limited. Generally also the surface is treeless, with great expanses of dry heaths on which the sheep feed. It is thus not unnatural that the population should be scanty, and that although many of the towns contain relics of a great past, yet most are small and only Valladolid exceeds the 100,000 limit.

It has been already emphasized that the surface rocks are tertiaries laid down on a sunken part of the core. They consist of soft clays and marls in addition to limestones and sandstones. The limestone areas are particularly barren and parched, and often form minor uplands called *páramos*, the Torozos hills near Valladolid (Fig. 83) being an example. *Campos* which appears in many place-names is a general term for the higher areas as contrasted with the river-valleys, especially those given over to grain production. The lake of Nava shown on the figure is a shallow fresh-water lagoon, containing water only at certain seasons, but salt pools also occur in places. The tertiary beds are not, however, everywhere exposed at the surface, for the mountain streams bring down a heavy load of debris, deposited in great alluvial fans as they leave the hill country. This is especially true of the northern streams, which have a multitude of parallel tributaries, each running on the surface of its own cone. Thus the tertiary deposits are most obvious in the central area, where the final convergence of the large tributaries takes place, and towards the east.

The first important right-bank tributary of the Duero is the Pisuerga. It rises in the Cantabrians to the east of Reinosa and its headstream is followed by the Santander-Palencia railway. Palencia is placed not on the main stream but on the Carrión above the junction. The Arlanzón tributary, on which stands Burgos, similarly allows for the passage of the San Sebastián-Valladolid railway, by the Pancorbo gap. The road here crosses at a height of 995 m. (3,265 ft.), but the summit level of the railway is a little lower (963 m., or 3,160 ft.).

Valladolid (116,000) stands on the Pisuerga just before its junction with the Duero. Almost opposite the Adaja, draining from the Central Sierras, comes in on the left bank. Ávila is on the upper course of this river, while Segovia is on the upper Eresma, one of its tributaries. Past these towns, as already seen, go the two railways to Madrid. The importance of Valladolid as a nodal point is thus made clear. It is the great grain market, wheat being grown especially round Palencia to the north. The latter town again is connected to León and Astorga by a railway which crosses the rivers of the basin transversely, a proof of the general ease of communication here as contrasted with the need for utilizing valley lines on its borders.

Westwards, the chief Duero tributary is the Esla, which has a course parallel to the Pisuerga, and like it rises in the Cantabrians. León stands on a right-bank tributary which permits of the passage of the railway to Oviedo. Astorga, farther west, is on another tributary followed by the trunk line to Galicia. Zamora is on the Duero itself upstream from the Esla confluence. In the vicinity is the *tierra del vino* or chief vine-producing area of the basin, as distinct from the *tierra del pan* or bread-yielding lands farther north. Salamanca (72,000) lies nearly due south of Zamora on a bend of the Tormes, and at an interesting convergence of routes, though its small size as compared with Valladolid shows that nowadays these are of minor importance. It stands (cf. Fig. 68) where a small bay

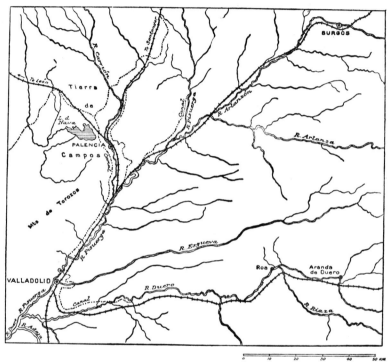

FIG. 83. PART OF THE BASIN OF OLD CASTILE, TO SHOW THE
POSITION OF VALLADOLID

(*From the 1/500000 map.*)

of tertiary rocks extends over the core, and thus commands the easiest route into Portugal. It should be noted that Zamora is on the edge of the core, and beyond the Esla confluence the Duero begins to cut that deep gorge which forms the international frontier. Further, on the other side of the frontier lies the thinly-peopled Tras-os-Montes province of Portugal, cold, remote, treeless, with Bragança as virtually the only town in its eastern section. Salamanca, on the other hand, affords access to the well-peopled part of Portugal. Again its position in the plain gives it easy connexion with Zamora, with Valladolid, with Madrid via Ávila, and the upper Tormes, as we have seen, assists the connexion with Plasencia and the middle Tagus valley. Salamanca is thus the second city of the basin, and its old university speaks to its wide connexions. In size, however, it is little superior to Burgos (60,000), the third city.

It may be added that in the basin generally, in addition to wheat, sheep-rearing, and the limited wine production, such crops as rye, hemp, and flax are grown. There is little systematized irrigation, though flax is sometimes grown on watered lands. The Duero is too liable to sudden floods to be of any importance for navigation, and though canals have been constructed round Palencia and Valladolid they are little used.

The earlier importance of the basin is associated with the routes which converge upon it, and particularly with the fact that Christian resistance to the Moors, initiated in the hill country to the north, found here a basis for a farther advance. The Moors were indeed unlikely to make desperate efforts to hold a region which on account of its cold climate and small range of crops was so ill-adapted to their characteristic culture. Burgos, at the door of the hill country of the north-west, remained the Christian capital till 1087, when, after the capture of Toledo, that town became the base for a further advance. There was great rivalry between the two cities, and after the fall of Granada in 1492, when Toledo was no longer a Christian outpost, Valladolid became the royal residence. It occupied that position till Philip II in 1561 declared Madrid to be the *única corte*, and Old Castile steadily diminished in importance.

THE BASIN OF NEW CASTILE

Very striking are the contrasts between the two sections of this region. The northerly one, which includes the provinces of Madrid and Guadalajara, with parts of Toledo and Cuenca, may be said to recall, with certain differences, the northern part of the Old Castilian basin. Thus the Tagus, despite its oblique direction, has a position comparable to that of the Duero, Madrid shows at least some analogy to Valladolid, Toledo to Zamora. Just as the Duero receives powerful right-bank tributaries from the northern hills, so the eastern portion of the Central Sierras and the Iberic Mountains send much water to the Tagus, and here again considerable alluvial fans are laid down as the streams emerge on the lower ground. Many of the streams here (note the Manzanares, Henares, and Tajuña) are gathered up by the Jarama, which joins the Tagus at the 'oasis' town of Aranjuez, with its beautiful gardens. The rivers generally gain from their mountain sources sufficient force to cut considerable valleys below the general surface, which has an average height of under 700 m. These valley lands are productive, especially since they can be watered without difficulty, and are green with fruit-trees and vegetable crops, while the olive is grown extensively, and the drier intervening uplands are devoted to grain, becoming bare and steppe-like after the corn is cut.

South of the Tagus there is rapid change. The streams have no high catchment basin, and the parting between Tagus feeders and those reaching the Guadiana or Júcar is low, as is that between the two latter. The country becomes drier and more barren, and with

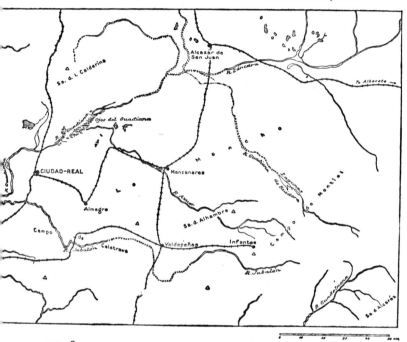

FIG. 84. PART OF THE MANCHA REGION WITH THE GUADIANA
HEADSTREAM
(*From the 1/500000 map.*)

southern Cuenca we definitely enter La Mancha, which includes also Ciudad Real and Albacete. The average elevation is now over 700 m., rising to 800–1,000 m. in the Campo de Montiel in the south. The aridity of the climate is accentuated by the nature of the rocks, which in this southern region are karstic triassic limestones. Thus the Guadiana headstream is a chain of pools (Lagunas de Ruidera), in part only with subterranean connexions, and further downstream the river disappears underground, reappearing later in the Ojos ('eyes') del Guadiana, a series of well-like pools (Fig. 84). The Záncara and Gigüela tributaries have so little fall that they tend to stagnate, and to recall the 'creeks' of the arid parts of Australia.

Everywhere minor streams dry up in summer, and lakes, swamps, and pools occur, often evaporating to form crusts of salt. Under such conditions it is not to be expected that the rivers will have much eroding power, and over large tracts the surface appears almost as flat as a table. Wherever slight swellings occur these are crowned by the famous windmills, for wind is the only motive force available. Conversely the depressions and swampy areas are signalized by their *norias*, or wells, for the water-table is not far below the surface, and even where the surface waters are salty, fresh-water can be obtained below by means of animal power. If the supply is adequate little oases of cultivation may appear, but much of the surface yields only winter pasture for transhumant sheep.

Such conditions prevail especially in the central area; to north and south, as the ground rises, the streams become more permanent and carry more water, surface relief is more marked, and the barren treelessness gives place to greater variety. Thus grain is grown both on the slopes of the Campo de Montiel (Fig. 84) to the south and on those of the Meseta de Ocaña to the north. Near Valdepeñas in the south wine with some local reputation is grown. It is of interest to note that it has a resinous flavour owing to being kept in goatskins impregnated with pitch. As we shall see the Greeks habitually add resin to their wines and assert that this increases their thirst-quenching quality. Esparto grass is produced, as one would expect, on a considerable scale, and other crops include flax, hemp, saffron, etc., with the olive locally and wine more generally.

In the northern area Madrid (1,100,000) and Toledo (26,000) afford an interesting contrast, alike as to size and position. The former is placed on a gently-swelling alluvial fan between the Manzanares—whose scanty content of water has prompted many local jests—and its even more insignificant tributary the Valle de Moro. It stands at a height of about 640 m., or some 2,100 ft., and prides itself on being 'nearer to heaven' than any other capital in Europe. Toledo is not much inferior in height, but in place of lying on a windswept and exposed slope, clings in most picturesque fashion to a rocky hill, encircled on all sides save the north by the Tagus, and rising some 200 m. above its rocky gorge. It was a Roman town; was the chief centre of the Goths; from 715–1085 ranked as the chief Moorish centre, and after its capture by the Christians became for a time the Castilian capital. Such sites indeed make a great appeal to deep-seated—possibly in part pre-human—instincts. But man would never have become fully man if, like the baboons, he had continued to make his home among the rocks. Such rock-sites, unless like Athens, like Edinburgh, like Salzburg and like many another, they have in their neighbourhood level ground over which they can spread, are doomed to fall to the status of museum specimens. The narrow, congested streets, the beautiful buildings and monuments of Toledo, know during the tourist season a brief period of great activity after the arrival of the morning train from Madrid, but soon fall back into somnolence after the flurry of the evening departure is over. That Philip II or his advisers showed more than a touch of genius in choosing as a capital a site which not only gathered up routes from all parts of the peninsula, but left ample space for a steadily increasing development, the story of the city since his time has fully proved. Very interesting also is the site of the great palace, monastery, church, and mausoleum of the Escorial—through which the tourists are again daily shepherded—so full of contrasts with the Moorish palaces of the south, so Castilian in its haughty aloofness from that great modern city which is the capital.

The towns of La Mancha are all small. The significance of Albacete (64,000) as a route centre has already been emphasized. Alcázar de S. Juan is the point of divergence of the railways to the south and the south-east, while Manzanares and Valdepeñas are on the main line to the south, which is necessarily forced to the east to avoid the mountains of Toledo. Something has been already said in regard to Ciudad Real. It will be noted (Fig. 84) that it is not on the Guadiana but some distance to the east; it is the point upon which railways converge.

THE MOUNTAIN BELTS AND INTERVENING VALLEYS

Of the three transverse hill ranges of the meseta the Central Sierras are much the highest. Their height diminishes towards the west, but since the bordering lands are also lower there the Serra da Estrella and connected groups, though not reaching the 2,000 m. contour, still present the appearance of imposing mountains. Within Spain the slope is remarkably steep towards the middle Tagus valley, increasing the isolation of that region, but much gentler towards the basin of Old Castile. North-eastward the high ground is continued into that of the Iberic Mountains, and the Horna tunnel on the Madrid-Saragossa railway passes through the Sierra Ministra at a height of over 1,100 m. The road-passes across the Sierra de Guadarrama, which reaches 2,405 m. in the Pico de Peñalara, are much higher. Thus the direct road from Burgos to Madrid via Aranda de Duero crosses the Puerto de Somosierra at a height of 1,430 m., that from Segovia to Madrid the Puerto de Navacerrada at 1,779 m., the latter being avoided by the railway by means of a westward bend and the tunnel already mentioned. The road-pass is often impassable in winter on account of snow. Segovia can also be reached by road over the Puerto de Guadarrama (1,527 m.), crossed by Napoleon and his army in the winter of 1808.

Pine woods, mingled with deciduous trees such as oaks, syca-mores, birches, etc., occur on the lower slopes of the Sierra de Guadarrama, giving place above to well-watered alpine pastures, utilized in summer by sheep which winter in the basins of Old and New Castile. The animals are now transported by train, thus avoiding the ancient conflict between shepherd and cultivator. These statements apply generally to the whole belt, though the Serra de Estrella is largely deforested.

The Sierra de Gredos reaches a greater height than the Guadar-rrama (Plaza del Almanzor, 2,692 m.), and offers a more serious obstacle to transverse traffic, mainly because the whole belt is much dissected by longitudinal river-valleys, which cut it up into an alter-nation of ridge and vale. Thus the Gredos range proper is separated to the north from a ridge including the Paramera ('moorland') de Ávila by the upper valley of the river Alberche. This river has a remarkable course, turning on itself at a right angle as it leaves the hills, and finally reaching the Tagus upstream from Talavera de la Reina. Its upper valley has the same direction as that of the upper Tormes, which flows westward instead of east, but shows a similar bend where it emerges from the hills; as we have seen, it passes Salamanca on its way to the Duero. A third ridge includes the Sierra de Ávila, separated off by the valley of the upper Adaja. To complete this account of the complex valleys we may note that the Tietar follows the southern base of the main Gredos ridge, and has for a time a course parallel to the Tagus. Its lower valley, before the Tagus confluence, forms the green and productive Vera region with the monastery of Yuste, to which Charles V retired in his last days. Thanks to the shelter of the hills the climate here is remark-ably mild—an 'eternal spring'—and orange-trees appear, accom-panied by palms and agaves.

The absence of easy transverse routes in the Sierra de Gredos is of the less importance since the land-forms between it and the Sierra de Gata facilitate communication there. The Roman road over the Puerto de Baños (980 m.), named from the Baños de Montemayor with its sulphur springs, is now replaced by the Béjar-Plasencia railway. The gap between the two ranges enables the Alagón tributary of the Tagus to push its way far back to the north; Béjar is on one of its feeders.

The next transverse hill belt, that formed by the Toledo-Guadalupe ranges, is much lower than the Central Sierras, few points rising much above 1,400 m., while the road-passes are correspondingly low. But the upper levels are dry and barren and settlements are remarkably few, large tracts being virtually unin-habited. Trujillo and Cáceres are the chief towns on the northern slopes. The latter, it will be recalled, is on the railway from

Salamanca via Béjar and Plasencia to Mérida. It lies in a productive area, yielding corn, fruit, and wine, while the reputation possessed by its hams recalls the fact that Spanish no less than Portuguese Estremadura rears many pigs in its oak forests.

More important is the Sierra Morena, or 'dark' range, which rises little over 1,100 m. To the south its slopes, often clothed with dense evergreen maquis, sink steeply down to the Guadalquivir, and are dissected by its numerous short and rapid tributaries. To the north the mountain appearance is largely lost, the slope being much gentler, especially towards the east, where the Guadiana cuts but a narrow gorge between the Sierra Morena and the Toledo-Guadalupe Mountains. Apart from the abruptness of the drop to lower Andalusia, and the unfruitful nature of the eroded slopes, the contrast between the productivity and the mild climate there and the barren slopes above is too great for any density of settlement to occur on the latter. The slopes and summit level are indeed very scantily peopled save where minerals form a local attraction. Almadén, on the slopes of the Sierra de la Alcudia, is famous for its mercury deposits. About 2,300 workmen are employed and the production is of the order of 1,200 metric tons of metal per annum. But when Italy possessed the Idria mines between 1919 and 1945 its production of mercury in some years surpassed that of Spain, formerly the chief European producer. The lead ores which occur on the slopes above Linares, the coal of Bélmez, the copper of the western area have been already mentioned. Where the slope towards the Guadiana becomes accentuated to the west, conditions improve to some extent, though the hard rocks yield but a poor soil. Local names often indicate areas of somewhat greater productivity and denser settlement. Thus La Serena is an upland area famous for its winter sheep pastures, and also producing wine and water melons. Apart from wide areas of heaths, and the oak forests, which include the cork oak and thus permit both pig-rearing and cork extraction, there is some local production of corn, wine, and olive oil wherever the conditions permit. With the appearance of tertiary beds in the Badajoz-Mérida basin the landscape undergoes a notable change. The splendid Roman bridge at Mérida speaks to its importance as a converging point of routes, and there are many remnants of Roman waterworks, the Guadiana lending itself here to use for irrigation. Orchards, market gardens, olive groves, prickly pears appear and give the area a definitely Mediterranean aspect. Grain is grown extensively. Badajoz (56,000) is chiefly a frontier town.

Of the last hill belt of the tableland, the north-eastern Iberic Mountains, little more need be said. As a whole they have an average height of 1,000–1,500 m., rising in Moncayo to 2,349 m. The slopes are steep towards the Ebro valley but gentler towards the basins of Old and New Castile, and the whole area is thinly peopled and has but little to offer. Deforestation has not been so extensive as in many other parts of Spain and considerable pine forests persist, especially on the triassic sandstones, while the limestone areas may be either thickly clothed with maquis or bare and barren. Central Teruel offers summer pasturage to the sheep which winter in the Ebro basin or in Castile. The scenery is often highly picturesque, especially in the much-denuded limestone hills of the Sierra de Gudar and around Cuenca on the upper Júcar, which acts as an intermediary town between hill country and plain. The significance of the towns of Calatayud and Teruel has already been indicated; all three have populations only of the order of 12,000–15,000.

Note.—The Spanish accents, often omitted in English, have been inserted here on the place-names, since they indicate the exceptions to the otherwise simple rules determining the stress. These rules are that in words ending in a vowel or in the consonants *n* or *s* the stress usually falls on the penultimate syllable, though the termination, *ia*, unless the *i* is accented, is a diphthong (cf. Valencia and Almería); in those ending in a consonant other than *n* or *s* the stress falls on the last syllable, as in Madrid. All names which do not conform to these rules should be accented, e.g. Cádiz, Málaga, Jaén, Júcar. The use of the Spanish forms of the consonants, particularly of the Castilian lisp, in ordinary speech may be regarded as pedantic, so far at least as the better-known places are concerned.

STATISTICAL SUMMARY

The most interesting statistics are those which emphasize the contrasts between the Iberian Peninsula and Italy.

POPULATION

The Iberian Peninsula has a much larger area, a smaller density of population, and the development of large towns is much less marked.

	Area sq. km.	Population in 1940	Density	No. of Towns with over 500,000 Inhabitants
Italy . . .	310,140	*c.* 44,000,000	141	5
Spain[1] . .	496,000	25,563,000	52	2
Portugal[2] .	88,620	7,175,000	81	1

[1] Without Canary Islands.　　　[2] Without oceanic islands.

LAND UTILIZATION

Spain is estimated as having about 12 per cent of the surface unproductive, as compared with about 8 per cent in Italy, but the productive surface is less fully utilized, and the yield, especially of cereals, is lower. This is in part because of the aridity and high mean elevation, and the absence of large, well-watered lowland tracts; but agricultural methods are less advanced.

In Portugal some 25 per cent of the total surface is ranked as unproductive; the yield, especially of cereal crops, is low; agricultural methods are of low standard.

CEREAL CROPS

	Italy (1940)	Spain (1941)	Portugal (1940)
Total area under Cereals (hectares) .	c. 7,400,000	7,220,000	c. 1,380,000
Under Wheat . .	5,085,000	3,821,000	502,000
Yield (quintals per hectare) . .	15	7·5	5
Under Maize . .	1,509,000	429,000	394,000
Yield . . .	17	14	9
Under Barley . .	203,000	1,582,000	61,000
Under Rice . .	161,000	26,000	25,000
Under Rye . .	105,000	602,000	116,000

Spain and Italy have a not dissimilar area under wheat, but the production in Spain (28,000,000 quintals in 1941, as against 76,000,000 in Italy), is much less. The small total area under maize in Spain is due to the fact that the crop is little grown save in the damper north and north-west. The heavier rainfall in Portugal gives maize a proportionately wider distribution there. Barley is a crop particularly well suited to the climate and relief of Spain, and is very largely produced, being used especially as fodder for live stock. The large area under rye (as under oats) is a result of the large extent of cool uplands, that is, of the plateau type of relief. Next to Italy, Spain ranks as the most important rice-producing and rice-exporting country of Europe, but in Spain rice is mainly produced in the area round Valencia. The area sown to rice in 1940 was over double that of 1941, which was a bad year. Spain has a considerable import of maize, especially from the Argentine. Wheat production scarcely covers the demand, despite the relatively small population.

FRUIT TREES

Spain ranks as the leading country in the world for the production of olive oil; the amount produced is about twice as great as in Italy, but the export is about three times as much. The area occupied by olive-trees is about 2,161,000 hectares, Andalusia being the greatest producer, followed by Catalonia. The figure of about 800,000 hectares, already given for

21

Italy, is quite deceptive, for this includes only land wholly devoted to olives, while it is characteristic of Italy as contrasted with Spain that olives are frequently mingled with other crops. In Spain pure plantations are much more frequent. The figures for the production of olives are of the order of 20,000,000 quintals for Italy and 32,000,000 quintals for Spain.

In regard to wine production Spain stands third among the world countries, but normally exports more than Italy. This is both on account of the smaller population and the lower home consumption (estimated as about 73 litres per head per annum in Spain as against 103 in Italy). Italy produces about 40,000,000 hectolitres per annum, as against about 17,000,000 in Spain. The area covered by vineyards in the latter country is about 1,509,000 hectares. In addition to wine Spain exports fresh and dried grapes very largely. Almería is the chief centre for fresh fruit, while Málaga owes to its freedom from late autumn frosts a large production of raisins. The cultivation of the vine in Spain is estimated to give occupation to 3,000,000–4,000,000 persons, while, despite the wealth of minerals, only 210,000 are engaged in mining.

Spain is the second world-producer of oranges after the U.S.A., but the largest exporter, about two-thirds of the total crop being exported. The production as compared with that of Italy in a normal year is in round figures as follows:

	Italy	Spain
Oranges (quintals) . .	2,720,000	14,350,000
Lemons (quintals) . .	4,310,000	550,000

It will be noted that the production of lemons in Spain is insignificant as compared with Italy, while the production of oranges is more than five times as great.

Among other fruit-trees in Spain, figs, almonds, hazel nuts (exported especially from Tarragona), pomegranates, etc., are all important.

INDUSTRIAL CROPS

Spain is the largest world producer of cork, the chief areas of production being Andalusia, especially Cádiz, and Catalonia, especially Gerona. Some 575,000 hectares are devoted to esparto grass, especially in Murcia, Albacete, and Almería. In 1942 the yield was 91,000 metric tons. In addition to being exported, especially to England, for paper-making, esparto grass forms the basis of a number of minor local industries. It is widely used for making the sandals used by the peasants, for matting, bags, etc., for cordage, and so on. Silk production is very small as compared with that of Italy, Spain producing only some 470,000 kilos of cocoons, as against about 30,000,000 in Italy. Both sugar-beet and sugar-cane are grown, the former to an increasing extent, though the production of beet-sugar is much less than in Italy, about 1,450,000 quintals as against 4,150,000 quintals.

LIVE STOCK

	Italy (1939)	Spain (1940)	Portugal (with Islands) (1940)
Horses, Mules, Asses . .	2,019,000	2,582,000	453,000
Cattle	7,879,000	3,014,000	973,000
Pigs	3,303,000	5,613,000	1,253,000
Sheep	9,875,000	24,237,000	3,948,000
Goats	1,867,000	6,249,000	1,244,000

The figures for Italy for horses are based on a return made in 1938. The statistics show how relatively unimportant cattle are in Spain. They occur especially in the cooler, damper north; the general unsuitability of the arid parts of the south is shown by such facts as that in the province of Badajoz they form but 3 per cent of the live stock, and in Guadalajara only 1 per cent. On the other hand, the number of sheep is a direct reflection of climate and relief; goats have not yet been ousted, as is happening increasingly in Italy; the number of pigs in both Spain and Portugal reflects at once the abundance of nut-bearing forest trees and the somewhat primitive type of agriculture. The highest density of pigs is found in the cooler north and north-west, where they are fed on potatoes, sweet chestnuts, and garbage.

MINERAL RESOURCES

Spain is rich in minerals, especially metals, containing both a large variety and a fair wealth of important ores, particularly iron. After the U.S.A. and Peru, it is the greatest world-producer of lead. During the Italian possession of the Idria mercury mines there was great competition between the two countries as to supremacy in the production of mercury. In the table overleaf the figures for Spain refer to 1943 and those for Italy to 1938. The table shows that despite Spain's resources both of coal and iron ore more pig-iron and steel are produced in Italy. It is indeed generally true that smelting industries are but little developed in Spain, most of the ores being exported in the raw or but slightly modified state. Further, the mines themselves are often in foreign (especially English) hands. The export of ores is facilitated by the fact that these occur mainly near the seaboard.

EXTERNAL TRADE

By value, Great Britain normally takes the largest proportion of Spain's exports, followed by France, the U.S.A., Germany, Italy, and Belgium. Minor amounts are taken by the Argentine, Holland, and the Spanish Colonies. The largest export is southern fruits, including especially oranges and grapes (fresh and dried); metals, metal wares, ores, etc., come next, followed by wine. Other important items are olive oil, cork, and cork wares. Wolfram ore ranked very high in 1943. Iberia is the world's chief supplier. In 1943 Portugal produced 5,671 metric tons and Spain

4,038 metric tons. Wolfram was the leading export of Portugal, while in Spain its value exceeded that of all other minerals except coal.

The largest import is food and drink (over 18 per cent), followed by machinery and mechanical apparatus (over 15 per cent), minerals, including coal (12 per cent), followed by chemicals, cotton, and cotton goods and tobacco, the Spanish production of tobacco being relatively small. The United States normally supplies about 17 per cent of the imports and then (pre-war) Germany, followed by Great Britain, France, the Argentine, and the Spanish colonies.

In 1942–3 the exports were valued at 755 million pesetas and the imports at 762 million pesetas.

MINERAL PRODUCTION

	Spain Metric Tons		Italy Metric Tons (1938)
	(1929)	(1943)	
Coal . . .	6,609,000	10,702,000	1,480,000
Iron Ore and Pyrites	6,559,000	2,650,000	1,920,000
Copper Ore[1] . .	4,270,000	366,000	(metal) 1,000
Lead Ore . .	181,000	48,000	67,000
Zinc Ore . .	145,000	72,000	201,000
Sulphur . . .	74,200	42,000	2,364,000
Rock Salt . .	983,000	266,000	614,000
Pig-iron ⎱1942 .	557,000	528,000	865,000
Steel ⎰ .	772,000	638,000	2,323,000
Mercury (1941) .	2,195	2,950	2,315

[1] There has been a great decrease in the output of copper and many other metals in Spain since the Civil War.

REFERENCES

MAPS

About 600 sheets are available of the official 1/50,000 map which has been in course of publication since 1875 (1,078 sheets projected). Just over 40 of the 345 projected sheets of the 1/100,000 map have been published. The most generally useful map is the *Mapa General de España*, 1/500,000, eight sheets (or nine including the Canary Islands), which has the contours somewhat obscured by the brown colouring. There are various road maps, e.g. *Mapa Michelin España*, 1/400,000, in eleven sheets, but this shows no relief. There is a good official map of Portugal on the scale of 1/50,000, in process of revision, and a Staff map on the scale of 1/250,000, in twelve sheets; the latter does not show relief.

The 6 sheets of the 1/1,000,000 map, which cover Iberia, are all published and revised.

BOOKS

General. The fullest description of the peninsula as a whole is that by T. Fischer (op. cit., p. 212), largely utilized by Maull (1929), with more recent material added. The three short articles in Fischer's *Mittelmeerbilder* are also useful. Philippson in Sievers' *Europa* and Hans Praesent in *Seidlitz'sche Geographie* give briefer accounts, with new material, the latter having a useful bibliography and a number of maps and diagrams. Of recent guide-books mention may be made of the two volumes of the *Blue Guides—Northern Spain and the Balearic Isles* (1930) and *Southern Spain and Portugal* (1929), with excellent maps, and the single volume of Cook's *Traveller's Handbook to Spain and Portugal*, new edition, 1930, also with good maps. Classics such as George Borrow's *The Bible in Spain* (1843), Richard Ford's *Gatherings from Spain* (1846), and Théophile Gautier's *Voyage en Espagne* will not be neglected by those who wish to realize the features of the older Spain. Albert Mousset, *L'Espagne dans la Politique Mondiale* (Paris, 1923) gives some indication of pre-revolutionary trends.

R. Staub's important article on structure, 'Gedanken zur Tektonik Spaniens', with its coloured map, is published in *Vierteljahrsschrift d. Naturforschenden Gesell., Zürich*, 71 (1926).

For vegetation see Moritz Willkomm, *Grundzüge d. Pflanzenverbreitung a. d. Iberischen Halbinsel*, in Engler u. Drude, *Die Vegetation der Erde* (Leipzig, 1896), the standard work, with coloured maps; also R. Chodat, *Excursions Botaniques en Espagne et au Portugal* (Geneva, 1909); F. F. Laidler, 'Notes on the Limits of Certain Cultures in Spain' in *Studies in Regional Consciousness and Environment: Essays presented to H. J. Fleure* (London, 1930).

For old and new routes of sheep migration see J. Klein, *The Meseta* (1920), and review article by Robert Aitken in *The Geographical Journal*, CVI, July–August 1945, pp. 59–69.

Statistics are given in *Anuário estadístico de España*, Madrid, yearly since 1914. In *Regioni e Stati d'Europa*, by L. De-Marchi and F. Milone (Padua, 1931), some of the outstanding economic contrasts between Spain and Italy are well brought out.

Regional. M. Sorre, *Les Pyrénées Méditerranéennes: Étude de Géographie Bibliographique* (Paris, 1913); *Les Pyrénées* (Paris, 1922); the former is a larger work, of more limited scope, with coloured map. E. E. Evans, 'The Pyrenees: A Geographical Interpretation of their Role in Human Times', in *Regional Consciousness*, etc., see above. H. Ormsby, *France* (London, 1931), the section on the Pyrenees.

E. Scheu, 'Das Kantabrische Gebirge u. die nord-spanische Riviera', in *Mitteil. d. Gesellschaft f. Erdkunde zu Leipzig* (1925–9). M. Chevalier, *Les Paysages Catalans* (Paris, 1929). P. Vilar, 'La Vie Industrielle dans le Région de Barcelone', in *Annales de Géographie*, XXXVIII (1929).

Interesting regional studies appear from time to time in the *Boletín* de la Real Sociedad Geográfica; cf. Alvaro de las Casas, 'La Provincia de Orense', LXVII (1927); E. Hernández-Pacheco, 'Los Cinco Principales Ríos de España', LXVIII (1928), etc.

Among the wealth of literature published recently on the geography of Iberia are the following:

L. Martin-Echeverría, *Geografía de España* (1928), 3 vols.

E. Hernández-Pacheco, *Sintesis Fisiografica y Geológica de España* (1934).

M. Sorre and J. Sion, *Espagne, Portugal* (1934). Tome VII, Pt. I. of *Géographie Universelle*.

B. H. and F. M. Gescher, *L'Espagne dans le Monde* (1937).

J. Dantín Cereceda, *Ensayo acerca de las regiones naturales de España* (revised 1942).

E. H. de Viller, *Soils of the Lusitano-Iberian Peninsula*, English version by G. W. Robinson (1937).

E. H. G. Dobby, 'Galicia . . .', *Geographical Review* (1936); 'Agrarian Problems in Spain', *Geographical Review* (1936); 'The Ebro Delta', *Geographical Journal* (1936); 'Catalonia . . .', *Geographical Review* (1938).

For Portugal, there is a remarkably complete geographical account by H. Lautensach in *Petermann's Mitteilungen (Ergänzungsband)*, XLVI (1932), No. 213, and L (1937), No. 230.

PART V
GREECE AND ALBANIA

CHAPTER XIV
GENERAL SURVEY OF GREECE

Modern Greece—Stages in Expansion—General Characters of the
Lands—Structure and Relief—Climate

MODERN GREECE

GREECE, like the other Balkan States, has arisen and expanded
with the successive stages in the collapse of the former
Ottoman Empire. Three sets of facts have to be borne in
mind before its development can be understood. In the first place,
it took a century (Protocol of London, 1830, Treaty of Lausanne,
1923) for the national territories to attain their present size, and
prior to 1912 expansion was slow, the European powers at each
stage striving to keep down frontier disturbance to a minimum.
Second, while in Europe as a whole it was the 1914–18 War which
led to notable frontier and other changes, in the case of Greece, as
with the other units of the peninsula, that war appeared but as a
continuation of the Balkan wars of 1912–13, and the country was also
involved in a later conflict with Turkey. Finally, if in eastern
Europe generally the two wars and their sequelae led to considerable
movements of population, Greece was unique in that mass movements occurred which altered completely the ethnical character of
certain territories.

Between 1912 and 1923 the national territories were doubled in
area, from about 25,000 sq. miles to some 50,000 sq. miles. In 1947
the Dodecanese, 1,022 sq. miles and with a population of about
115,000, were added. In the census year 1907 the old territories
included over 2,500,000 people; in the census year 1928 the total
reached 6,250,000. But the increase was not due only to the population of the added lands, for over 1,000,000 people entered as refugees
from areas which remained Turkish. There had also been an
emigration of a much smaller number from the new lands, mainly
to Asia Minor.

That Modern Greece was at first very small and expanded but
slowly, that from 1912 onwards great changes have occurred alike
in area and in population, are facts of great importance. Athens,
with a population to-day approaching 500,000, has been the capital
almost from the beginning; but Salonika, the only other large city,

with nearly 270,000, is in the new territories. But this has not quite
the significance which it might appear to have at first sight. Emphasis
on the recent enlargement of Greece is apt to give a wrong impression of the nature of the change. In the sense of the area in
which Greeks lived, Greek lands have shrunk rather than expanded,
resources have been reduced rather than increased; for from parts
of the shores of the Aegean, the Greek Sea, Greeks have now been
expelled. By so much also has one of the sources of national prosperity diminished, that which depended on the presence in non-
Greek lands of Greeks willing to lavish on the homeland wealth
earned elsewhere. There is indeed a certain analogy—if with well-
marked differences—between the Greeks and the Jews, for the
individuality of the former, in the absence through long centuries
of an independent national territory, was preserved by the bond of
the Greek Orthodox Church. In addition to the cultivators and
fishers of what became the first Greek lands, Greeks innumerable
infiltrated Turkish territory and Turkish social polity, carrying on
the occupations and fulfilling the functions for which the nominal
rulers were unfitted. To these Greeks of the dispersion the first
small Greece became a sacred symbol, a Zion of the hills. An ill-
advised and unsuccessful attempt to extend the national territories
into Asia Minor in the area round and including Smyrna, which
contained many Greeks, led to the existing position of affairs.

STAGES IN EXPANSION

Fig. 85 indicates broadly the successive boundaries of the Greek
State in the period 1830–1923. Growth was not due to the progressive addition of natural units, so that it is not possible to base a
description of the physical aspects of the country on the elements
shown on the map. At the same time some notes on them may
serve both as an introduction to the topography and as an indication
of the problems the country has to face.

The first Greece (1830) consisted mainly of the Peloponnesus or
Morea, now an island because of the Corinth canal, plus a strip lying
to the north of the central depression, the large island of Euboea,
and the smaller islands of the northern Sporades and the Cyclades.
The limits of the northern strip were at first a line from the Aspropotamo river, which enters the Gulf of Missolonghi (Fig. 91), along
the crests of the mountains Oxia and Oeta to the Spercheios river
(Fig. 90), which enters the Gulf of Lamia. Two years later this
section was enlarged by the shifting of the frontier to a line from the
Gulf of Arta along the crest of the Othrys Mountains to the Gulf
of Volos, thus giving better protection to Athens. The Ionian
Islands, from Corfu to Zante, were under British protection, and

were not ceded to Greece till 1863, being finally handed over in 1864.

The essential features of this first Greece were that its peninsular and narrow northern sections included relatively little productive land suitable for cereals; that the currant islands, particularly Zante

FIG. 85. THE GROWTH OF MODERN GREECE

The dates are those at which the different territories were acquired.
S.=Salonika. V.=Volos. Y.=Yannina. A.=Athens. P.=Patras. K.=
Kalamata. The Dodecanese Islands became Greek in 1947.

and Cephalonia, were excluded; that the boundary was drawn through the Aegean in such a fashion as to exclude many of the islands, particularly Crete, the largest. A poverty of cereals, incomplete control of the area producing currants, the commodity of which the Greek lands had a world monopoly, a division of the Aegean islands which handicapped the highly important maritime traffic—these were the outstanding characteristics.

The cession of the Ionian Islands having been already noted, the further points are the gradual spread farther and farther to the north and east, with the resultant acquisition of plains capable of producing cereals, tobacco, and a number of other crops, and the degree to which control of the islands was acquired. Of the plains —the precise equivalent of those fertile, hill-girdled, but generally sea-bordered areas to which the Italians give the name of campagna, or champaign—Thessaly (Fig. 96) was the first to be acquired, and with it a hill belt extending westward to the Gulf of Arta (Fig. 97). The delay was due to the fact that the outer and inner plains of Thessaly, with a climate of continental rather than of typical Mediterranean character, like the similar plains of southern Macedonia and of Thrace, were areas to which on the one hand the Turk clung closely and on the other were not likely to give rise to spontaneous nationalist movements. The explanation is to be sought, not only in the productivity of such plains, but in the fact that the level surface and the general uniformity of the conditions made it both possible and profitable for land-owning Turkish *beys* to exploit the labour of semi-servile cultivators. Ottoman rule pressed less hardly on peasants in areas of definitely Mediterranean climate and relief, where nothing in the way of large-scale production of bread crops was possible. In such areas the nationalist spirit, owing to the looser control, was less effectively crushed, and liberation was more easily attained.

Not till the period of the Balkan wars was a further northward extension possible, and then Greece acquired the Epirus in the west, with southern Macedonia (1913). Final adjustment of the eastern frontier of the new territories was only achieved in 1923 when eastern Thrace was returned to Turkey, the frontier being drawn along the lower Maritsa, leaving the town of Adrianople, with the railway station and surrounding territory on the right bank, to that power. The adjustment was accompanied by agreement for the compulsory exchange of populations, Turkish and Greek, the Greeks of Istanbul being excluded from this agreement. As already indicated, the Greek immigrants far outnumbered the Turkish emigrants.

After the Balkan wars Greece at last secured Crete and the eastern islands. But Italy retained the Dodecanese and Rhodes which only became Greek in 1947.

As against Bulgaria and Yugoslavia the boundary is mainly a mountain-crest one, both these States being shut off from the Aegean shore. In other words, the European shores of the Aegean, as contrasted with the Asiatic one, are, except for a small area in the north-east, controlled by the essentially maritime power of Greece.

GENERAL CHARACTERS OF THE LANDS

As this summary account shows, Greece expanded till it experienced a very definite check in eastern Thrace and on the mainland of Asia Minor, where a land power reacted strongly. From the peninsular nucleus expansion was mainly eastward, across and around the Aegean, that miniature Mediterranean within the greater one. The most serious frontier problems, as in all such Mediterranean States, arose from the difficulty of finding suitable limits towards the mainland interior. Before making any detailed study of the structure and relief of the Greek Lands, it is necessary to look a little more closely at their relations to the surrounding seas and continents.

North of a line marked by the towns of Vlonë, Salonika, and Istanbul, the Balkan peninsula is broad, massive, almost rectangular in shape, and because of the way in which it widens northwards, continental rather than truly peninsular in character. Westward, between Valona and Salonika, it gives rise to a secondary peninsula of very different character. On its western side the coast, though broken by the Gulfs of Arta and Patras, the latter expanding beyond the narrows into the long and wide Gulf of Corinth, is generally fairly uniform. It is fringed by the Ionian Islands, relatively few in number, but beyond them looks out upon an island-free sea. Alike in ancient and in modern times this coast has been relatively unimportant. To-day the sea-routes turn inwards to the Gulf of Patras, and so to the greater gulf beyond and the Corinth canal, or pass southwards to round the Peloponnesus.

Eastwards and southwards there is a great contrast. Here the coast is dissected and island-fringed in a fashion unique in Europe, though the same phenomenon is repeated on the opposite Asiatic shore. Everywhere the sea penetrates far into the land, giving rise to peninsulas of fantastic shape (note particularly that which almost closes the Gulf of Volos), bordered by narrow channels or wide gulfs, sometimes, like that of Aegina, themselves sprinkled with many islands. The large island of Euboea again presents the appearance of a double peninsula, owing to the narrowness of the strait which connects the Euripus and Atalante channels. The dissection of the coast increases from north to south, but it should be noted that the three prongs of the Chalcidice peninsula, on the south coast of the main peninsula, seem to repeat the divergent 'fingers' which spring from the south of the Peloponnesus. East of the Chalcidice peninsula, with its bounding gulfs of Salonika and Orfani, the Balkan peninsula proper displays a mainly uniform coast till a new finger-like process is thrust out in the peninsula of Gallipoli.

A significant point about this remarkable Aegean coast is the relation of the shore features to those of the interior of the lands on the one hand, and to those of the sea on the other. Thus the depressions indicated by the gulfs and channels are continued landwards in plains and basins. As examples note how the Gulf of Salonika is continued into the Salonika Campania; that the Atalante Channel leads to the Gulf of Lamia and so to the plain crossed by the river Spercheios; that similarly the Gulf of Laconia has at its head the lowland watered by the river Eurotas. Conversely, the mountain ridges of the interior can be followed into the peninsulas which bound the depressed areas, as is well seen in the case of the Parnon and Taygetus Mountains of the southern Peloponnesus, which are prolonged into the finger-like peninsulas. Thus, as contrasted with the generally inhospitable Ionian coast, it is characteristic of the other shores that the most productive lands are so placed as to make access to the sea easy. At the same time the generally mountainous interior, together with the varying direction of the ranges, now nearly north-to-south, now west-to-east, accentuates the tendency for traffic to be sea rather than land traffic.

Again, the islands of the Aegean show a certain relation, both in number and arrangement, to the contiguous coasts, and tend to direct coasting traffic along certain well-marked lines. In the north, in harmony with the generally uniform coast, islands are few, only Thasos and Samothrace being of any importance. Where, as in the region of the Gulf of Volos, the coast begins to show the characteristic peninsulas and islands, Aegean islands increase in number, and a series leads from the northern islands of the Sporades through Lemnos and Imbros towards the Gallipoli peninsula. Still farther south, as dissection of the coast increases, the almost circular mass of the Cyclades points the way to Nicaria and Samos and so to the Asiatic coast. Finally, the eastern finger of the southern Peloponnesus points to Crete, itself obviously part of an arc leading once again, by Carpathos and Rhodes, to Asia Minor. In that greater peninsula again there recurs the correspondence between bay and gulf and lowland behind which we noted on the Grecian shore. Beyond the coastal strip, however, in this case lies not a land of great complexity, as in the Greek peninsula, but a much more uniform high plateau.

Further, just as the west coast of Asia Minor is a transition zone, linked on the one hand by its islands and peninsulas, with their intervening channels and gulfs, to the Aegean, but on the other hand bound to the continental part of the Balkan peninsula by that broad isthmus within which the Bosporus makes so insignificant a gap, so also is Crete an area of transition. Its long, northern coast, with the ruins of Cnossus almost centrally placed, is Aegean. But its southern less-indented shore looks out on water barren of islands, upon an 'ocean' rather than upon an island-flecked inner sea. This double character, half-Mediterranean, half-Aegean, goes far to account for the delay in the attachment of Crete to Greece, just as the analogous feature in the Ionian Islands, where Corfu, for example, is at once a Greek island and a stepping-stone to the Adriatic, led to hesitation in admitting that they should be included in Modern Greece.

As contrasted with such marginal islands the Cyclades offer some points of special interest. Syros, nearly in the centre, with the small island of Delos to the east, affords an illustration—of which there are many in the area—of the way in which geographical position, not supported by notable local resources, determined political and economic importance at different periods of history In the Aegean Copper Age (about 3000–2400 B.C.) Syros was the great centre of Aegean trade. In the fifth century B.C. Delos was the centre of the marine confederacy established under the presidency of Athens, and some centuries later became a great trade centre. During the Turkish period both Syros and Delos were notable centres of piracy, piracy always tending to take the place of legitimate trade when there is no strong maritime power able and willing to police the seas. Finally, in the early days of Modern Greece, when Athens, with its port of Piraeus, was as yet unable to form a centre of traffic, it was on Syros that one of the chief ports of the Eastern Mediterranean was established. Such facts make it clear that the Aegean is an area on which traffic routes necessarily converge. Historical 'accidents' determine both the characters of the traffic and its focal point at any particular period, but geographical conditions ensure its persistence throughout the ages.

But if Greece, in any sense of the word, is essentially the mistress of the Aegean routes, the land-ways to and from the continental interiors tend to escape from her control. The Turkish re-advance to the Maritsa line, despite the treaty of Sèvres, was determined by the need of holding that ancient route whose modern significance is indicated by the railway to Istanbul and its Asiatic continuation beyond the Bosporus. The Greek-Yugoslav frontier similarly gave the former power but a fragment of the Salonika-Belgrade route, as also of the transverse route indicated by the ancient Via Egnatia (p. 363).

STRUCTURE AND RELIEF (FIG. 86)

The origin of the features just outlined is to be sought in the same factors as those which have given the Mediterranean Lands in general their characteristics. That is to say, there has been folding of the younger and softer beds while ancient crust-blocks have acted as centres of resistance to the folding process, but have fractured under the pressure, parts of the fractured areas being upthrust as horsts, while others have sunk below sea-level. But the conditions here are peculiarly complex, partly because of the crowding together of the different sets of phenomena within a narrow space, and partly because fracturing with depression of segments has taken place on a very large scale.

Within the Greek Lands proper two crust-blocks can be recognized. A third is represented in western Macedonia, but it lies, at least in great part, across the frontier, and has not been completely investigated. The two named are that whose splintered fragments form the greater part of the Cyclades, and the massif of Thrace. The former, or Cycladean crystalline massif, in addition to the Cyclades, includes also the southern parts of the Attic peninsula and of the islands of Euboea and Skyros. It is thus largely sunk below sea-level, and it is to its collapse that this part of the Aegean owes its origin. The constituent rocks are schists, marble, granite, and gneiss, and the marble, the widely-distributed potter's clay, and the limited mineral deposits, notably the silver of Laurion in the Attic peninsula and the copper of Serifos, were of considerable importance in early days as stimulating Aegean trade. From the shallow shelf on which the Cyclades stand the sea-floor drops abruptly to the deep basin north of Crete, and, as would naturally be expected, the descent is marked by a belt of volcanic islands. Thus in the Gulf of Aegina the islands of Aegina and Poros, with the peninsula of Methana, are of volcanic origin. The chain is continued through Melos, of which only a portion is volcanic, to the partially submerged volcano which forms Santorin and the adjacent islands, and to Nisyros and Kos near the Asiatic coast. Santorin was active in 1866 and the following years, and after sixty years of quiescence recently showed new signs of activity; but vulcanism is much less marked here than in the western basin of the Mediterranean and appears to be dying out.

The northern crust-block, built of similar crystalline rocks, includes western Thrace, southern Macedonia with the Chalcidice peninsula, the islands of Thasos and Samothrace as well as the hill country of eastern Thessaly and the northern part of Euboea. Though far less shattered and fragmentary than the land-mass of whose former existence the Cyclades afford proof, traces of the same processes are discernible in the alternation of mountain or hill country and sediment-filled basins, the latter being often wide and fertile. As contrasted with the area occupied by the Cycladean Massif, which rises to no great heights, the maximum being about 5,000 feet in southern Euboea, the northern crust-block includes in Olympus (2,911 m., or nearly 10,000 ft.) the highest summit of Greece, while Ossa (1,978 m.) and Mt. Athos (2,033 m.) rise well above 6,000 ft.

The Hellenides or Greek fold-mountains are a continuation of the Dinaric folds farther north, and fall into an eastern and western series, trending nearly at right angles to one another. Philippson subdivides the western series, which have a longitudinal or diagonal direction, separating the central chains of the Peloponnesus, which are continued into the Parnon and Taygetus ranges, from the

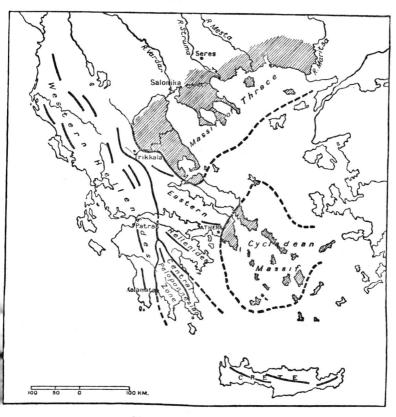

FIG. 86. THE STRUCTURE OF GREECE

For explanation, see text.

western series proper. But though the subdivision is indicated on Fig. 86 for our purpose it may be neglected.

The western mountains have a north-north-west to south-south-east trend, and at the southern end of the Peloponnesus swing round in the great curve indicated by the islands of Crete, Carpathos, and Rhodes to enter Asia Minor. The curve may be associated with the presence of the resistant Cycladean massif to the north. These western fold-mountains display a certain broad simplicity of structure. Their seaward border is composed chiefly of massive limestones and dolomites of triassic age, giving rise to the characteristic scenery of Epirus, Acarnania, western Messenia, and the Ionian Islands. Farther east, and thrust over a band of eocene flysch beds, are the schists, cherts, and limestones which build up the lofty central axis represented by the Pindus range, the Aetolian mountains, and across the gulf by the Olonos group of the Peloponnesus, continued southwards into the mountains of central Arcadia, and so into the divergent ranges of the terminal peninsulas. The rocks were strongly folded in the oligocene period.

The eastern chains are more complicated. They have a general west-to-east trend and include palaeozoic rocks such as schists, greywacké, limestones, and serpentine, in addition to mesozoic beds. Their folding seems to be older than that of the western belt, having apparently begun in eocene times. The area concerned extends from the south of Thessaly to the Gulf of Nauplia, eastward includes the centre of the island of Euboea, while to the west the folds are drawn in towards the longitudinal folds of the Pindus-Olonos series. With this eastern transverse folding some well-marked relief features are associated. In east central Greece three belts of mountain country can be recognized. The most northerly is the Othrys range which, as already seen, formed at one time a Greek frontier, and separates Greece proper from the wide plains of Thessaly. Farther south, beyond the Spercheios lowland, a second belt can be traced from Mt. Oeta (2,115 m., or 7,000 ft.) in an east-south-east direction along the shores of the Atalante Channel. Finally, from Mt. Ghiona (8,240 ft., or 2,512 m.) and Parnassus a third extends through the Helicon, Cithaeron, and Parnes mountains, separating the plains of Attica from those of Boeotia (Fig. 90). It used to be stated that the Othrys folds could be traced through the islands of Skipelos and Lemnos, that is, north of the Cycladean crust-block, to Asia Minor, but according to Maull this is now doubtful.

South of the areas mentioned the eastern folds are represented also in the isthmus which links Attica to the Peloponnesus as well as within the latter. There they may be regarded as indicated by the belt of high ground which, starting from the lofty plateaus of Khelmos and Ziria (2,376 m., or nearly 8,000 ft.) extends into the Argolis peninsula, separating during part of its course the low ground round Corinth from the plain of Argos (Fig. 93).

We have thus made clear the structural basis of the contrast already noted between the relatively uniform Ionian coast and the complexity of the Aegean shores. To the west are the parallel longitudinal folds of the Hellenides, swinging round in the south in the eastward arc; but on the Aegean side the short transverse ridges and the fragments of the faulted and shattered crust-blocks combined with the processes of erosion and deposition to which later earth movements have given rise, result in confused topography. But that confusion, with all that it has meant to man, is a result rather of the later earth movements and their effects, than directly of the contrast between young fold-mountains and ancient crust-blocks. One cannot, that is to say, assume off-hand that the folds necessarily correspond to mountain ridges, the crust-blocks to denuded uplands, for, in the first place, movements of elevation and depression, and in the second the varying action of surface agents upon the different rock-types exposed, have exerted great influence on the existing land-forms.

Two stages can apparently be recognized in these later tertiary movements. During miocene and early pliocene times there was a slow process of elevation, such that denudation more or less kept pace with uplift. Only where the rocks were particularly resistant did plateau-like hill-masses arise. Simultaneously with the slow rise and the active processes of denudation marine sediments were deposited over wide areas, so that, for example, in parts of Thrace the old rocks were completely buried beneath tertiary deposits.

At a later stage elevation was greatly intensified and accompanied by faulting and the sinking of blocks, with the result that the older surface of denudation became transformed into one showing accentuated relief. Thus in the Peloponnesus some of the lower pliocene conglomerates have been elevated some 1,800 m. above sea-level, while at the same time two series of fractures developed, cutting up the land into series of compartments. Some of these rifts have been already noted incidentally, but a more complete survey will bring out their complex interrelations.

The longitudinal or diagonal series is well represented in the south of the Peloponnesus. Note as examples: the Gulf of Messenia, continued into the Messenian lowland; the Gulf of Laconia, continued into the Eurotas trough, which, beyond the high basin of Megalopolis, can be followed into the lowland of Elis along the valley of the Alpheios, a river which has captured streams formerly flowing to the Eurotas (Fig. 92); the Gulf of Nauplia, continued into the lowland of Argos. Farther north the fractures become transverse. The most conspicuous is represented on the west by the Gulfs of Patras and Corinth, separated from the Gulf of Aegina on the east only by the low and narrow isthmus now pierced by the Corinth canal. The phenomenon is repeated farther north, if less markedly. Here the Euripus channel on the east is extended landwards into the lowlands of Boeotia and has a western counterpart in the depression north of the Zygos Mountains in Aetolia (Fig. 91). The

22

Atalante channel—Gulf of Lamia—Spercheios depression has a similar western counterpart in the Gulf of Arta and its bordering lowland. Farther north again the longitudinal trend reappears in the Gulf of Volos and the basins of Thessaly, in the Gulf of Salonika and the Salonika Campania, and in the high basins of Macedonia beyond the Greek frontier, while the transverse is clearly indicated to the east of the town of Salonika (Fig. 98).

The alternation of uplifted and depressed areas has naturally given rise to many peculiarities of the drainage system. Rivers have in some cases been able to maintain their earlier course by cutting through boundary ridges in gorges, in others have been forced to find new outlets, or have had some of their waters captured by neighbouring streams. Many detailed examples will be given later, but even at this stage attention may be directed to the Peneus in Thessaly (Fig. 96), the Vistritsa (Aliakmon) farther north, and the Crna Reka in Yugoslavia just north of the Greek frontier; all have very remarkable courses.

It should be added that, particularly on the eastern and thus drier side of the Greek peninsula, the rivers are of uncertain flow, coming down as torrents after the winter rains, and the melting of the mountain snows, but shrinking or even disappearing during the summer drought. In flood they carry much sediment, and not only are deltaic deposits formed at their mouths but heavy deposition occurs upstream of the gorges so often found on their courses. Thus while small lakes appear numerous and are indeed a natural consequence of the blocking of the antecedent drainage-lines by the earth movements, those shown on the map are but remnants of earlier water-bodies now filled by sediment. Man has often accelerated the process, as in the case of Lake Copais (Fig. 90), in order to increase the cultivable surface.

A final factor in producing the diversity of the Greek landscape is the variety of rocks represented. The massive limestones, weathering to form a thin, poor soil and therefore scantily clothed with vegetation, and often displaying typical karstic phenomena, are an outstanding feature, especially of the higher grounds. With them contrast the flysch beds where the sandstones break down to form fine soil, rivers are more fully developed and the relief is often softened, though on high ground flysch beds may give rise to striking rock scenery. The crystalline rocks are notable as furnishing abundant supplies of water and are often deeply dissected by valleys. The late tertiary (neogene) beds consist of marls and conglomerates, and while the former on slopes sometimes form typical 'badland' terrain with gutter-like hollows and intervening sharp ridges, the latter tend to be dissected by gorges and canyons whose walls sometimes break up into fantastic pinnacles and towers,

affording sites for almost inaccessible monasteries, such as those of
Meteora in north-west Thessaly (Fig. 96).

Generally, indeed, it may be said that Greece is as remarkable
for the variety of its scenery as for its constantly changing land-
forms. The frequent earthquakes (note that of Corinth in 1928)
show that the internal forces to which its peculiar features are due
have not yet ceased to act, while the historic changes, especially in
the form of the coast-lines, show that surface agents have not had
time to smooth out, by erosion and deposition, the irregularities to
which those forces gave rise at the period when they acted most
strongly.

CLIMATE

Though the climate may be described generally as typically
Mediterranean, in detail it displays well-marked minor variations.
The diagrams (Figs. 87, 88, 89), representing as it were cross-
sections of the lands, are intended to bring out the influence of
latitude and longitude on temperature and rainfall conditions.
They are based on the data given by Maull, which differ slightly
from those in Kendrew's *Climates of the Continents.* In studying
the diagrams it is important to bear in mind that the stations are
not strictly comparable as regards height above sea-level. Thus
Yannina has an altitude some 400 m. greater than that of Larissa.
On the usual basis of a decrease of 0·5° C. for every 100 m. of ascent,
the mean January temperature of the former would be higher than
that of the latter, and the mean temperature of the hottest month
(August in the one case and July in the other) would be practically
the same.

With such qualifications the diagrams may be said to show the
following points as regards temperature conditions.

1. Temperature range increases from west to east.
2. The effect of latitude in raising mean monthly temperatures
   is more marked in winter than in summer.
3. It is also more marked in the east than in the west.

1. The easterly increase in temperature range results from the fact
that winter temperatures decrease more rapidly in this direction than
summer temperatures increase, as is shown by the following table.

TABLE VII

Lat.	Western Stations			Eastern Stations		
		January	July		January	July
39½°	Corfu	10·2° C.	25·9° C.	Volos	7·4° C.	26·0° C.
38°	Cephalonia	11·0° C.	26·2° C.	Athens	8·6° C.	27·3° C.

But this relation depends upon a measure of 'continentality', even if the term may at first sight seem hardly applicable to Athens. An

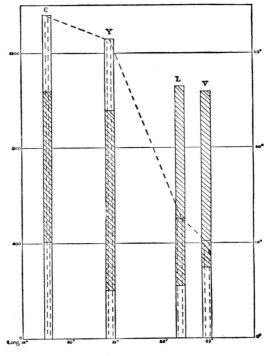

FIG. 87. TEMPERATURE RANGES AND MEAN ANNUAL PRECIPITATION FOR GREEK STATIONS IN LAT. 39½°

The longitude of the station is shown by the horizontal figures, the mean rainfall (in millimetres, figures to left) by the parts of the columns which are shaded vertically, and the temperature range (difference between mean January and mean July figures, in degrees C., to right) by the parts shaded obliquely. The broken line emphasizes the contrast between the heavy rainfall of the western stations and the lighter one of the eastern stations.

C.=Corfu (30 m.). Y.=Yannina (485 m.). L.=Larissa (75 m.). V.=Volos (8 m.). The figures after each name indicate the height of the station above sea-level in metres.

island position modifies the effect, as may be seen by comparing the following stations, noting their situation and the fact that Tripolitsa in Central Arcadia stands at a height of 664 m. above sea-level.

TABLE VIII

Station	January	July
Zante . .	11·5°	26·6°
Tripolitsa . .	4·6°	22·8°
Nauplia . .	10·0°	26·7°
Syros . .	11·7°	26·7°

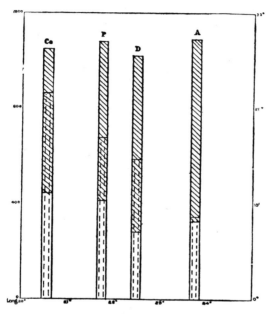

FIG. 88. TEMPERATURE RANGES AND MEAN ANNUAL
PRECIPITATION FOR STATIONS IN LATS. 38°–38½°

Symbols as in Fig. 87.
Ce.=Cephalonia (11 m.). P.=Patras (5 m.).
D.=Delphi (557 m.). A.=Athens (107 m.).

The fact that Zante and Syros have practically identical temperature conditions, despite the 4° of longitude which separate them,
should be noted, and also the relatively 'extreme' conditions at
Tripolitsa, even when its height above sea-level is allowed for.

2. The effect of latitude may be realized by comparing the figures
given for Volos and Nauplia, or, similarly, the two places named in
Table IX.

This means, in effect, that cold winters are confined to the north-
east, the winters warming up rapidly towards the south.

TABLE IX

Lat.	Station	January	July
$39\frac{1}{2}°$	Larissa	$5\cdot5°$	$26\cdot5°$
$37°$	Sparta	$9\cdot4°$	$27\cdot2°$

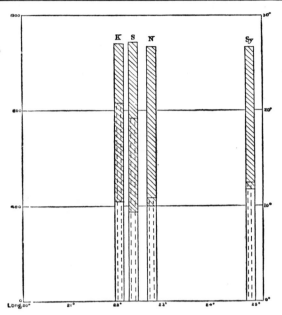

FIG. 89. TEMPERATURE RANGES AND MEAN ANNUAL
PRECIPITATION FOR STATIONS IN LATS. 37°–37$\frac{1}{2}$°

Symbols as in Fig. 87.
K.=Kalamata (32 m.). S.=Sparta (170 m.). N.=
Nauplia (6 m.). S.=Syros (24 m.).

3. The fact that in the west, as a natural consequence of the
warmth of the winters even in northern stations, latitude appears to
have comparatively little effect in increasing mean annual temperatures is well seen by comparing Kalamata, in lat. 37° (January 10·9°,
July 27·1°) with the figures for Corfu given above.

Summing up, it may be said that the essential features as regards
temperature conditions are that the north-west has winters remarkably mild for the latitude, while in the north-east winter temperatures
are low for the latitude. The latter condition, already indicated at
such stations as Volos, is accentuated in Greek Macedonia and
Thrace. Thus Salonika (January 5°, July 26·2°), in a latitude
slightly lower than that of Naples (January 8·2°) has much colder

winters, and night frosts are frequent in January. During the same month Corfu, which lies some three degrees of latitude north of Palermo in Sicily, shows an average temperature quite comparable to that of the latter town.

The figures for precipitation emphasize once again this contrast between north-west and north-east, a contrast becoming more and more marked with the passage from the north-eastern section of the Greek peninsula proper into the Greek Lands lying along the southern shore of the greater peninsula.

The diagrams indicate only the total rainfall at the different stations, and show that this is heaviest in the north-west (Corfu and Yannina) and decreases to the east and south-east. In the case of the Cyclades the insular position does not increase the total much, as may be seen by comparing Syros with Nauplia. The main points as regards distribution throughout the year may be indicated as follows:

TABLE X

Station	Per cent of Total Falling in 3 Summer Months	Per cent of Total Falling in 6 Winter Months
Salonika . .	21·6	52·6
Corfu . .	3·9	78·7
Athens . .	8·3	77·8
Naxos . .	0·8	86·6

This comparison shows that summer drought is well marked at Corfu despite its high total precipitation, and is accentuated at Naxos in the far south. Athens, though both July and August have low mean rainfalls and one or both months may be rainless, lies beyond the limit of the truly rainless summer. The percentage falling during the summer months increases to the north-east, and at Salonika is so high that the station must be regarded as definitely outside the limit of the typically Mediterranean climatic area. June is indeed here a rainy month, while February is nearly as dry as July. Thus the rainfall *régime* approaches the eastern European type.

The highly accentuated summer drought of the Cyclades is due to the prevalence then of the winds called Etesian by the Ancient Greeks (cf. p. 23), which are remarkably constant. Since they blow over but a narrow sea, and since, further, the summer temperatures in the islands are moderate as compared with those prevailing in Asia Minor, they deposit but little moisture. Off the west coast of the Greek peninsula the northerly winds of summer have often a westerly component, and the summer drought, though well marked, is less prolonged and less severe than in the Cyclades.

CHAPTER XV

CENTRAL GREECE, THE PELOPONNESUS, AND THE ISLANDS

Natural Regions—Central Greece: Attica; The Boeotian Plains; the Spercheios Plain and Euboea; the Western Area; the Ionian Islands—The Peloponnesus: General Characters: Town Sites, Communications, and Products—The Aegean Islands: The Cyclades, Crete and the Dodecanese

NATURAL REGIONS; SUB-DIVISIONS

FROM what has been said in regard to the new territories in Macedonia and Thrace, it is clear that in structure, climate, and relations they have an individuality of their own, which is accentuated by the mere fact of their recent acquisition. We must therefore regard them as a distinct unit, continental in character, and contrasted in many ways with the Greek peninsula and the islands. Again, in the northern belt of the peninsula hilly Epirus to the west is equally a recent acquisition, and is in many ways aloof and marginal. It may be grouped with Thessaly to the east, made up of fertile plains and encircling hills, and also very different from the more diversified lands to the south. From them Thessaly is separated by the transverse Othrys range, and they in their turn are naturally divided by the great gulfs, separated only by the narrow Isthmus of Corinth, into Central Greece and the Peloponnesus. The latter, despite the contrasts between its coasts and the hilly interior, must be regarded as forming a single division.

We are thus left with the islands, which are not easy to fit into any simple scheme. It seems best to regard the Cyclades, Crete, and the Greek Asiatic islands as forming a separate region and to discuss the others, including those of the Ionian Sea, with the peninsular areas with which they are contiguous.

This gives us the following five regions: (1) Greek Macedonia and Thrace; (2) Northern Peninsular Greece, including Thessaly and Epirus; (3) Central Greece; (4) the Peloponnesus; (5) Crete, the Cyclades, and the Asiatic islands. The last three constitute Greece proper, the area within which the typically Greek mode of life prevails in which climate, relief, and tradition have combined to imprint so definite a stamp as to make the question of the actual ethnic composition of the present population one of purely academic importance. That Greece, now as always, looks seaward.

Though it is impossible to separate Epirus and Thessaly from each other, they have little in common save the fact that both are somewhat remote from the main centres of Greek life, a remoteness not greatly modified by the fact that through Thessaly there passes the line of rail which connects Athens with the Salonika-Belgrade route. This railway links Athens to 'Europe', which in the cultural sense is regarded in the Balkan peninsula as beginning only to the north of the Danube. As regards Macedonia and Thrace, the essential point is that here Greece comes into contact with Balkan problems, particularly, as already noted, that peculiarly Balkan problem of migration of peoples associated with changing frontiers. Westward lies Albania, almost roadless and still without any con-nexion with the European railway system. It is at once a buffer State and a point of contact with the great power of Italy, which also abuts upon Greece in the Italian Aegean islands. The large island of Corfu, with its heavy rainfall, included here with the Northern Peninsular region, lies close to the Albanian coast and also points the way to the Adriatic Sea.

These brief notes indicate that a discussion of the five sub-divisions recognized in the order in which they have been numbered above, though apparently logical, would give a wrong impression of their relative importance. At the time of the foundation of Modern Greece, Athens was a mere huddle of miserable huts, and the Piraeus as a port had practically ceased to exist. But though for a short period Nauplia served as the capital the transference was soon made to Athens, for above the squalid settlement towered as of old the Acropolis with its crown of splendid, if ruined buildings, half buried in later constructions, and to the politically-minded Greek its symbolic value was obvious. If in point of fact a new Greece had to be constructed from the foundations, in theory the task was the far simpler one of reconstruction. Since within Attica lies, and has lain in the past, the heart of the essential Greece, it is with the surrounding region that a description of the Greek Lands should begin.

CENTRAL GREECE

This broad east-to-west strip includes the three peninsular depart-ments of Attica and Boeotia, Phocis and Phthiotis, Acarnania and Aetolia, with the large island of Euboea to the east and the Ionian Islands of Cephalonia, Levkas (Santa Maura), and Ithaka to the west. For the reasons already elaborated its eastern and western sections, separated by the high ground through which runs the eastern frontier of Acarnania and Aetolia, are sharply contrasted with one another. In the eastern area mountain ridges with a general east-to-west, or north-west to south-east, trend separate three sets of plains and basins from one another, while the articulation of the coast, with its gulfs and channels, makes access to the sea easy. But on the west the trend-lines show a north-to-south direction; the chief lowland is the Aetolian depression (Fig. 91) traversed by the rapid and silt-laden Aspropotamo, and opening to the unsheltered Gulf of Patras; to the north of the lowland forbidding mountains fringe the Ionian shore.

In the east the transverse Othrys range forms an obvious northern boundary (Fig. 90), and its steep southern slopes overlook the

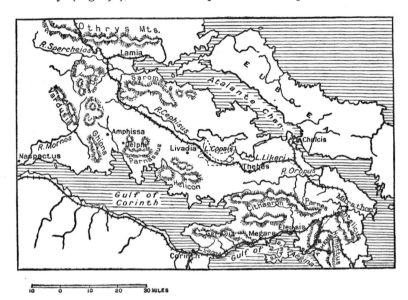

FIG. 90.　EAST CENTRAL GREECE

Spercheios plain. This in its turn is bounded to the south by Mt. Oeta, the hill country being continued, beyond the gap through which the railway passes, by Mt. Saromata and a belt which stands a little back from the shores of the Atalante Channel and dies out where that channel narrows towards Chalcis. South of Mt. Oeta are Mts. Vardusia and Ghiona. In the intervening valley the river Mornos flows first southwards and then south-westwards to the narrows between the gulfs of Patras and Corinth, having the little town of Naupactus or Lepanto to the west of its deltaic mouth. Ghiona is in its turn separated from the great mountain mass of Parnassus by a small stream which passes near the market centre of Amphissa before entering the gulf of the same name. High above a lateral valley, on the slopes of Parnassus, from whose limestones come the waters of the Castalian spring, lies the village of Delphi. Parnassus itself is the end of the hill belt which, continued through

Helicon, Cithaeron, Parnes, and Pentelicus, separates the plains and basins of Boeotia from the smaller and more isolated plains of Attica.

The whole region, from the Othrys to the Gulf of Corinth, from the Atalante Channel to the Gulf of Aegina (Saronic Gulf), has been of inestimable importance in the history of mankind, and the geographical factors may be regarded as twofold. On the one hand, the arrangement of the mountains has exerted, and still exerts, a profound influence on land-routes, forcing traffic into a few limited ways, readily blocked at strategic points. On the other hand, there are limited areas of considerable productiveness, protected on the landward side but open to the sea, within which experiments in the art of living could be practised with a measure of security and yet without harmful isolation, for the sea-roads lay open. The cult of the Corn Mother at Eleusis reminds us of the enormous significance of those fundamental discoveries on which all settled life must depend. But that the Eleusinian Mysteries, however elemental was their starting-point, came to include those concepts which lie at the base of all religions is a proof of the success attained by those first experimenters who in fear and trembling committed the precious seed corn to the stony ground.

1. *Attica.* A description based upon these two elements of protection and the presence of productive lowlands naturally begins with Attica, where protection reaches its maximum. Four mountain walls guard Attica from the north, those ramparts playing in the long history of the Greek Lands a part comparable to that of the narrow seas which separate England from the Continent. In neither case, that is to say, was there an absolute barrier, whether looked at from within or from without, so that isolation was not complete and action and reaction constantly occurred. But in both cases there was that measure of security which permits of the development of a definite unit within, and gives opportunity for the growth of patriotism, and of an inspiring tradition.

The first of the mountain walls is outside the area immediately concerned. Its position is indicated by the way in which the railway is forced to the coast by the flanks of Mt. Olympus, and has then to find a way above the narrow vale of Tempe (Fig. 96), where Ossa blocks the direct route to the south. Then come in order the Othrys range, the Oeta-Saromata range and the belt indicated by the scarped limestone blocks of Ghiona, Parnassus, Helicon, Cithaeron, and Pentelicus. Between Saromata and the Gulf of Lamia, now greatly silted up as compared with its form in classical times, the old route led past Thermopylae—then really a narrow strip between mountain and sea—the hills being crossed farther east or the coast road continued till they ceased to present a serious obstacle. But the railway, as already indicated, takes the pass between Oeta and Saromata, and thus traverses through its whole length the lowland occupied by the Boeotian Cephisus, which is now without outlet to the sea, Lake Copais (now drained), Lake Likeri, and the river Oropus. The southern edge of this lowland is marked by an almost continuous series of battle-grounds, marking the strategic points in the inner-most wall of Attica.

Southwards, Attica faces the Gulf of Aegina, the eastern penin-sula, with the white marble columns of the ruined temple of Poseidon at its extremity at Cape Sunium, at once giving shelter within and marking the transition to the stormier waters without. Of the dangers of those outer waters to early navigators the inscriptions of the temple afford ample evidence.

On the south-eastern side of the peninsula is Laurion, with its silver-lead ores which are smelted on the spot—the only activity of this kind in Greece.

Westwards the mountains of the isthmus made the passage from Attica to the Peloponnesus difficult till the construction of the modern railway and road, for the old path, after leaving Megara, was obliged to skirt the Scironian cliffs, high above the sea and dropping sharply down to it. Until the middle of last century the cliff path, known as the 'Evil Staircase' (*Kake Skala*), was dreaded by travellers both on account of its inherent difficulty and because of the risk of brigands.

Within its mountain girdle Attica includes a series of small plains on all of which the three basal Mediterranean crops, corn, vines, and olives, grow freely. The most fruitful, and that offering the greatest opportunities for irrigation, is that of Eleusis, through which the Cephisus flows. It is, however, somewhat less favourably placed as regards both land- and sea-routes than that of Athens. The Bay of Eleusis is bounded to the east by higher ground, terminating in Mt. Aegalus, which is thrust forward towards the island of Salamis. The Aegalus ridge separates the plain of Eleusis from that of Athens, and the modern road, like the ancient Sacred Way, the line of which it follows, crosses this ridge by a low pass near which is the deserted Byzantine monastery of Daphni, with fine mosaics in its church, placed probably on the site of the sanctuary of Apollo.

The plain of Athens, though larger than that of Eleusis, is some-what more arid. It has, however, two outstanding advantages, its two ports and the isolated hills which rise from the surface, one of which forms the Acropolis. Of the ports Frazer (*Studies in Greek Scenery, Legend, and History*, p. 207) says: 'The fortification of Piraeus and the transference to it of the port of Athens from the open roadstead of Phalerum constituted one of the most momentous steps in the history of Athens.' The Piraeus is now virtually continuous with Athens (combined population in 1940 was over 1,100,000) and receives about two-thirds of the total imports of Greece.

Piraeus is now the chief industrial centre of Greece, with large modern factories concerned with the working up of agricultural produce—including brewing, distilling, sugar refining, and tobacco manufacture; and also chemicals, soap, textiles, and engineering.

The other plains of Attica are the Mesogia, lying to the east of Mt. Hymettus, before the peninsula narrows and becomes hilly, and the small coastal one of Marathon. Though none of the plains can be described as extensive, and the kinds of crops which can be grown are somewhat limited, yet their presence makes Attica a considerable producer of wine and olive oil.

2. *The Boeotian Plains.* To the north and north-west of the Helicon-Cithaeron-Parnes ridge, in Phocis and Boeotia, lies the second series of plains and basins of eastern Central Greece. Originally the whole series seems to have been traversed by a greater Cephisus flowing eastward to the Euripus Channel. But earth movements, combined with the presence of porous limestones which permit of underground drainage, have brought about great changes and broken up this originally continuous hydrographical system. The upper stream flows through a narrow, mountain-bordered valley, and then breaks through a defile to enter a wide plain, once largely occupied by Lake Copais. Lake Copais in its varying forms, historic and prehistoric, is to be regarded as a water-body of typical karstic type, varying in extent both from season to season and from year to year. Since the Cephisus, its affluent, is turbid and silt-laden, the underground channels through which the water escapes are always tending to be blocked up. Further, as is generally the case in karstic lands, they are in any case unable to carry off the waters brought during the winter wet season as rapidly as they accumulate. Apart from human interference, therefore, such areas tend to show wide expanses of water and swamps during the winter and in wet years, the margins drying out to a greater or less extent in summer as the waters sink down into the underlying rocks. The accumulation of alluvium, enriched by humus derived from marsh plants, and the thorough moistening of the soil which results from the winter flooding, makes such areas productive. Here, in addition to autumn-sown cereals, and to a considerable amount of pasturage, such summer crops as cotton, maize, tobacco, and rice can be grown. Obviously the amount of land available for such crops can be increased by drainage and regulation works, and the recent drainage of Lake Copais seems to have been anticipated in pre-Hellenic times. Drainage is a somewhat complicated process, for it must be combined with the possibility of irrigation for the

water-demanding crops mentioned above. The drainage is now gathered in marginal canals, whence it is let through a tunnel to Lake Iliki and thence through another lake and a tunnel to the sea.

The extensive Copaic plain is separated by a broad terrace on which stands the town of Thebes from an easterly basin drained directly by the river Oropus. Now, as in earlier times, the whole area is agriculturally rich, but it is without that easy access to the sea which has always meant so much to Attica. Settlements tend to be small market towns, placed usually on the drier ground at the base of the mountain rim. There is little to correspond with the modern development of industry and commerce which has transformed Athens and affected Eleusis, if to a much smaller degree. Of such settlements Livadia, the ancient Lebadea, is the most important. It lies at the opening of a tributary glen to the south of the upper section of the Copaic plain, while the ruins of ancient Orchomenos, placed on the extremity of a ridge which runs out into the plain, lie to the north. The stream on which Livadia stands is fed by powerful springs, two of which are believed to be the classic waters of Memory and Forgetfulness. In Turkish times, when Athens was insignificant, Livadia was the most important town of east Central Greece and the seat of the governor. It has now about 13,000 inhabitants as compared with the 500,000 of Athens.

From Livadia it is possible to penetrate the western mountain block and reach the fertile valley, famous for its olive groves, in which Amphissa (Salona) lies. This would be more important were it not for the relative difficulty of access, outlets from the Copaic plain and upper Cephisus valley to the west and south-west not being easy. The tourist route to Delphi, high up on its arid mountain shelf above the valley, used to be chiefly from the shores of the Gulf of Amphissa. Here lie the small shipbuilding centre of Galaxidi and the little port of Itea. During the 1914–18 war, however, when the Aegean was infested by submarines, a motor road was built by British troops from the shores of the Gulf of Amphissa across the mountains to Bralo on the Athens-Salonika railway, in order to ensure free communication with Salonika without crossing the Aegean. The road, which passes through Amphissa and has a connexion up the steep hillside to Delphi, affords, in combination with the railway journey to Bralo, an easier connexion with that famous site from Athens than the sea-journey to Itea.

Apart from the valley in which Amphissa lies, and the corresponding one opening into a smaller bay farther east, the mountain block formed by Parnassus, Ghiona, Vardusia, and Oeta is scantily peopled and yields little. There is some wood and sufficient pasture to support stock-keeping, but the Mediterranean climate, and with it the possibility of Mediterranean crops, has only a limited extension except within the two valley areas. It is not without interest to note that in the neighbourhood of Amphissa camels are used as transport animals, a very unusual condition in Greece.

3. *The Spercheios Plain and Euboea.* The third considerable plain area in eastern Central Greece is that traversed by the river Spercheios. This river, like the Aspropotamo (Achelous) of the west, is heavily laden with silt, and the Gulf of Lamia into which it opens has been extensively silted up in historic times, so that more land than formerly is available for crops, which are now of considerable value and variety. Lamia is the chief town and was for long the frontier fortress of Greece, since it commands a pass over the Othrys range.

Euboea, with its three mountain masses to the north, centre, and south, and intervening lower and narrower sections, is fertile and owes to its position a somewhat heavier rainfall and milder winter than Attica. Thus citrus fruits can be grown in its southern section, while they are excluded from most of Attica save for a narrow strip along the shores of the Gulf of Aegina. Chalcis, at the narrowest part of the channel, serves as a link with the mainland, and Kyme, on the eastern shore, with the northern Sporades, particularly the high island of Skyros, on which Rupert Brooke is buried.

The Western Area. Strikingly different from the east, with its natural route-lines along which the fertile basins are strung, is the complex and mountainous western section of Central Greece. To the early Greeks it was at best semi-civilized, and one of the exploits of Hercules has been associated with the vagaries of the powerful and turgid Aspropotamo. In the tale of his cutting off the horn of a savage wild bull it has been suggested that there is an allusion to the work of some early engineer in reconquering lands devastated by floods due to the piercing of a diked bank of the river. It is certain that alike in prehistoric and historic times there have been great changes in the local topography here.

The essential structural features are threefold. West of Mt. Vardusia, and extending southwards to the shores of the great gulf, lies the Aetolian mountain belt, made up of a central limestone area with bordering strips of sandstone. Much farther west the karstic Acarnanian Mountains confront the Ionian Sea, the adjacent Islands representing the higher parts of their submerged seaward edge. Finally, the centre includes a complex depression, as is shown by two series of basins almost at right angles to one another (Fig. 91). The one extends from the south-eastern angle of the Gulf of Arta through two partially silted-up lakes to the lagoon of Missolonghi, while the other is indicated by the lakes of Agrinion (Vrachori) and Zygos, or Anghelokastron, with the intervening swamps and surrounding lowland.

Three powerful streams, with remarkably zigzag courses, traverse the area. The Mornos has been already mentioned (p. 330). The Phidaris rises to the east of Vardusia and appears to be making for Lake Agrinion, but then changes direction and, cutting through the high ground of the Zygos Mountains between that lake and the shore, enters the Gulf of Patras by a more extensive deltaic plain. The Aspropotamo, arising far to the north, and having many large tributaries, is especially interesting in the lower part of its course. As Fig. 91 shows, it avoids what would appear to be the natural route, which would bring it into the Zygos lake, and, skirting the north-western prolongation of the Zygos Mountains, enters the sea by a large delta to the west of the complex lagoon of Missolonghi. But this is not all. The lagoon, which has a very typical sand-spit across its seaward opening—quite comparable to the *lidi* of Venice —narrows landward to a bottle-neck which leads to the inner lagoon or lake of Aetoliko, with the town of that name at the entrance. To the north a very remarkable gap through the Zygos hills leads to the swamps between the lakes of Agrinion and Zygos. This Klissura, or defile (K on map), whose steep walls rise to a height of nearly 1,000 ft., is not now occupied by a through stream, but must have been excavated by a powerful river. The silting-up of the inner and outer lagoons, that is, the pushing out of the land surface seawards, must have been the work of this earlier river, for no important stream now enters the Aetoliko lake.

This description makes clear the fact that Aetolia contains a considerable amount of potentially fertile land, alike around the inner lakes and where alluvial deposits occur on the coast. But the deposits brought down by the three major rivers and the smaller streams do not coalesce to form a continuous coastal plain. Between the fan of the Mornos and the larger one of the Phidaris two masses of limestone, Varassova and Klokova, confront the shore. The former, though the lower, is particularly steep and bare. According to the local legend it represents a block of rock flung by the Titans, in the hope of making a stepping-stone across the narrows, which missed its mark owing to its weight. The immediate point is to emphasize the fact that access to the interior from this southern coast is not easy: neither eastward because of the hills which approach the shore, nor westward because of the lagoon coast. Naupactus is merely a small haven without effective connexion either coastwise or northwards. Because of the difficulty of skirting the mountainous strip of coast to the west, it was not chosen as the starting-point of the short 'north-western' railway. This begins farther east, at the insignificant hamlet of Kryoneri, placed at the western base of Varassova and having steamer connexion with Patras, nearly opposite. From Kryoneri the line runs to Missolonghi ('the middle of the marshes'), which is very difficult of access from the sea, and from there to Aetoliko and Agrinion, with a branch westward from Aetoliko to Katokhi.

One other point should be noted. In the last chapter the contrast

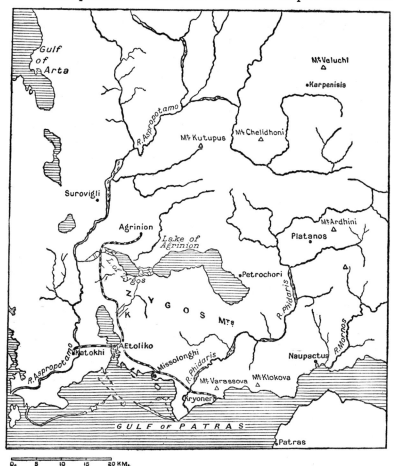

FIG. 91. WEST CENTRAL GREECE, INCLUDING A PART OF ACARNANIA AND
AETOLIA TO SHOW THE SOUTHERN LOWLAND AREA
K. = the Klissura or defile mentioned in the text.

between the longitudinal folding of western Greece and the transverse structure lines of the east was emphasized (Fig. 86), and we have seen that the transverse ridges played an important part in ensuring protection for the plains of Attica. Here the conditions are of course reversed. The mountains of the Pindus range in the large sense extend from the shores of the gulf without obvious break

23

north-westward through Epirus into southern Albania, the physical conditions being broadly similar throughout. It is not only that, on account of the converging river-valleys, there is no obvious line of demarcation between the lowland areas capable of carrying a settled agricultural population and the upland with its mountain folk. We have in addition the fact that the lowlands, with their uncertain and varying drainage, their absence of a natural centre from which the whole could be dominated, their difficult access to the sea, are not easy to organize as against the continuous and extensive mountain hinterland. Within it, both because of the climatic conditions as modified by relief, and the limited amount of productive land, the typical Mediterranean culture cannot establish itself, and the main dependence must necessarily be upon live stock rearing, with but a limited amount of agriculture. Even to-day transhumance exists on a scale which is 'Balkan' rather than Greek, for the summer pastures of the uplands feed great flocks which with their herds must winter on the marshy lowlands round the Missolonghi lagoon. It is obvious therefore that Aetolia was not fitted for the early development of a State of the Mediterranean type.

Even in modern times the geographical conditions have tended to check development. The area was extensively devastated during the war of Greek liberation, and recovery has been slow. Both facts can be readily explained. It was particularly suited for the operations of the Turkish troops, who at one time seemed to have mastered the insurgents, the latter being in any case divided among themselves, as one would expect in such a country. As in Macedonia neglect, with all that it means in flooding, swamp-formation, and malaria, had a cumulative effect which makes reconstruction difficult.

Much progress has, however, been made, and such crops as maize and tobacco are now grown extensively in the lower, damper areas of the south, in addition to vines, both for currants and wine, olives, and fruit-trees which here include, in suitable localities near the coast, citrus fruits in addition to carobs, figs, walnuts, and so on, all grown on the drier slopes. The central mountain belt is well wooded both with broad-leaved and coniferous trees, but, as already stated, is mainly pastoral and in consequence thinly peopled. The Acarnanian Mountains are peculiarly barren and arid, forming a true land of drought (*Xeromeros*), for surface water and soil are alike scanty. Light oak forests occur and animals, including many pigs, are reared; but there is little cultivation.

The Ionian Islands. Conditions are considerably better in the Ionian Islands. Limestones of karstic type are not indeed absent, and are especially notable in Cephalonia, the highest of the islands. But much depression has taken place, as is indicated by the curious shapes both of Cephalonia and Ithaka, and younger beds, including sandstones, marls, and conglomerates, have been laid down in the sunken areas, giving rise to fertile soil, present especially round the bays. Currants, olives, citrus fruits, etc., are grown extensively. In Cephalonia, Mt. Elatos, called Monte Nero by the Italians because of its dark fir woods, reaches a height of over 5,000 ft., but its limestone rocks absorb much of the rainfall, the water, as on the Dalmatian coast, reappearing in springs sometimes below the level of the sea. Near the port of Argostoli occurs the curious phenomenon of two powerful salt-water streams, possibly due to the re-emergence of springs after their waters have mingled with the sea. Argostoli is of considerable importance for local traffic owing to the absence of suitable ports on the mainland.

The island of Levkas is separated from the mainland by a very narrow channel which is, however, not man-made but natural, and a result of the movement of depression which has detached this and the numerous small islands to the south-west from the adjacent Acarnanian coast. In this connexion it is interesting to note that near the mouth of the Aspropotamo a number of low, rocky heights protrude from the fine-grained alluvial deposits of the plain. It is clear that these were once islets which have become attached to the land by the accumulation of fluviatile detritus around them.

THE PELOPONNESUS

General Characters. From the point of view of administration the Peloponnesus is divided into the six departments of Argolis and Corinth, Achaia, Elis, Arcadia, Laconia, Messenia. Structurally, as already indicated, it displays certain general resemblances to Central Greece. Thus the north-east, corresponding roughly to Argolis and Corinth, falls into the Eastern Folded Zone, that is, is comparable to east Central Greece. Similarly the west, that is, Achaia and Elis with a part of Messenia, shows the same north-west to south-east fold-lines as Acarnania and Aetolia. The centre, including Arcadia, Laconia, and eastern Messenia, is, however, more complex. As Fig. 86 shows, it corresponds to Philippson's Central Peloponnesian Zone, and from the point of view of relief is characterized by two diverging belts of high ground, prolonged southwards into the eastern or Parnon, and the central or Mani peninsulas. Both belts originate in the region of Mt. Khelmos. The eastern is the more continuous, and its parts receive various names—Artemisium, Parthenium, and Parnon (Malevo, the highest peak of the last, rising to 1,935 m., or well above 6,000 ft.). Of the western ridge the Taygetus is the most important element. It is higher (Agios Ilias, 2,409 m., or nearly 8,000 ft.), but extensively dissected by river action and thus more broken up.

Still farther west, that is, within the Western Folded Zone, the elevation decreases steadily from north to south (Olonos, 7,000 ft., Lykodhemo in Messenia, 958 m., or over 3,000 ft.), and the high ground is quite definitely cut up into blocks by intervening lowlands, such as that traversed by the lower course of the Alpheios and that behind Kyparissia (Kokla gap, Fig. 92). Further, the north-western

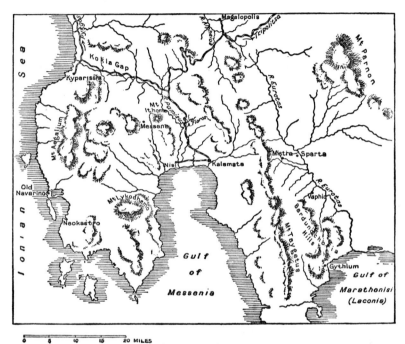

FIG. 92. PART OF MESSENIA AND LACONIA

part of Elis is lowland, corresponding closely in general character to the 'new land' of the opposite or Aetolian shore; for it has been made in the same fashion by the rivers coming down from the mountainous interior.

Farther east the coastal plain becomes narrow, the mountains approaching the shores of the gulf. It is, however, wide enough to support a number of towns, including Patras, and to permit of the construction of a continuous road and railway. But access to the interior is not easy till the wider plain round Corinth is reached. Even here the mountain mass of Kyllene (Ziria) sends eastward a lower prolongation which, if it does not block the passage, at least makes it necessary to cross a pass before the plain of Argos (Fig. 93) can be reached. A spur forms the fortress-crowned Acrocorinth, the guardian of the pass alike in classical and medieval times. The ridge may be compared to the Cithaeron-Parnes ridge, for it functions as a northern protecting wall to the Argos plain as the former does to the plains of Attica. Apart from the plain of Argos most of Argolis is a dry, karstic upland; but the bordering islands and the secondary peninsulas include fertile tracts.

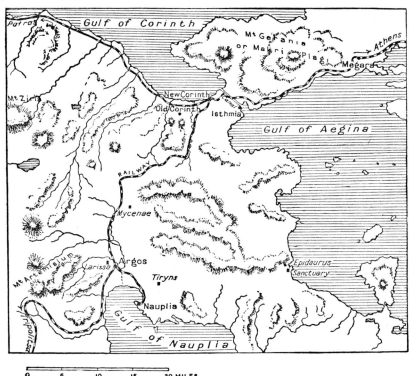

FIG. 93. CORINTH AND ARGOLIS

Just as the plain of Argos lies at the head of the gulf of Nauplia, so the two southern gulfs are backed by similar plains, bordered by the ridges already described. The eastern plain, that of Laconia, is drained by the Eurotas (Fig. 92), which breaks through an upland in mid-course, so that the inner plain of Sparta is separated by a defile from the swampy coastal plain, once the home of the despised and enslaved helots. The Eurotas is of no great size, for it has been decapitated by the large Alpheios river which, fed by the heavier rainfall of the west, has been able to cut back far into the hilly interior of Arcadia. The Pamisus, the corresponding river of the Messenian plain to the west, is similarly small, but in its lower course is swollen by the water received from the powerful springs called Agios Floros, which water the 'blessed land' of the ancient Greeks. In consequence the Pamisus is 'navigable'—if in a very limited sense—for a few miles from its mouth, near which stands the little port of Nisi (Messini).

In Arcadia drainage conditions are somewhat complex. As already indicated the Alpheios, which has a number of large tributaries, including the Ladon, has succeeded in carrying off most of the water of the west-central area. To the north, especially in the Ladon basin, the country is highly mountainous. Farther south the headstreams of the main river traverse the high (425 m.) but fertile basin of Megalopolis; though from the standpoint of human geography this has always tended to be attached either to the Laconian or the Messenian lowland (note the existing railway connexion). The reason is not far to seek. Because of the way in which the Alpheios, on its journey to the west, cuts through the mountains in narrow gorges and with constant changes of direction, its valley is of no use as line of communication. On the other hand, Megalopolis can be reached with relatively little difficulty from either of the southern lowlands.

No river comparable to the Alpheios finds its way eastward through the Parnon ridge to the Gulf of Nauplia. East-central Arcadia indeed forms a basin of interior drainage, so far at least as surface water is concerned (Fig. 94). Apart from the two points already noted, the greater height of the eastern ridge and the lower rainfall, a third factor plays its part in causing this state of affairs. In the west the penetration of the Alpheios has been assisted by the variety of rocks represented; but here they are predominantly karstic limestones, riddled with swallow-holes, or *katavothras* as the Greeks call them. The water lost in this way tends to reappear in *kephalaria* or springs, on the eastern flank of the Parnon ridge, that is on the shore of the Gulf of Nauplia. Such springs sometimes give rise to short streams, or gush out near or even below sea-level. The Lernaean marsh, near the south-eastern edge of the plain of Argos, is fed by such springs rising quite near the shore.

As in other areas of similar character (cf. Boeotia, p. 333) this part of Arcadia is characterized by a series of basins, moistened or even flooded by the winter rains but drying out more or less completely in summer. The largest and most southerly is that of Tripolitsa (Tripolis), with the considerable (about 15,500 inhabitants) town of that name on its western border and Tegea in its swampy centre (Fig. 94). It is separated by a slight constriction from the basin of Mantinea to the north and stands at a height of about 600 m. The central and flatter parts of the basin produce corn and maize, while the margins bear vineyards and fruit-trees of the Central European rather than the Mediterranean type, for the olive, which is present in the lower basin of Megalopolis, does not thrive at this elevation. The basin is a valley water-parting, for some water seems to soak through to the Alpheios system, though most travels eastward by subterranean channels to the Gulf of Nauplia.

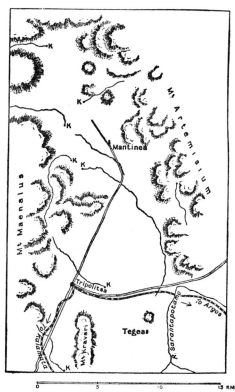

FIG. 94. THE BASIN OF MANTINEA

K.=the Katavothras or swallow-holes into which the streams disappear. The River Saranta-potamo disappears into such a swallow-hole to the east of the map.

Of the other basins the most interesting are the two northern ones of Symphalus (height 700 m.) and Pheneus, both containing lakes. The Pheneus lake has shown great variations in size in historical times, for its katavothras are always tending to become choked. When this occurs the lake increases in size and floods the areas which at other times are available for cultivation.

Town-sites. This brief description indicates the main physical features of the Peloponnesus. The historical changes which have occurred in the position of the centres of gravity within it are peculiarly interesting. They illustrate both the persistent effects of the relief and the varying values of particular sites as external conditions change, while the prolonged period of time throughout which observation is possible is an additional element of interest. A few examples may be given to illustrate the nature of the changes.

Just as in Central Greece, the chief classical and pre-classical sites lay to the east and south-east, that is facing the Aegean, which was crossed by the main traffic routes of the early civilized world. The west, particularly the north-west, despite its better rainfall and its considerable amount of potentially productive land, was unimportant in early days, except where Olympia, on the lower course of the Alpheios, owed to its distance from the main centres the possibility of becoming a friendly meeting-place for rival and often warring groups. Otherwise the swampy coast of Elis, the absence of harbours, the remoteness from traffic-routes, played precisely the same part as in Aetolia.

Of the eastern areas the plain of Argos shares some at least of the advantages of Attica, though it is more arid, and the spring-fed streams of its western border have no great value for irrigation. Here occur three important sites of the Mycenaean period—Argos, Mycenae, Tiryns (Fig. 93). Argos, now a considerable market town and railway junction (12,000 inhabitants), lies on the western margin of the plain at the foot of a spur of the Artemisium range, with the citadel peak of Larissa nearly a thousand feet above. Ruined Mycenae, with its impressive beehive tombs and the famous Lion Gate, stands at the north-eastern border of the plain, on a rocky spur between two deep ravines. The ruins of the citadel of Tiryns occupy a low, rocky hill rising from the surface of the plain itself, and believed to represent a former island, the head of the Gulf of Nauplia having been extensively silted up. Nauplia, now only a small port and town, is the outlet of the plain, which is productive. The whole area appears at first sight to be well protected from the north (p. 341); but this position did not avail to protect the Mycenaean culture against the Dorian invasion. Although long afterwards the Venetians made Nauplia one of their trading-centres, and still later it became the first capital of Modern Greece, the plain has never recaptured its pristine importance. But neither the plain itself nor any site on or near it possesses the same combination of advantages as Attica and Athens. Among other points the way in which the Argolis peninsula turns its back on the important Gulf of Aegina should be noted.

The inner basin of the Eurotas valley in Laconia has had a similar long and fluctuating history, but to an even greater extent has failed to attract population in the present period. It is exceedingly fertile and the streams from the Taygetus give much water. Thus vegetation is luxuriant, and to the typical Mediterranean crops are added citrus fruits, though the oranges are said to be inferior to those of Messenia. But the productive area is of limited extent; communications are difficult landwards, this being at once an advantage in early days as giving protection and a disadvantage in a unified Greece; finally, the existence of the Bardunochoria ridge and the swampy, deltaic coast make access to the sea difficult. No port can be established near the mouth of the river, and Gythium or Marathonisi, the ancient Kranae, lies to the west where the coast becomes rocky. Like modern Sparta, re-established on the old site about a hundred years ago, it is a small town (about 9,500 inhabitants), though somewhat larger than the former.

The ancient sites are of extraordinary interest, not only because of their antiquities but on account of the evidence they afford of a secular ebb and flow of population, accompanied by comparatively small shifts in the position of the centre. Thus Vaphio (Pharis) was an important Mycenaean centre on the right bank of the Eurotas, a short distance downstream from Sparta. Ancient Sparta lay on a small plain, also on the right bank, but where the stream makes a bend and thus gives some protection. 'About an hour's ride to the west', on a rocky spur of Taygetus, stands the fortress of Mistra, with the almost deserted town on the slopes below. The fortress was built in the thirteenth century by William de Villehardouin, and thus carries the story down to the days of the Franks and Byzantines. Everywhere, that is to say, there are signs of the alternation of splendour and decay. The green garden surrounded by barren mountains has always been a prize to be fought for, but contains within it the seeds of its own decay—its successive conquerors have never been able to remain long in their limited and isolated Eden.

The interest of the story is increased by the fact that modern Messenia has, as it were, avenged itself on Sparta for the ancient conquest. If Sparta is to-day an insignificant township, aloof from main traffic lines, Kalamata, with some 33,000 inhabitants, is the second city of the Peloponnesus, is connected with the main railway system of Greece and thus of Europe, and has been converted into a considerable port.

At first sight the topography of the Pamisus basin seems broadly similar to the Eurotas one. There is a corresponding division into an inner and outer plain, separated here by the calcareous mass of Ithome; Messene, though its site is different, being the analogue of Sparta. Kalamata, again, though it lies to the east of the river mouth, instead of to the west as does Gythium, is the analogue of that port, Nisi being unimportant. Further, the Messenian lowland enjoys a somewhat better climate than the Laconian one, and its vegetation is even more luxuriant. Two sets of facts, however, make clear the reason why on the one hand Messenia neither showed the precocious development of Laconia, nor was able later to maintain itself against the latter, while on the other it has now completely outclassed it. The one is the easier exit landwards, alike to the north-west and the north-east (note the railway connexions), and the other the nature of the sea outlook. Laconia looks towards Crete and so to the Aegean world; Messenia is on the margin of a sea which was once empty, but is now a great highway.

One other point is of some interest. Gythium does not face the Aegean Sea directly, any more than Kalamata faces the Ionian. But on the east coast of the Parnon peninsula and on the west coast of the Messenian one respectively lie two ports, both now only of historical interest, which represent past efforts to find better sites. The one is Monemvasia, the other Navarino. In both cases the present insignificance is due to the absence of a hinterland, combined with those modern advances in navigation which make a slight lengthening of a sea voyage of little account, if it leads to a port with good internal connexions. In both also the historical importance at various periods reminds us that till those advances occurred calling stations at short distances apart were essential.

Monemvasia can never have been a harbour of much value. Marine erosion has here separated a rocky island from the mainland, on a peculiarly inhospitable coast, with the result that a measure of shelter, with a site for a protecting fortress, is present. The port is associated chiefly with Malmsey wine, never produced here, however, but brought from the Cyclades, especially Tenos, and carried by the Venetians to western Europe, where it was greatly prized. But Minoan Crete had also a centre here, presumably both a naval port and a trading settlement—a striking example of the effect of the position.

Navarino, or rather the ports for which the name has been used, has a very different position. On the west coast of the Messenian peninsula, opposite the gap between the Lykodhemo upland and that lying to the south of Kyparissia, is an almost circular gulf across whose entrance lies the island of Sphakteria. Within is an admirable deep and sheltered harbour, with 'sandy Pylos', or Old Navarino, near the northern entrance, and Neokastro, or modern Navarino, near the southern one (Fig. 92). The chief modern association is with the great naval battle of 1827, when the Turkish and Egyptian fleets were annihilated. But as early as the second half of the sixteenth century B.C., that is, near the beginning of the Early Mycenaean Period, there was an important trading centre here, amber coming down the Adriatic and the relations with the Gulf of

Corinth being close. In other words, even if the commodities carried and the trade relations were very different, Pylos was then playing the part which Kalamata plays now—as interesting an example of a comparatively small shift from an outer to an inner port, as Minoan and Venetian Monemvasia is of the rejuvenation of an old site.

Continuing northwards, we find that though the lowlands of Elis are now well cultivated and populous, the historic lack of ports remains a disadvantage. Pyrgos (19,000 inhabitants); a market centre lying near but not on the lower Alpheios, is connected by rail to its shallow and unimportant harbour of Katakolo.

The outstanding feature of the north, however, is the predominance of the former Augustan colony of Patras, now the third largest city in Greece—if Athens-Piraeus be regarded as one—and the largest in the Peloponnesus, with over 61,000 inhabitants. This rise is quite recent, and is associated with a relative decrease in the importance of Corinth. The site of the latter appears at first sight much more advantageous, even apart from the presence of the canal. The growth of Patras was associated with the development of the currant export trade. Even though the importance of currants among Greek exports has diminished in favour of tobacco, Patras still serves as the great collecting centre for exports from the Peloponnesus to the west, and has also much local traffic, especially to the islands and the opposite shore (cf. p. 336). The Corinth canal is of less importance than might be expected, owing to its small size, and the tendency of the high and steep banks to slip, a tendency increased by the frequent earthquakes. It is only some 80 ft. wide (minima 24·6 m. at surface and 21 m. at bottom) and under 30 ft. (8 m.) deep, and is traversed by a strong current. Modern Corinth, nearer the shore than the old city at the base of its fortress-crowned hill, is a small town, which has been several times devastated by earthquakes.

Communications and Products. An atlas map suggests that the Peloponnesus has a fairly complete railway system. From Athens the line runs past Eleusis and Megara, skirts the rocky coast of the isthmus, crosses the canal by a lofty bridge, and so reaches Corinth. Here it bifurcates, one branch running across the Tretus or Dervenaki pass to Argos, with a branch to Nauplia, and then traversing by a difficult route the hill country of Arcadia, passing Tripolitsa and sending a branch to Megalopolis, but having no connexion with Sparta. It then runs south to Kalamata, with a connexion to Nisi. But the Kokla gap, north of the Kyparissia upland, allows a branch to reach the western coast, which it follows past Pyrgos. This line is continued along the whole of the northern coast, reaching Corinth by way of Patras.

Despite, however, the presence of a considerable number of short branch-lines this system leaves large tracts unserved by rail, and the railways themselves, which are metre-gauge, are not comparable to those of western Europe. In the Peloponnesus, as elsewhere, great efforts are now being made both to improve the existing roads, and to replace the rough mule-tracks by new ones capable of carrying motor traffic. But much still remains to be done.

Transport difficulties doubtless have much to do with the tendency to concentrate on products such as currants, sultanas, tobacco, dried figs, and so on, of small bulk. It is usually stated that the Greek habit of adding resin from the Aleppo pine to much of their wine —which makes it undrinkable to foreigners, and thus cuts off the outside market—is due to the need of improving the keeping qualities of the lighter brands, in this land of great aridity and high mean temperatures, both during summer and winter. That the added resin increases the thirst-quenching properties of the wine is also asserted. But anyone who has seen the grape harvest of the Peloponnesus being carried to railhead, and the subsequent transportation by rail to the wine-making centres, will be inclined to doubt whether the two suggested reasons form the whole explanation. The amount of contamination with dust and dirt is such that a heavy dose of a disinfectant may well be required to correct it. Currants and sultanas are dried, still too often by slovenly methods, in the areas of production, so that transport difficulties are less important. Currant vines, which demand rather specialized climatic conditions, are extensively grown along the western and northern coasts.

The Ionian island of Zante lies off the coast of Elis, which it resembles in structure no less than in its products, mainly currants and wine. Its port faces the mainland.

THE AEGEAN ISLANDS

The Cyclades. Of these little more need be said. Their interest is twofold: structurally, as already seen, they represent the fragments of an intensely fractured crust-block; historically, they have served at many successive periods as cradles of a nascent culture, in a region where cultural units have constantly tended to develop and to decay as a result of external impacts. The essential structural features have been already indicated. From the human standpoint they mean that everywhere apparently sterile but pasture-yielding hills alternate with narrow lowlands capable of supporting the typical Mediterranean crop-plants; harbours are also numerous. But although—combined with the stimulus of the island climate— the conditions thus favour human effort, the small area is a drawback. Thus, if the metaphor may be continued, historically the child outgrows its cradle; Crete or one or other of the adjacent mainland areas becomes the homeland, and the islands sink in importance, till a new catastrophe is followed in due course by a rally and the cycle begins anew. Without attempting any historical survey in illustration, we may simply recall the fact that Syros, with its port of Hermoupolis (21,000 inhabitants), was the great trade-centre of Modern Greece till Athens and the Piraeus could take over their normal function. The present size of the town, contrasted not with Athens alone, but even with Patras and Kalamata, is evidence enough of relative decay. Further, the change in the nature of the sea traffic is clearly illustrated by the fact that there is little inter-communication among the islands, and access from the mainland is not easy.

Nevertheless they must always be of great importance to the geographer, if only because of the way in which they illustrate the origin of the Mediterranean city-state and of the typical Mediter-ranean culture. Though their inhabitants are now mainly peasant-farmers, they tend to be town-dwellers, many islands containing one considerable town which lodges most of their occupants. The towns are generally placed on barren, rocky slopes, and are not infre-quently invisible from the sea as a protection from the pirates of an earlier day. The position obviates the need of sterilizing parts of the scanty tracts of productive land by buildings; it keeps also the farmer in contact with his two sources of livelihood, for stock animals, especially sheep and goats, are numerous. Other factors play their part—exposure to cool breezes during the summer heat, avoidance of the risk of malaria, access to mountain springs. But this com-bination of agricultural pursuits and town life, which has meant so much to Mediterranean man, would have been physically impossible had it not been for the intensive nature of the methods. During a large part of the year the Mediterranean peasant is almost as mobile as the shepherd, wielding his mattock or pruning-knife where the latter carries his crook. Even threshing operations need but a flat surface, paved with the omnipresent stones, and the easily trans-ported flails. One has but to glance at the farm buildings of the rural districts of our own islands to see wherein the fundamental contrasts lie. The Mediterranean peasant is freed from the double menace of summer rain and winter cold, and his labour if continuous can yet be leisurely.

It need only be added that the islands, especially Santorin, Tenos, Melos, and Naxos, share with some of the Ionian Islands and also with Messenia in the production of non-resinated, heavy wines which command some external market.

Crete. This large island, with its lofty peaks, snowclad for much of the year, and built mainly of limestones hardly less white, has changed much since the days when it could be described as 'Fair, fat, well-watered, it has men beyond numbering and ninety cities'. The palace cities of Cnossus and Phaestus have lain in ruins for more than three thousand years, and gone is the age when from the latter 'the dark-prowed ships were borne to Egypt by the force of the wind and the waves'. The interest of the island, in other words, even more than is the case with the Cyclades, lies in the past rather than in the present. Of that past this is not the place to speak in any detail; we can do no more than indicate some of the geographical features which promoted its greatness.

Structurally, as already seen, Crete is a prolongation of the Western Hellenides, and is the most prominent section of the broken land-bridge which extends from the Parnon peninsula through Cythera and Anticythera, and is continued by the islands of Casos, Scarpanto, and Rhodes to Asia Minor. But save in its effects on the relief this is less important than the sea-relations. These have two aspects. In the first place, as compared with the Cyclades, so favourable to early point-to-point navigation, Crete looks both north and south to an empty sea. Once, however, seafaring had lost its first terrors, the position became superb. It lies at equal distances between Troy and the Nile mouths, between the Gulf of Argolis or Nauplia and Cyrenaica, between Cyprus, the copper island, and Sicily, between Syria and Italy; midway, that is, between areas which had much to exchange, more especially when the Copper Age brought new needs.

The detailed relief, particularly in that eastern half which was important in the periods of its greatness, favoured concentration of effort. The island extends from west to east for about 150 miles, or some 250 km., and shows an alternation of swellings and constrictions, from a maximum width of about 35 miles to a minimum of some 6 miles in the isthmus of Hierapetra in the east (Fig. 95). Mountains extend throughout and fall into four main groups. To the west are the White Mountains with the peak of Agios Theodorus; then comes the Mt. Ida group, the highest (2,498 m.); still farther east are the Lasithi Mountains (Dicte), with the Sitia Mountains (Afendis Kavusi) on the hither side of the isthmus. If the forests which once clothed the mountains, especially Ida, are mostly gone, we know that they were once abundantly present; upland pasture is available, while the valleys and small karstic basins permit of some cultivation at considerable heights.

The essential feature, however, is the way in which the high ground encircles and largely isolates the chief productive areas. Between the Ida and Lasithi groups is a lower upland belt, with Mt. Iouktas (under 3,000 ft.) as its chief element. To the north of this upland is the plain on which Cnossus stood, now functionally

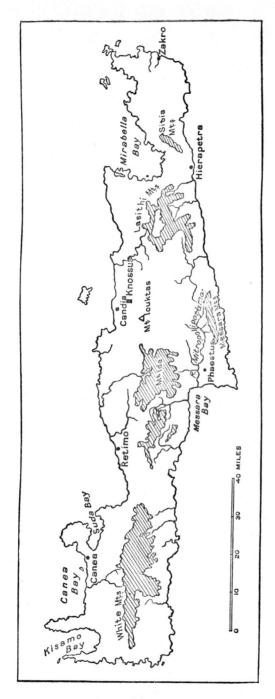

FIG. 95. THE ISLAND OF CRETE

replaced by Candia (Iraklion—about 33,000 inhabitants). To the south is the comparatively large Messara plain, about 37 miles long and 9–12 miles wide, watered by the permanent river Mitropolipotamo. On this plain stood Phaestus, which rivalled Cnossus in splendour, and it is the largest and most productive lowland of the island. Its position should be noted. It does not, like that of Cnossus, directly confront the sea, for a mountain belt intervenes between it and the south coast. But, while the southern coast generally is remarkably straight and inhospitable, and thus contrasted with the northern one with its peninsulas and bays, there is here a well-marked bend, giving rise to an open bay. The Mitropolipotamo runs from east to west, and the plain, like the river, has a western outlet, despite the hills to the south.

It is believed that the Bronze Age culture of Crete originated in this plain, perhaps owing to the settlement of immigrants from Egypt in the predynastic period. In later days it was connected with the Cnossus plain by a well-constructed road which crossed the intervening upland.

Of the other productive areas we may note to the west the little plain of Retimo, with the town of that name, and the similar plain behind Canea (about 27,000 inhabitants). Eastward the Hierapetra isthmus, already mentioned, has small lowlands both to north and south, with Minoan sites on both. The narrowing here was important, since the journey round the eastern end of the island by sea is not easy. There, nevertheless, is another small plain, with Zakro, once an important trade-centre.

All told, however, the productive areas are not large, nor easily linked together. Thus the prosperity of Minoan Crete depended upon the early start, the sea empire, and the overseas relations. After the thalassocracy was overthrown, and the hegemony passed to the Mycenaean culture of the mainland, there was no subsequent rally on any equivalent scale. The long Turkish period was one of continuous retrogression, and the attachment to modern Greece has not caused much improvement, though this may come. Curiously enough, one effect has been to reduce the population, and that for the usual reason. During the Turkish period a considerable number of the Greek inhabitants adopted the religion of the ruling power, and with the transference of rule these tended to emigrate to Asia Minor. Settlement of Asiatic Greek refugees is, however, taking place on a considerable scale.

One other point may be mentioned. Since limestone rocks are widespread, typical karst phenomena recur, some being of special interest. As an example we may take the Dictaean Cave or Cave of Psychro. Psychro is a village not far from Cnossus in an upland basin within the Lasithi Mountains. As so often happens, the basin was once a lake, and the cave, which lies above it, is a now function-less katavothra. It may well be that the draining of the lake took place with catastrophic suddenness owing to the opening of some lower exit at a time of flood. The cave, which is divided into an outer and inner, deeper part, is the traditional birthplace of the Cretan Zeus, the son of the Great Mother, and was a sacred place throughout a long period of time, objects derived from Egypt having been found within it. A delightful account of the first excavations is given in Hogarth's *The Wandering Scholar*. As elements which must have gone to the making of the sanctity we have to note both that feeling of the exposure of earth's mysteries which all limestone caverns give, and also the fact that the possibility of access to it must have been associated with the freeing of a new surface for man's use, fertilized by the fine debris derived from standing water. Since the princes of Cnossus claimed to be descended from the Cretan Zeus, by whose authority they ruled, the sacred cave brings us back once again to the great agricultural discoveries on which all civilization is based.

The Dodecanese (='twelve islands') passed to Greek control on 31st March 1947. They have an area of 1,022 sq. miles and consist of Astypalaea (Stampalia), Calymnos (Kalymnos or Calino), Carpathos (Scarpanto), Casos (Kasos or Casso), Chalki (Khalki), Cos (Kos), Leros, Lipsos (Lipso), Nisyros (Misiros), Patmos, Symi and Tilos (Piscopi). Castellorizo and Rhodes (Rhodos) are not historically Dodecanese islands, but have long been included. Rhodes (545 sq. miles), Carpathos (118 sq. miles) and Cos (111 sq. miles) are the largest islands. Rhodes has undergone much economic improvement in recent time, but the other islands are very poor. The total population in 1937 was 135,622 and in 1947 about 115,000. The Italians who were formerly nearly 10 per cent of the population have now left, as also some of the Turks who likewise accounted for nearly 10 per cent of the population in 1937. Jews of Spanish origin were important commercially in Rhodes, which has nearly half the total population of the islands. Calymnos (49 sq. miles) and Cos have another 30 per cent.

The islands are the prolongation of the ridges of Anatolia, and as the valleys have been submerged there are deep inlets verging on high, rocky, and barren mountains or hills. Cool northerly breezes temper the dry summers. Cereals are grown for home consumption, and grapes, citrus fruits, tobacco, olives, and vegetables for export. Sponge fishing is an important and ancient occupation. There is the usual seafaring tradition of Greek islands and Rhodes was for long and should again become a great entrepôt centre for the Eastern Mediterranean. Carpets in beautiful designs and woven with local wool, together with good pottery are well-known exports. Under the Italians, roads and hotels were built and the ancient sites of Lindos on Rhodes and sites on Kos and other islands were excavated. An important tourist industry developed and Kalithéa (Celitea) spa near Rhodes city became a great resort.

The islands were colonized by Dorians in the tenth century B.C. They were parts of the Roman and Byzantine Empires, passing thereafter to the Venetian Republic in 1082, to the Genoese Republic in 1248, to the Knights of St. John of Jerusalem in 1308, to the Turkish Empire in 1522, to the Italian Empire in 1912, and reverting finally to Greece in 1947.

Of the other islands of the Aegean little need be said. Their products are similar to those of the Peloponnesus, with an increasing tendency for the production of tobacco to extend, especially in Samos and Mytilene. Chios has long been famous for its mastic gum, produced by *Pistacia lentiscus*, which grows here very freely. Apart from its other uses, especially for making a kind of liqueur, it forms the basis of a glutinous sweetmeat, said to be greatly appreciated by the Turkish ladies of Istanbul, though Chios is of course now no longer Turkish. It is particularly fertile and densely peopled. It might also be noticed that Cyprus, although occupied by the British since 1878, is peopled mainly by Greeks who have long agitated for inclusion in Greece.

CHAPTER XVI

NORTHERN PENINSULAR AND MAINLAND GREECE

Thessaly—Epirus—Corfu—Greek Macedonia and Thrace—Sub-
divisions: South Macedonia, East Macedonia, Greek Thrace, West
Macedonia—Summary

THESSALY

E PIRUS and Thessaly are sharply contrasted with each other; for while the former is occupied by the Western Hellenides, the latter is part of the North Aegean crust-block. In Thessaly this has not been shattered into fragments, like the Cycladean Massif, but has been extensively faulted, and shows an alternation of up-thrust and depressed areas. In consequence, alike in its physical features and in the possible modes of life, Thessaly forms a region of transition between the essential Greece to the south and the new territories to the north.

Its relatively late acquisition by the modern Greek State was the political consequence of this fact, just as the relative slowness with which its peculiar problems have been tackled was the social and economic one. These problems, again, difficult though they are, are less serious than those of Macedonia. The agrarian problem—a Turkish heritage—has been largely solved, and drainage schemes, carried out between the two World Wars, have done much to improve the state of the countryside.

GENERAL FEATURES OF THESSALY

The essential points may be easily made out from Fig. 96. From the north of the Vale of Tempe, where the flanks of Mt. Olympus approach the seaboard, southwards to the Trikeri Channel, there runs a belt of high land, with Ossa, Mavrovuni, and Pelion rising notably above the general level. This belt forms the eastern edge of the crust-block, which is tilted westward, so that while the sea-ward side is steep and the coast thus inhospitable and harbourless, landwards there is a more gentle slope to a plain. But the southern part of that plain is sunk below the sea as the Gulf of Volos (Pagasaean Gulf), which has its entrance constricted by the hook-shaped pro-longation of the Magnesian peninsula. Apart then from the com-plexities of the interior, where lowlands alternate with moderate uplands, the combination of coastal mountain ridge and gulf means that there is at once a contrast and a resemblance to the Greek lands already described.

Thus, whether we think of Attica or Boeotia; of the Amphissa valley or lower Aetolia; of the plains of Argos, Sparta, or Messene; of the small lowland areas of Crete—everywhere we find as a common characteristic the sea outlook. Even where, as at Sparta, direct access either for man or commodities is not easy, yet sea influences penetrate, modifying the climate and influencing the life of man and the growth of plants. But Thessaly has a steep sea-wall, while southwards the Othrys range, westwards the Pindus, and northwards the mountains of Macedonia encircle it, excluding the vivifying breath. Here is the essence of the contrast with the southern lands.

None the less there is also a real resemblance. South-eastwards lies the gulf, the legendary home of the Argonauts, a miniature sea on whose calm waters the Hellenes first learnt the craft of seafaring (Stählin). While the inner plains are steppe-like, on the lower slopes of the hills around the gulf the Mediterranean evergreen scrub occurs. While they are mainly grain-producing, here, thanks alike to shelter from the Etesian winds and from the foehn-like *Livas* which blows down from the Pindus and may blight the corn of the plains, the olive and even the orange flourish. Here, then, cultivation is of the intensive garden type, as contrasted with the large estates of the interior, themselves in essence a response to the natural conditions; for dependence on one crop which may fail is a terrible risk for the man of small means. But these are not the only resemblances between the habitable strip round the gulf and the true Greek Lands. To the north, in the region round the present port of Volos, we find repeated that succession of historical sites throughout the ages which we have already discussed in the south. Not only, also, is the succession peculiarly long and complete, but the small changes in the position of the dominant centre illustrate the stages in the development of the 'Greek' mode of life. The area indeed served as a training-ground in which the successive immigrants learnt the art of adapting themselves to their new environment. Conversely, the decay and subsequent rejuvenescence of Volos in quite modern times illustrates the fact that the latest immigrant, the Turk, proved incapable of this process of adjustment.

Only the barest outline of the story can be given. The first settlement was apparently at Sesklo (S on map), on a hill site to the south-west of Volos, just south of the gap through which the railway to Larissa now passes. It was occupied in the early Stone Age. Nearer the gulf, and already on the plain, though with a low hill to serve as a site for the fortress, stood Dimini (D on map). Both sites were occupied by neolithic peoples, who entered from the Danubian region during the course of the third millennium B.C. According to Dawson (*The Age of the Gods*), 'Sesklo and Dimini . . . are the first

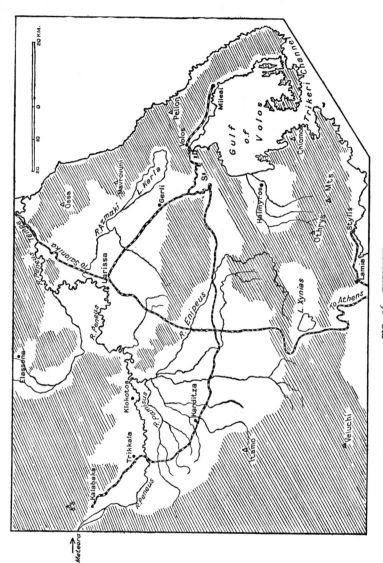

FIG. 96. THESSALY

The stippled areas lie above 500 m. The letters S and D indicate the ancient sites of Sesklo and Dimini.

walled "towns" of Greece, and the earliest forerunners of the historic Greek Polis'.

Dimini continued to be important during the Copper Age, but by the late Minoan period Iolcus became the centre, and its princes had their beehive tombs within ruined and deserted Dimini. Iolcus is virtually identical in site with Volos, that is, is on the gulf. Thus we have the sequence—primitive hill settlement; plain town with fortified mound; port at edge of plain. From this time onwards the centre was always a gulf port, though its precise position varied a little from time to time throughout the ages, never, however, being far from the existing Volos. In 1881, when Thessaly passed from the Turk to Greece, Volos was a squalid township with some 2,000 inhabitants—a sign of the general degeneration of this once-prosperous region. It is now the fifth port of Greece, has about 51,000 inhabitants, and in addition to its external trade has some minor industries, dependent on local raw material, such as flour-milling, cigarette-making, and so on. It, like its historic predecessors, is of course the outlet for the whole of Thessaly (note the railway connexions).

A ridge of high ground extends from the coastal range near Pelion towards the Othrys Mountains, and this separates the Volos basin from the inner plains of Larissa and Trikkala. Just to the west of the town of Volos, however, this ridge drops to a saddle well below 500 ft. in height (137 m.), which allows for the passage of the railway.

The plains themselves are somewhat complex. The uplifted and westward-tilted crust-block which forms the coastal range has an inner counterpart in the ridge of high ground which separates the eastern and western plains. Both these areas of uplift are margined by north-west to south-east fault-lines, whose direction is indicated by the Azmaki, which flows into Lake Karla (Voiviis), and by the almost parallel course of the lower Enipeus, which unites with the Peneus. In each case depression on the downcast side of the fault was sufficient to cause the present plains to become lakes. Drainage has been a slow process, but much progress has been made, and by 1939 some 13,000 acres in the upper basin and 50,000 acres in the lower or Larissa basin had been given regulated irrigation. The river Peneus appears to represent an old consequent which has been able to preserve, broadly speaking, its original direction, despite the subsequent faulting and differential movement. But this involved the necessity of cutting through the two uplifted areas in gorges, both of somewhat complicated nature. The one is indicated on the map east of Klokotos, and is remarkably winding; the other consists of two separate parts with a small intervening plain, the lower forming the vale of Tempe. The Peneus is a powerful stream, fed by the abundant rainfall of the Pindus, and its numerous tributaries drain the whole of the upper plain, converging towards the main stream at the north-east angle.

This upper or western plain stands at an average height of nearly 500 ft. (150 m.), and has an area of about 600 sq. miles (1,600 sq. km.). Owing to the clay subsoil it is liable to become swampy in winter and to dry out and fissure in summer, when large tracts take on the appearance of a thistle steppe. There is some evidence from classical writers that it was once wooded, but now trees are confined to the stream-banks (gallery forests); whether the change is due to a diminished supply of water or to Turkish influence is uncertain. Except for the main stream and the great Enipeus tributary most of the mountain streams become dry in summer, while in winter and spring, swollen with melted snow, they tend to flood the land and spread over it deposits of sand and gravel. But this upper plain has the great advantage of copious and unfailing springs, especially round its margins, which give a constant water-supply.

In the north-west angle, at a height of over 1,800 ft. (570 m.), lie the Meteora Monasteries, perched on pillar-like rocks dissected out of tertiary conglomerates (p. 323), and extremely difficult of access. Of the original twenty-three, four only remain, housing only about thirty monks. As no more novices are accepted, the occupation even of these four must shortly cease, and this picturesque protest against a changing world will be only a memory. As in similar institutions elsewhere the ban against the female sex is complete, extending even to animals. Thus there can be no renewal of life; death is never counterbalanced by birth.

After cutting its way through the hard rocks of the central ridge the Peneus emerges on the Larissa plain, receiving no right-bank tributary within the plain proper, which has a relatively low rainfall. After many windings, and receiving a mountain left-bank tributary with the town of Elassona on its upper course, it breaks through to the sea. This lower plain stands at a height of about 300 ft. (100 m.), and has an area of some 340 sq. miles (880 sq. km.). Parts of it are exceedingly dry, without possibility of irrigation, while the region round Lake Karla is swampy and the lake itself occupies a considerable area of what might be productive ground, though the drainage of the area between the lake and the Peneus, by depriving the lake of some of its inflow, will no doubt cause it to decrease in area. It is stated that the shrinking of the water surface in classical times increased the winter cold, so that while the olive once flourished at Larissa it was later killed out. At present the climate is certainly extreme, with hot, dry summers and winters sometimes of such severity as to kill the flocks of the Vlach herdsmen who migrate here from the mountains to seek winter pasturage. The *Livas* wind and locusts are also great plagues. On the other hand, the loamy soil is extremely fertile and provided the spring rains are adequate yields good crops of wheat. Larissa (27,000), on the Peneus, till recently presented a markedly Turkish appearance, with its numerous tall, white minarets, but is now rapidly changing in character. The site is a very ancient one, and the town has taken on a new lease of life since it passed from Turkish control. Owing to the abundant water of the river it presents in summer the appearance of a green oasis in the midst of the brown and dusty steppe.

EPIRUS

Like Macedonia Epirus is but a name taken from ancient geography to serve as a convenient designation for an area with some physical but no political or administrative unity. To the Greeks of Corfu the karstic and somewhat forbidding upland, in part forested both with broad-leaved (beech and oak) and coniferous trees, which extends from the Bay of Valona to the Gulf of Arta was 'the continent', with an implication of difficulty of access and of utilization. A small south-eastern part of this tract, forming the department of Arta, passed to Greece with Thessaly in 1881. The remainder, the Epirus of the modern political geographer, forms one of these debatable areas in which the retreat of the Turk gave rise to many difficult problems. Its southern section is included in Greece as the department of Yannina, its more northerly falls into southern Albania. On Fig. 85 the date 1913 is given as that of the acquisition of the Greek segment. But this was then nominal rather than real, and it was only in the post-war period, after various incidents and vicissitudes, that a final settlement was achieved, and the boundary between Greece and independent Albania demarcated. Greek Epirus is thus emphatically a 'new' territory, thinly peopled, and with very imperfect communications, both internal and external.

It is separated from Thessaly by the Pindus range, the name being used in various senses. Some geographers restrict it to the high ground which extends from the Peristeri Massif (2,530 m., or over 8,000 ft.), east of Yannina, to Mt. Veluchi (Fig. 96). This belt forms a great obstacle to east-to-west traffic, the chief pass being the Zygos (the name means 'pass'—1,551 m., or over 5,000 ft.), on the northern slopes of the Peristeri group. This leads, if hitherto only by mule-paths, from the upper Peneus, via the Vlach village of Metzovon, to Yannina. But the central range is continued northwards, beyond the pass, into the higher peak of Smolika, while Grammos (2,526 m.), on the Albanian border, may be regarded as a further prolongation.

In this larger sense the Pindus is throughout a thinly-peopled area, inhabited chiefly by migratory Vlach shepherds, and retaining parts of its original forest cover. A scheme has been put forward to extend the railway from its terminus at Kalabaka (Fig. 96) to Yannina, not by the Zygos but by a much more circuitous route farther north, with an extension down the Kalamas valley to Goumenitsa, a small port south of the deltaic mouth of that river.

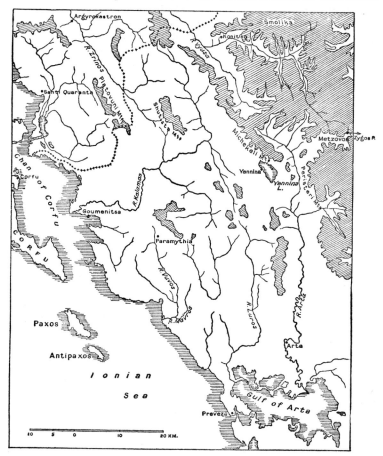

FIG. 97. GREEK EPIRUS

The stippled areas lie at heights over 1,000 m. The Greco-Albanian frontier is shown, but only a part of the Greek island of Corfu.

Meantime, however, Greek Epirus is devoid of railways and not effectively connected to Thessaly across the Pindus barrier, for the proposed motor-road over the pass has not yet been constructed.

The essential features of Epirus can be deduced from Fig. 97. The first point to be noted is the presence of the Gulf of Arta, the northern shore of which shows an obvious resemblance to the lagoon coast of Missolonghi (Fig. 91). It will be noted that the river Arta, the largest stream of Greek Epirus, is a smaller analogue of the Aspropotamo, while a second and smaller river, the Luros, has a similar southerly direction and is also a silt-carrier. But there is one obvious difference from Aetolia. The lagoon coast there confronts the wide Gulf of Patras; but the Arta gulf has a narrowed neck, at which stands the small port of Preveza. Though there are some minor havens on the east and south sides of the gulf, it is clear that both because of its shallow lagoon coast to the north and its narrow and inconvenient exit, it cannot form a good outlet for southern Epirus. On the other hand, the lowland which borders the gulf to the north affords considerable opportunities for cultivation. Its centre is the small town of Arta, situated (cf. Agrinion) on the edge of the higher ground to avoid the risk of flooding.

North of the gulf lowland is a peculiarly inhospitable area, less because of its elevation, which is only moderate, than because of its karstic nature and the narrow valleys, which afford little opportunity for either cultivation or settlement. They have a southerly trend, and it should be noted that the river Mavros, though it breaks through to the western sea in its lower course, has for the most part, both in itself and its tributaries, a similar direction. Its Vuvos tributary waters a plain of some fertility, with the small town of Paramythia as its centre.

With this southern section northern Epirus, beyond the Yannina–River Kalamas line, is sharply contrasted. The elevation is greater, but the valleys are more open and inviting, communications are somewhat easier, and in particular the upland basin in which Yannina lies offers considerable opportunities for settlement, the town containing some 21,000 inhabitants.

It is in this part of Epirus that the greatest difficulty in frontier-drawing has been experienced, and the compromise achieved has cut natural lines of communication. Because of the continuity of the physical features there has been in the past reciprocal interpenetration by Greeks and Albanians. Greek Epirus has still a considerable Albanian population; but, certainly till quite recent times, Orthodox Christian Albanians have adopted Greek culture very readily. But the fluctuating fortunes of the independent Albanian State, and particularly Italian 'interest' in its maintenance in the area where the Ionian Sea narrows to the Strait of Otranto, have given rise to serious problems. Two illustrations may serve to indicate the nature of these. In Northern Epirus, both Greek and Albanian, the ridges have a north-west to south-east trend, as have, necessarily, the intervening valleys. The easiest lines of communication from Yannina thus tend to run north-westwards into Albania. In particular the considerable Albanian river Vijosë (Vynsa) (cf. Figs. 97 and 102) has headstreams rising well within Greek territory. Gjinokastër on one of these is connected by a good road with Yannina, and the most convenient sea-outlet of the latter is the Albanian port of Sarandë (Santi Quaranta, the Hagii Saranta of Greek maps). But this lies within the Strait of Otranto, and the Italians were as little likely to consent to it becoming Greek as the Greeks were to agree to Yannina becoming Albanian—though the latter town was at one stage occupied by Italian troops.

The other illustration is of a different nature. In Greek Epirus, particularly in the port of Goumenitsa, are found Moslems called Chams. These are said to be the descendants of Greeks who embraced Islam in the late seventeenth century, but they speak Albanian and have Turkish sympathies. The Chams were expressly exempted from the exchange of Christian and Moslem peoples. Such an exchange would have taken them into Albanian territory, where they would not have been welcomed.

A few words may be added in regard to the site of Yannina. The town is placed on a promontory jutting out into the lake of the same name. This is of the ordinary karstic type and occupies a varying part of a considerable upland basin standing at a height of some 1,600 ft. (485 m.). To the north-east lie the Michekeli Mountains, rising to 4,000 ft., and it is their drainage-water which accumulates to form the lake. This has no visible outlet but is said to leak through the limestones both to the Kalamas (north-western part) and to the Luros (south-eastern part). The essential point, however, is that while much of the basin is water-covered in winter and spring, in summer considerable areas of moistened land are exposed, well suited to the cultivation of maize and other cereals. The vine is also grown on the slopes and the pastures are particularly rich. This combination of local resources and converging routes makes Yannina the natural centre of Greek Epirus, though, as already indicated, the actual routes leave much to be desired. The relation of the Yannina basin to the Kalamas valley is of some interest. It will be noted that this valley has a similar direction to the Shkumbi (Fig. 102) in Albania, followed by the Via Egnatia. The proposed railway to Goumenitsa would give Yannina a direct outlet to the channel of Corfu.

CORFU

This curiously-shaped island, elongated in the direction of the trend-lines of the continent, is the most densely-peopled part of Greece (466 per sq. mile in 1938), owing to its favourable climate, its fertile soil and its position on the route between the Ionian and the Adriatic Seas. In contrast to the inhospitable mainland its eastern coast is mostly low. Between its two open bays, on a peninsula, with a safe if somewhat shallow harbour, lies the capital and only important town (about 35,000 inhabitants) which shares the name of the island. Formerly strongly fortified, and acting at various periods as one of the great route centres of the Mediterranean, it has now lost much of its earlier significance, being relatively remote alike from the land- and the sea-ways of modern times.

The island is particularly noted for its olive groves and production of olive oil, though other southern fruit-trees are grown extensively. Its surface is generally undulating rather than hilly, though in the wider, northern part the limestone mass of Pankrator rises to about 3,000 ft. (906 m.), and there are other elevations in the centre and south. There is no railway, but roads, perhaps as a result of the British control of the island from 1815 to 1864, are better developed than in most parts of Greece. The small islands of Paxos and Antipaxos lie to the south-east.

GREEK MACEDONIA AND THRACE

Before attempting a description of these mainland territories, two general points may be emphasized. In the first place, though the Greek advance into Macedonia, with the capture of the great prize of Salonika, dates from the Balkan wars, and the year 1920 gave her in theory a large accession of territory in Thrace, yet the fixing of the present frontier along the line of the lower Maritsa was the work of the Lausanne conference in 1923, and a small adjustment at the mouth of the river took place only in 1926. Further, though a considerable amount of interchange of populations had been going on from the period of the Balkan wars, the great influx of Greek refugees from Asia Minor only occurred in the disastrous year 1922, and the compulsory interchange of Greek and Turkish peoples was one of the provisions of the Lausanne treaty. Necessarily, therefore, the new territories are still, socially and economically, in a state of flux.

Again, a word may be said about the use of the name Thrace. By historians and political geographers, it is often used as synonymous with the old Roman province, which in the south extended westward to the line of the lower Mesta (Kara Su). In that sense southern Thrace can be divided by the river Maritsa into a western or Greek and an eastern or Turkish portion. But the line of the lower Mesta has no present-day significance, and there is some tendency to limit the word Thrace to Turkish territory, and to extend 'Macedonia' to the lower Maritsa. The point is only of importance because the varying uses of the name may give rise to misconception as to the position of the eastern frontier of Greece.

SUB-DIVISIONS

Twelve departments are recognized in the new territories, and there is a certain convenience in grouping these to form the basis of a general description.

Six departments, those of Salonika, Pella (capital Edessa or Vodena), Kilkis, Seres, and the two into which the Chalcidice area is divided, Chalcidice and the small, isolated Agion Oros or Mt. Athos, may be grouped together as forming South Macedonia. This is a fairly natural unit with well-marked characteristics. In the first place, its rivers, particularly the Vardar and less markedly the Struma, open up pathways into the hilly interior. The size of Salonika is a clear indication of this nodal significance. Secondly, the climate, though not typically Mediterranean, approaches the type sufficiently to permit of the growth of the characteristic crops. These include the olive, where shelter from the Vardar winter wind is obtainable, and are of very varied nature, owing to the wide tracts of actually or potentially productive lowland. Finally, though the whole of the lands included are not low nor level, there is yet a sufficiently definite rim of higher ground, especially to the north, west, and south-west to make the limits obvious on an atlas map.

To the west the departments of Kozani and Florina constitute the Greek part of West or High Macedonia. This extends westwards to the Pindus and southwards is separated from Thessaly by the hills which girdle the plains of the latter. The special features are the elevation and the reduction of the cultivable land to upland basins and valleys lying between ridges. The ridges tend to have a southerly or south-easterly trend, the basins being elongated in a similar direction. This is a contrast to South Macedonia, where the lakes and basins tend to be elongated from west to east. Further, as a natural result of the run of the surface features, frontier lines are not easy to draw, and the same type of country is continued into Yugoslavia and the Albanian borderland.

To the east of South Macedonia lie the departments of Drama and Kavalla, forming East Macedonia. This shares some of the features of the former, but to a diminishing extent. Thus access to the interior is less easy, productive lowlands are less extensive, the climate is less favourable to varied production and tobacco becomes the outstanding crop. The port of Kavalla (55,000) is small, as compared with Salonika, as a natural result of these conditions.

Still farther east, between the Mesta and the Maritsa, lies the comparatively narrow strip of southern Thrace which is attached to Greece. This is made up of the two departments of Rhodopi with Komotini (formerly Gumuljina) as its capital and Evros with Alexandroupolis (formerly Dedeagach). As already suggested there is no essential contrast between this area and East Macedonia. Tobacco is again an important crop. Alexandroupolis is an insignificant port (about 15,500 inhabitants).

SOUTH MACEDONIA (FIG. 98)

This as defined is highly complex. We may note first that the frontier with Yugoslavia crosses the river Vardar in the region of the Chingane Derbend gorge, which is 6 miles long and bordered by hills rising to 1,100 ft. West of the river the frontier runs along a ridge, which extends south-westwards to Lake Ostrovo (Vegorritis) and has as its outstanding feature the high peak of Kaimakchalan (2,517 m., or about 8,200 ft.). From the north-east end of this ridge, which bears various names, there stretches southwards an upland mass (Payak Planina) which separates the high basin of the Moglenitsa river from the Vardar. South of this upland lies the broad and formerly swampy Campania. Its western border is formed by the Agostos Mountains, separated from the great ridge just mentioned by the narrow Vodena valley. The centre of the Campania plain was formerly occupied by a lake (Yenije or Yiannitsa) which has now been drained. To the south lies the river Vistritsa (Aliakmon), which emerges on the plain from a narrow valley lying between the southern end of the Agostos Mountains, and the great block of high ground to the south of which Mt. Olympus is the outstanding feature. The Vardar runs from north to south at the eastern side of the plain, its delta, which has a new straight artificial mouth, being virtually continuous with that of the Vistritsa.

The plain is exceedingly productive though seasonal flooding and the prevalence of malaria were formerly great obstacles to its full utilization. The crops include such fruit-trees as figs, almonds, vines, with the olive on well-drained and sheltered marginal slopes; the mulberry for silkworm-rearing; cotton, opium poppy, tobacco, sesame, and rice, in addition to other cereals. The wide tracts of pasture were formerly used in winter by transhumant Vlach shepherds, but the increased density of settlement due to the influx of refugees from Asia Minor has tended to check such movements.

The chief settlements, necessarily, are pushed to the hilly margins. In the west, standing on terraces of travertine (sinter, deposited by lime-laden waters), are Berroia (Verria), Niausta (Agostos), and Edessa (Vodena). The last is much the most interesting. It stands at the opening of a transverse valley leading from Lake Ostrovo to the plain, on the Salonika-Monastir railway. But the lake has no surface outlet. Powerful springs emerge at the surface a little to the east to form the river which passes Edessa. Its Slav name of Vodena (*voda*=water) is an allusion to the splendid waterfall near the town.

Much more important than this narrow belt of lowland is the basin of Seres, which extends from the Butkovo lake to the Strimon gulf and is traversed by the lower Struma (Strimon). This river, rising far within Bulgaria, enters Greek territory in the region of the Rupel gorge formed by the approach of the eastern end of the Belesh Planina to the southern extremity of the Pirin Dagh of Bulgaria. After its emergence on the plain the river is deflected by the outlet from Lake Butkovo (Kerkini) and flows in a south-easterly direction, expands into the wide lowland formerly occupied

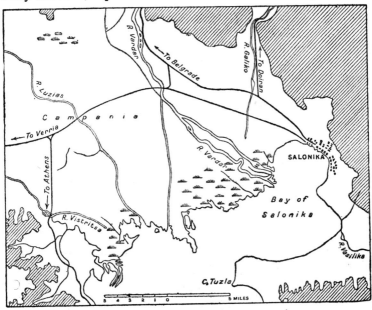

FIG. 99. SITE OF SALONIKA (THESSALONIKI)
Heights above 300 ft. are stippled. (*From the War Office map.*)

by the now drained Lake Tachinos (Akhinos), and then turns south to the gulf. The lowland which it waters is bounded to the north-east by an upland which may be regarded as the last outpost of the Pirin Dagh. In its southern part, however, occurs yet another of the characteristic transverse valleys, beyond which the land rises again towards the coast. This valley allows the effluent of the Drama basin, the Angitis, to reach the Struma, and also affords a passage to the Salonika-Istanbul railway.

The Seres basin as thus defined is exceedingly fruitful, wine, tobacco, and rice being the chief products. The drainage of Lake Tachinos has provided 46 sq. miles of new land for cultivation, and other works in the Struma valley (notably the impounding of Lake

24

Butkovo) have given irrigation water to 1,700 sq. miles. The town of Seres (Serrai) (32,000) is beautifully situated on the hill-slopes above the lake, and has increased considerably owing to the settlement of refugees. Orfani, though at one time regarded as a possible outlet for Bulgaria, has no importance as a harbour, though Amfipolis, on the mouth of the Struma, is now linked by a branch to the main railway.

The Chalcidice peninsula, with its three prongs, forms an appendix to South Macedonia. Separated from the mainland by the swampy, lake-filled depression already described, and deeply interpenetrated by the sea, it served as a refuge for an almost purely Greek population as contrasted with the racial complex of the interior. In its climate, in its vegetation, which includes both high forest and dense maquis, and in its generally hilly nature, it is Aegean rather than Macedonian, and, as in Greece proper, the absence of plains capable of large-scale cultivation tended to exclude the Turk. The most interesting feature is the cluster of twenty monasteries which occupies the extremity of the Agion Oros, or Mt. Athos prong. This prong is connected to the peninsula proper by a narrowed neck, crossed by the remnants of Xerxes' canal, so that exit and entrance is readily controlled. Mt. Athos is still an autonomous province under Greek sovereignty; its population numbers about 3,500 monks.

EAST MACEDONIA

The essential features of East Macedonia, the area between the hill country bounding the plain of Seres to the east and the Mesta river, may be gathered from Fig. 100, which shows its southern section. The wide deltaic plain of the Mesta is thinly peopled and of little importance, but the two towns of Drama and Kavalla are of much interest.

Drama (35,000 inhabitants), occupying a position at the base of the hill country quite analogous to that of Seres, is the centre of a productive basin, continued south-eastward into what is sometimes called the plain of Philippi, from the ruins of that once famous town. This plain was formerly occupied by the Philippi marshes and the Bereketli lake, one of the worst malarial districts in all Greece; the drainage of the area and its conversion to agricultural land is amongst the most noteworthy of all the recent engineering works of this kind. Tobacco of fine quality ('Turkish') is the special product of the area, though with the extensive settlement of refugees new crops have been introduced, including roses for attar. The special point of interest, however, is that tobacco forms the basis of an extensive export trade, so that a convenient exit is essential. This is found in

Kavalla, the chief tobacco port of Greece, which has grown rapidly
in recent years. Its position should be noted. Everywhere along
this coast the presence of a considerable river is a great menace to
the maintenance of a port. Even Salonika, despite its position, is
exposed to the danger of silting, which has furnished one of the
motives for the undertaking of the elaborate flood-control measures.
It is, then, of great importance that the Drama basin is drained, if
incompletely, south-westwards, and that a considerable ridge of
high ground skirts the coast to the south of the town. Kavalla
stands on a rocky cape on this hilly coast, a gap in the hills behind

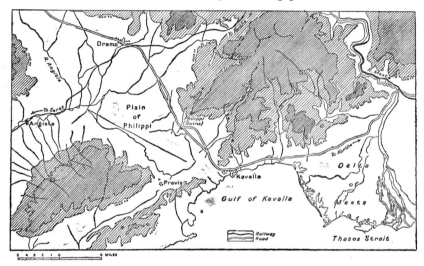

FIG. 100. THE BASIN OF DRAMA AND THE PORT OF KAVALLA

Note that there is as yet no railway to Kavalla. (*From the War Office map.*)

permitting of communication with Drama without being low enough
to allow of the development of a considerable river.

The port is not good and requires extensive improvements, and
it is a remarkable feature that there is no rail connexion, the main
line lying inland, where it passes Seres and Drama but sends no
branch to the coast. Thus all traffic has to be carried on by motor
vehicles. But such anomalies are common in Greece, old and new,
and remind us once again that it is a country in a state of transition,
not comparable to the lands of western Europe.

South of the Mesta delta lies the large, hilly, and wooded island
of Thasos. Like Laurion (p. 332), it was famous in ancient times
for its silver mines; during the present century there has been a
small zinc-mining industry.

25*

GREEK THRACE

East of the Mesta the frontier with Bulgaria, which here follows the water-parting of the Rhodope Mountains, approaches nearer the coast, thus narrowing the strip of Greek territory, and reducing the size of the rivers which flow direct to the Aegean. Between the mountains and the sea the land is mainly level or undulating, but the wide and swamp-encircled Boru (Vistonis) lake (Fig. 101), opening into Lagos Bay, reduces the area available for cultivation. It divides the lowlands into two basins, that of Xanthi to the west

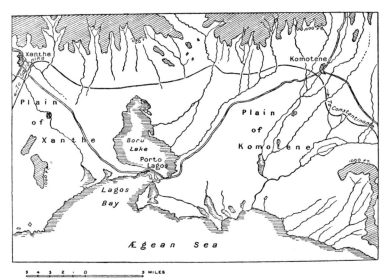

FIG. 101. PART OF GREEK THRACE. (*From the War Office map.*)

and that of Komotini (Gumuljina) to the east. Tobacco is again an important crop. Both towns are similar in size and position to Drama, and both lie on the railway, which is pushed to the base of the mountains by the presence of Vistonis lake. From Komotene the railway runs through a gap in hillier country to the port of Alexandroupolis (Dedeagach), which is thus, in striking contrast to Kavalla, on the direct Salonika-Istanbul line. It is nevertheless but a small and insignificant town, while Porto Lagos is a potential rather than an actual 'port'. East of Alexandroupolis lies the river frontier of the Maritsa (Gr. Evros). The fact that by the Treaty of Lausanne, Karagach, a suburb of Adrianople, but placed on the right or Greek bank of the river, was assigned to Turkey, should be noted (cf. p. 314). It means that a Turkish enclave, including part of the railway, is pushed into Greek territory.

WEST MACEDONIA

As compared with the areas just described, with their considerable towns, their great influx of refugees, both urban and rural, their large-scale production of industrial raw material, their considerable reclamation works, and their political problems in relation to the interior States, which can only reach the Aegean through them, West Macedonia seems unimportant. Its main interest lies rather in the physical geography than in the economic possibilities, and the departmental capitals of Florina and Kozani are small towns. Except also for the railway which, following the line of the ancient Via Egnatia, penetrates the Vodena valley and finds a circuitous route to Monastir in Yugoslavia, lines of communication are imperfectly developed, and the region has something of the aloofness of Epirus on the hither side of the Pindus.

The essential feature of the relief is the presence of two parallel belts of high ground. Of these the more easterly is that already described as forming the western border of South Macedonia. Farther west is the Neredska Planina with its higher southern continuation. Between the two, and also between the latter and the Pindus range, lie two series of basins and valleys showing highly anomalous drainage conditions.

We may begin with Lake Ostrovo (Vegorritis), of which something has been already said. It is fed by a stream flowing north and watering a considerable basin (height 650 m.) on whose margin lies the town of Kozani. But a comparatively low saddle separates this basin from the larger and highly fertile Pelagonian basin, or basin of Monastir, which has always acted as a centre of attraction for all the various racial groupings represented in the neighbourhood. It is watered by the river Crna, which, in Yugoslav territory, flows by a remarkably circuitous course to the Vardar, its two sectors, with the intervening acute angle, being wholly comparable in direction to those of the Vistritsa farther south. The southern part of the Pelagonian basin has a Greek population and the Yugoslav frontier, here drawn on an ethnological basis, crosses its floor. Florina is the chief Greek settlement, placed on the slopes of the Neredska Planina in the south.

On the western side of that range, forming as it were the counterpart of the Pelagonian basin, lies the wide but shallow Lake Prespa, surrounded by high mountains. It has no surface outlet except to the smaller, narrower Ventrok (Mikri Prespa) lake to the south, which has a partially underground connexion with the Albanian river Devole (Devoll) (Fig. 102). The frontier crosses the lake, and in this region Greece, Albania, and Yugoslavia abut on one another. South-east of Lake Prespa the headwaters of the river Aliakmon rise from the surrounding mountains, and to it the small circular lake on which the town of Kastoria stands sends a tributary. The Aliakmon flows south-east, and appears to be making for the plains of Thessaly from which it is separated only by the low Khasia Mountains. But it turns suddenly on itself at an acute angle, and instead flows north-eastwards to the Salonika Campania, as already described.

Throughout, where cultivation is possible, the main crops are cereals, vines, the less delicate fruit-trees, and so on, but there is necessarily much stock-rearing. As usual, this is associated with a considerable Vlach element, both nomadic and settled, the nomads having hitherto tended to move up to the hill pastures in summer and down to the lowlands of the Campania or even Thessaly in winter. To their prime function as shepherds their ownership of beasts of burden enables them to add that of porters, pedlars, and generally agents of transport in this and similar areas of difficult communication. In addition to the Vlachs, who are readily hellenized, there is a considerable Slav element.

CONCLUSION

The above detailed accounts of the natural units of the Greek Republic make clear the two essential facts of its great diversity, and of the great changes which, initiated by the Balkan wars, have been taking place with accelerated momentum ever since. The nature of these changes is indicated by a whole series of economic data. Thus the area of cultivated land doubled (from 3 million acres to 6 million) between 1921 and 1937; much of this increase was due to drainage, reclamation, and irrigation works, which also had the effect of considerably reducing the incidence of malaria. Tobacco has far outdistanced currants as the chief export, and the output of cereals for home use has greatly increased, though not in proportion to the increase of the population. The establishment of factories for the making of fertilizers at the Piraeus points to a marked change in Greek agriculture. Not long ago fallowing was the chief means used of restoring fertility, and half the land was said to be in fallow every year. Other new industries, such as carpet-making, pottery, copper-work, have been founded by refugees from Asia Minor, who have also been instrumental in increasing the supply or improving the quality of such products as sultana raisins (especially in Crete) and dried dessert figs, now boxed like those of Smyrna. Silkworm-rearing has taken on a new importance, especially in Macedonia and Thrace, and the former export of cocoons has ceased with the rise of the silk industry.

But it is easy to exaggerate the importance of such facts. Despite increased agricultural production and various changes in the nature and relative importance of the products, despite an increase in the number of industries, the new Greece shows fundamental resemblances to the old. It remains a mainly agricultural State, exporting the products of its specialized farming, and importing cereals, especially wheat, textiles, coal, metals, and machinery, and paying, at least in part, for the surplus imports by the profits of its shipping and carrying trade.

The essential change lies deeper. Before the Balkan wars there were two Greek communities—the territorial and the extra-territorial. Though the Greeks of Istanbul were exempted from the compulsory interchange of population, it may be said broadly that the latter has almost disappeared, for Istanbul no longer occupies its former position. This has meant much to Greece. Emphasis on the 'blighting' effect of the Turk in Europe is apt to lead one to overlook the fact that Turkish rule did afford ample opportunity to traders and business men of other races. This is particularly, though not exclusively, true of the Greeks, who share with the Jews and Armenians the type of mentality which takes naturally to trade.

There are of course still difficulties, which have been accentuated by the devastation of the 1939–45 war. That Athens-Piraeus and Salonika are the only large cities is symbolic of the new dualism, of the Greece which is at once a Mediterranean and a Macedonian State. On the one side it makes contact with Italy, pre-eminently a Mediterranean power, and on the other with Yugoslavia and the comparatively small Bulgarian State. But its political problems lie on the margin of the geographer's sphere of interest. To him the prime importance of Greece must always lie in the fact that it is the most typically Mediterranean country of Europe, showing the essential features of the characteristic structure, relief, climate, vegetation, and products in their most pronounced form.

Note.—The mapping of the Greek lands is still somewhat incomplete, precise levelling not having been carried out. Many of the figures given for heights are doubtful. In the text they have often been given in feet, in round numbers, in order to indicate that they are not more than approximations. The figures given on the various existing maps often differ very notably, and this is also true of books of reference. The figures in metres in the text are taken from *Annuaire Statistique de la Grèce*, first issue (Athens, 1930).

CHAPTER XVII

ALBANIA

Coasts—Frontiers and Relief—Towns and Resources

ALBANIA (Fig. 102), with an area given officially as 27,540 km., or 10,630 sq. miles, and a population of some 1,045,000 (1938), is, as a political unit, roughly comparable to the Republic of Estonia, though the commercial importance is less, and the density of population considerably greater. As a modern State it dates, in theory at least, from the period of the Balkan wars, Albanian independence having been proclaimed in the autumn of 1912. Brief as its existence has been, however, it has been chequered and interrupted, the mode of government oscillating from principality to republic, republic to kingdom, and back to republic, with periods of chaos and of occupation by other powers. Such conditions may seem to offer little assurance of future stability, and the country is indeed primitive and backward, its resources imperfectly utilized, effective lines of communication almost non-existent. On the other hand, the Albanian folk have behind them a long history. According to many writers they are the little modified descendants of the ancient Illyrians, and it is at least certain that throughout the long period when their lands were included in the Turkish Empire they preserved their individuality intact, and, so far as certain clans were concerned, were virtually independent within their mountain fastnesses. Nor did this even involve, as with some other stocks of the peninsula, the acceptance by all of the religion of the invaders, for there are Catholic Albanians in the north, and members of the Orthodox Church in the south, in addition to the Moslem majority (Fig. 103).

There is still another anomaly. Although the undeveloped communications and the poverty are the outstanding features, and the former go far to explain the persistence of the Albanians as an entity, their lands have been coveted by other States, mainly because of the possibility of running through them routes to the interior. The notion has a sound historical basis. From Durrës (Durazzo—the Roman Dyrrhachium) through Elbasan there runs eastward what remains of the Via Egnatia, which led to Byzantium, and this is but one of the old Roman roads which traversed the country. Traces of much earlier contacts with the outside world also occur, for round Shkodër (Scutari) evidence has been obtained that trade was carried on with the Etruscans, and objects made of Baltic amber have been found.

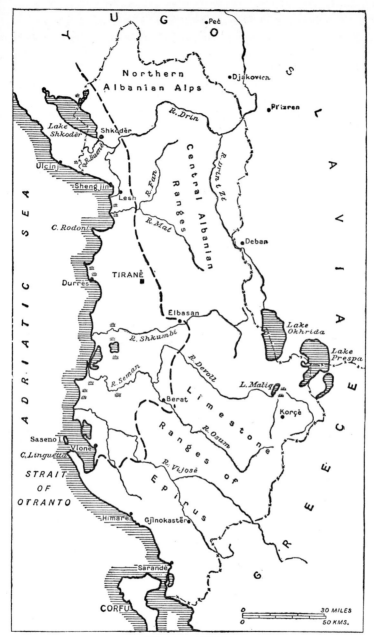

FIG. 102. ALBANIA

The broken line divides Lowland Albania, with its low, flat and often marshy plains and NW–SE ranges of soft Tertiary hills, from Highland Albania, which falls into the three divisions named. Note how the market towns in the north-east are all on the Yugoslav side of the frontier.

From these facts we can deduce the chief points of geographical interest presented by the country. The mention of Durrës and Shkodër suggests that the coast-line affords points of ingress into the interior of the peninsula from the west, and the coast-line of Albania indeed presents certain peculiar features. The Via Egnatia and other Roman roads suggest the presence of valleys by which that interior can be reached. But the persistence of a well-marked Albanian stock must mean isolation and therefore mountain country. A peculiar coast, an interior mainly mountainous but traversed by large rivers some of which afford possible routes—these are the essential features of the country.

COASTS (FIG. 102)

In the neighbourhood of the small port of Ulcinj (Dulcigno) on what was formerly the narrow coastal strip of independent Montenegro, the west coast of the Balkan peninsula undergoes a marked change alike in direction and character. Northwards it is typically Dalmatian, steep limestone hills with a north-west to south-east trend confronting an island-fringed, deep-blue sea. Rocky inlets and sheltered channels are frequent, rivers are few and may burst from the limestone hills in springs practically at sea-level. Near Ulcinj the coast takes a sharp easterly bend, and then, beyond the lower Buenë (Boyana), the boundary between Albania and Yugoslavia, and the effluent of Shkodër lake, trends almost due south. The Albanian port of Shengjin (San Giovanni di Medua) at the base of a hill ridge running parallel to the coast, stands at the point where this second change of direction occurs. The southward trend continues from Shengjin to Cape Glossa, the end of the tongue-like peninsula which bounds the long but narrow Bay of Valona. Southwards, again, a south-easterly direction is resumed, and the boundary between Greece and Albania, which crosses the northern part of the channel of Corfu, does not correspond to any notable change in the characters of the coastal belt.

These two sections of the Albanian coast, that from the Buenë and Yugoslav frontier to Cape Glossa, and that from Cape Glossa to the Greek frontier, are markedly different. The first is fringed by turbid, silt-laden waters, as contrasted with the clear blue farther north, and the shore lands are mainly flat and marshy, with salt lagoons and reed-choked, malaria-infested swamps. Mountains are no longer coastal but retreat to a distant horizon.

The second section is of the normal, hill-backed Mediterranean type, a strip round the small town of Himarë, forming one of those Riviera coasts which tend to occur wherever adjacent mountains give shelter from land-winds, and throw back the sun's rays. Here

citrus fruits, olives, and vines flourish, with wheat growing round
the trees. The rivers are small and short, rising but a few miles
inland and flowing swiftly to the sea. Inland, the landscape is
characterized by bare limestone
ridges, rising to heights of over
6,000 ft., and separated by long
valleys floored by sandstones
and clays. This southern region
is Albanian Epirus, which, as
already seen, does not differ
notably from Greek Epirus,
with which it is continuous
across the frontier.

The northern coastal strip is
crossed by a number of large
rivers, coming from the distant
interior and carrying a heavy
load of silt, to which the
turbidity of the shore waters is
due. This silt is in part deposited round the mouths of
the rivers, and in some cases,
as with the Drin and the Mat,
and the Shkumbi and the
Seman, the deltas of adjacent
rivers are virtually confluent.
Since a great flood in 1858,
however, most of the Drin
water has been carried off by
the Buenë, to which then it
became linked by a new channel
called the Drinasa.

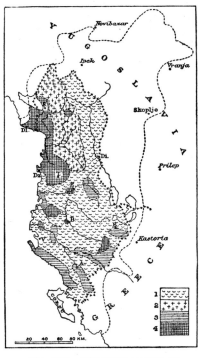

FIG. 103. RELIGIOUS FAITHS IN
ALBANIA

1. Moslems. 2. Catholics. 3. Orthodox. 4. Mixed.

The clear space between the present
frontier and the dotted line shows the
area, now included in Yugoslavia and
Greece, which in the latter part of the
nineteenth century was regarded as
having a solidly Albanian population.

The chief towns of Albania are indicated by their initial letters only, cf. Fig.
102. (*After Almagia.*)

A summary statement of this
kind gives the impression that
the Albanian coast from the
Buenë mouth to the Bay of
Valona is wholly low and
alluvial. The actual conditions are much more complex,
and to understand them it is necessary to note the chief relief
features.

FRONTIERS AND RELIEF

The most striking element in the relief is the massive wall of the
North Albanian Alps. On the west this mountain block approaches

Scutari lake; eastward it overlooks the Metoya basin, drained by the
White Drin (Drin i Bardhë), one of the two headstreams of the
Drin river; north-westward it is continued into the barren karst of
Montenegro, and to the south sinks with great abruptness to the
tremendous gorge in which the Drin flows.

Since the mountains rise to a maximum height of about 9,000 ft.
(2,700 m.), and, though not technically above the snow-line yet,
like the higher mountains of Scotland, are flecked with snow even
in summer, and display quasi-permanent fields, they would appear
at first sight to form an admirable boundary. The actual Yugoslav
frontier, after leaving the lower Buenë and crossing Shkodër lake,
follows for the most part the line of the water-parting. It then turns
to the south-east, is for a time almost parallel to the White Drin,
and then crosses that river to bend south. Such crest frontiers are
rarely so satisfactory in practice as they appear to the boundary-
maker; but there are special difficulties here.

In the first place, the North Albanian Alps have throughout
much of historical time served as a natural fortress, within which
the purest and most primitive Albanian stocks have found refuge.
Their settlements, particularly in the west, where the valleys are
wide and the intervening crests narrow, ascend far into the mountains. To the east, where the valleys are narrower and large areas of
summit plateau occur, permanent dwellings are thrust to the margins,
but the upper levels form those summer pastures so essential to
mountain folk. To demarcate an international boundary based on
principles laid down in a protocol, but yet taking adequate account
of the need of access to such pastures, is a matter of peculiar difficulty,
accentuated when maps are imperfect and those most directly
interested are unable to understand them or to point out their
deficiencies.

Secondly the mountains, in addition to forming a refuge, have
also served as a centre of dispersion, especially during the Turkish
period, when the Albanians were a privileged people. It is clear
from what has been already said that such dispersion was most
likely to occur eastward, westward, and even northward (see Fig. 103),
while directly southward, the Drin gorge and the great limestone
cliffs form a natural barrier. In particular the Metoya basin was a
centre of attraction, and the towns of Prizren and Djakovitsa within
it include many Albanians. It is indeed stated that, all told, nearly
500,000 Albanians live to the east of the Yugoslav frontier. Further,
for the inhabitants of the eastern part of the Alps, Djakovitsa as a
market centre is much more easily reached than Shkodër, and the
inclusion of the former in Yugoslavia means that the hill Albanians
must make a long and difficult journey by mountain paths to the
latter, if a crossing of the frontier has to be avoided. How important

is this question of access to markets may be judged from the fact that in the days before independence, when some of the mountain folk carried on constant feuds with each other, paths leading to these towns were sanctuaries from dawn till dusk.

As the frontier lies just to the west of the town of Prizren a small part of the Metoya is Albanian. Since early days the routes from it have followed the White Drin, but, after its junction with the Black Drin (Drinizi), flowing from Lake Okhrida in the south, they are compelled to leave the Drin river, because of its gorge and the difficult mountain country within its northern bend, and run well to the south on their way to Shkodër. This emphasizes once again the defects of the Alps as a boundary zone. Their barrier effect is most marked in the south centre, that is, towards Albania proper; they leave open gaps to the west round Shkodër lake and to the east in the Metoya, both lowland areas crossed by the Yugoslav frontier; the White Drin drains fertile regions within Yugoslavia which otherwise have difficult access to the sea. The position is complicated by the fact that to the east there is a considerable Albanian population in Yugoslav territory, with a tradition of privilege dating from Turkish times, and that Yugoslavia is particularly concerned with the problem of sea outlets.

From the northern Alps the mountain country of Albania is continued in a great central belt, with a generally southward direction, to and beyond the Greek frontier. The elevation is lower here, though some peaks rise to over 7,000 ft., and a special feature is the abundance of green igneous rocks, sometimes transformed into serpentine, which are impermeable and give rise to softer outlines than the massive limestones which are also present. Several of the large rivers, such as the Shkumbi, Seman-Devole, and Vijosë, which originate far to the east, cut through this belt in great gorges on their way to the sea.

From the basins and mountains of Macedonia this central belt is separated by a long valley, formed successively by the basin of Korçë, Maliq 'lake' (in reality but a stretch of land flooded by the Devole as it rounds the northern part of the basin of Korçë), Lake Okhrida (Ohri in Albanian), and the valley of the Black Drin. The frontier sometimes runs along the valley, crossing Lake Okhrida, for example, and for a time following the Black Drin, and elsewhere rises to the crest of a westward or an eastward ridge. The valley is well peopled, Korçë (26,000) being the third largest town of Albania, after Tiranë, the capital, and Shkodër.

To the west of the central mountain belt the upper Mat river occupies a long valley, trending from south-east to north-west, which separates the central belt from a lower border range, at the westerly margin of which lies the town of Tiranë (about 35,000), the capital of Albania. South-east of a transverse upland which connects the central and border ranges the same valley feature is represented by a fertile depression traversed by the upper Shkumbi. Thereafter the Shkumbi breaks through the border range in a deep gorge and enters the basin of Elbasan, the town being placed not on the river but on the basin rim.

South of the Shkumbi the interior is mainly mountainous. The Devole river, rising across the Greek frontier in the Grammos Mountains, has a long and complicated course through this upland region. South of Elbasan it rounds the splendid Tomor Massif and approaches the Shkumbi, to which it is linked by a dry valley, probably marking its earlier course. Downstream the Devole is joined by the Osum, also draining Albanian Epirus, and having the town of Berat on its course. After the junction the river is called the Seman.

Finally, west of the border ranges there are a number of usually low ridges, which are as it were almost submerged beneath the alluvial deposits which lap them round, but prevent the coastal lowlands forming a continuous plain. It is in the shelter of such ridges that the ports of Shengjin and Durrës find a place; they are thrust out seawards to form Capes Rodoni and Laghi; inland their slopes afford sites for settlements above the swampy, malarious plains.

Here, then, we have the essential features of the relief of Albania. To the north is the wall of the North Albanian Alps, bordered by lowlands to east and west, virtually continuous, across the Drin, with a central mountain belt which merges southwards with the Pindus range of Greece. To the east lies a long furrow forming a line of separation from Macedonia, Greek or Yugoslav, and to the west a shorter and less marked depression bounded by border ranges cut through by the rivers. Finally, still farther west, in northern and central Albania, is the coastal strip of ridges and plains.

TOWNS AND RESOURCES

Nominally there are five ports—Shengjin, the nearest to Shkodër; Durrës for Tiranë, Elbasan and the interior; Vlonë, connected by road to Berat, to Gjinokastër (Argyrokastron), and by a very indirect route to Korçë; Porto Palermo, serving chiefly Himarë (p. 378) and the settlements of the Albanian Riviera; Sarandë (Santi Quaranta) connected, if by an indirect route, to Gjinokastër and to Greek Epirus (Yannina, p. 363).

Of the interior towns Shkodër (30,000) is the largest outside the capital. The selection of Tiranë as capital was due to its roughly central position between the Ghegs of the north and the Tosks of the south, who speak different dialects, and to its proximity to the port of Durrës, with which it is connected by a motor-road. Durrës (12,000) changed much between the two World Wars, chiefly owing to the reconstruction of the port, the rebuilding of much of the town, and the reduction of the incidence of malaria by letting salt water into the nearby lagoon. Korçë is beautifully situated and owes to its position near the Greek and Yugoslav frontiers considerable commercial activity

The generally mountainous interior has permitted the Albanians to survive the vicissitudes of a troubled history, and that history has led to the retention of all the primitive virtues. They are brave, hardy, faithful to their plighted word, and make admirable soldiers. But these characteristics in their turn have led the men to direct their attention to stock-rearing (combined with brigandage) rather than to agriculture, with its double demand of the bent back and the discarded rifle. Agriculture is best developed in the south, where the climate is definitely of the Mediterranean type, and it is interesting to note that the cultivator on watered land enjoys the *bessa*—the immunity from vendetta which is everywhere the privilege of the women and of men accompanied by women.

If, however, their fine qualities and their stock-keeping, with some generally primitive agriculture, have preserved the Albanians in the uplands, neither virtues nor social policy fit them to make the best use of the swampy lowlands, or to maintain or increase the resources of their lands. Deforestation has been practised recklessly and has been accentuated by the devastation of many wars, with disastrous results. Malaria and—a curious fact—tuberculosis and alcoholism are woefully prevalent, though the vendetta, in earlier days a handicap to all progress, has been virtually stamped out. The Turkish *régime* and the insecurity of life led to neglect of means of communication. The Buenë has been allowed to silt up, almost cutting off Shkodër from the sea, and the pouring of the silt-laden waters of the Drin into it by the Drinasa arm, which has been the main agent in the process, has led simultaneously to the decay of Leš at the mouth of the shrunken Drin main channel. Such roads as exist are mainly due to the activity of past invaders, especially the Italians, who also constructed some fine ferro-concrete bridges across certain of the rivers. It is also to outsiders that the ports owe what facilities they offer. Before 1939 Italy supplied the greater part of the imports, mostly textiles, motor-cars, petrol, etc., and took most of the exports, chiefly animal foods and fish, hides and skins, with cereals and fruits in good seasons. Minerals may become important in the future, for deposits of copper, mercury, iron, chrome, and lignite occur. Asphalt has been worked to a small extent at Selenicë, near Vlonë (Valona) and Italian oil concessions have tapped oil at several places in the centre and south.

Yugoslavia has long been desirous of sea outlets more easily connected with the interior than are the Dalmatian ports. In the past Albania resented the existing frontier with Yugoslavia since it excludes a number of their fellow-countrymen, while Yugoslavia objected to the lack of sea outlets in the south. But in 1946 these countries signed political and economic treaties. The latter provides for a customs and currency union and for Yugoslav aid in Albania's recovery. It also provides for a railway from Vlonë to Bitolj (Monastir) and for another from Durrës via the capital to a point on the Yugoslav railways to be determined. Construction of these railways will certainly be difficult across rough terrain. Albanians also live beyond the frontier in northern Greece. Greece absorbed these very easily in the past and saw in consequence little virtue in a frontier drawn upon a purely ethnical basis. For long Greece cast covetous eyes on the southern part of Albania, which is called by the Greeks 'northern Epirus'. Albania is now a republic organized on the communist pattern and there is acute tension between it and Greece.

STATISTICAL SUMMARY

GREECE

AREA AND POPULATION (INCLUDING THE DODECANESE)

Area: 132,496 sq. km., or 51,169 sq. miles.
Population: 7,451,000 (October, 1940).
Density: 56 per sq. km., or 145 per sq. mile.
Towns (estimated 1937): Athens, 494,080. Piraeus, 287,800. Salonika, 267,870. No other even approaches the 100,000 mark, the largest being Patras, 73,840, and Kavalla, 55,280.

The highest and lowest departmental densities were as follows in 1928 (per sq. km.):

Highest			Lowest		
Corfu	.	.	164	Mt. Athos	.	17
Attica	.	.	157	Chalcidice	.	20
Zante	.	.	100	Kozani	.	26

LAND UTILIZATION

In 1937 there were nearly 6 million acres of cultivated land in Greece, representing one-fifth of the total land surface; but even this meagre figure was almost double the 1921 acreage. Cereals were by far the most important crops, utilizing 67 per cent of the cultivated land, of which over one-half was devoted to wheat, and about one-sixth each to barley and to maize. Yields are low—wheat about 7 cwt. per acre and maize 8 cwt.

Vines cover 11 per cent of the cultivated area, but their produce during the 1930s represented one-sixth of the value of the total agricultural output; just over half the harvest consists of dried grapes. The olive is the most important fruit tree in Greece; perhaps one-seventh of the cultivated land is in olive groves, and the annual yield of fruit is of the order of 600,000 tons, yielding 100,000 tons of oil.

Tobacco cultivation is increasing, and in the 1930s the average annual production was about 60,000 tons, from about 240,000 acres. This is a light yield compared with other parts of Europe, but the quality is high. Cotton is also increasing in importance—180,000 acres with a yield of 16,000 tons in 1938; over half the crop is a fine long-stapled variety exceeded only by Egyptian in quality.

Among live stock there was a universal increase between 1928 and 1937, and this despite the increasing cultivation of the plains and the upsetting of much of the traditional semi-nomadism associated with stock-keeping. In the latter year, sheep numbered nearly 8½ millions and goats 5¼ millions; these two animals provide the bulk of the milk and cheese consumed in Greece. Cattle, numbering 1 million, are mostly draught animals in the north, with a few imported milch cows around the main southern towns. Horses, asses, and mules together number nearly a million, and there are half a million pigs.

Silk production, dependent on the mulberry-trees, is increasing, especially in the north, and the former export of cocoons has been replaced by an import to serve the thriving silk industry.

Food crops other than cereals and tree fruits occupy 8 per cent of the cultivated land; they comprise beans, lentils, etc., grown dry, and vegetables grown in irrigated gardens; among the latter onions and garlic are most important, also cucumbers, melons, etc.

The forest acreage of Greece is estimated at 5 millions, representing 14 per cent of the total land surface. Above 600 feet, much of the surface is covered with forest and scrub, but 'high forest' probably covers no more than 1½ million acres. Fires and the large sheep and goat population render the encouragement and maintenance of forest growth difficult, but a policy of conservation and afforestation has been adopted in part to counteract soil erosion.

MINERALS

Greece is relatively poor in minerals. The chief are iron ore and iron pyrites, magnesite, bauxite, chrome, nickel, lead, and zinc. Amongst minor products are the emery of Naxos, pumice, and Pentelicon marble. The minerals are almost all exported: iron ore from Serifos in the Cyclades; magnesite from Euboea and Chalcidice goes mostly to Western Europe; the bauxite is of low grade and is exported mainly for the manufacture of cement and refractories and not for aluminium. Only the Laurion lead is locally smelted.

INDUSTRY

The value of the industrial production increased nearly 14-fold between 1921 and 1939, and more than doubled during the second half of this period; to a large extent this was due to the influx of refugees and to the generally rising standard of life. Textile and chemical industries together make up half the total production by value, though food and drink industries employ more people than either. The most striking expansion has been in engineering and electrical manufactures. The number of industrial workers, nearly 500,000 at the 1928 census, now probably approaches the million mark.

TRADE

The foreign trade of Greece is distinguished from that of its Balkan neighbours by two things, first, the absence of large cereal and live stock exports, and secondly, the considerable adverse balance (which is rectified mainly by the income derived from such services as the mercantile marine, and from the remittances of emigrants).

The chief imports are agricultural products (especially cereals), textiles, metal goods, and minerals (coal and petroleum). During the 1930s Germany rose to a dominating position as a supplier of Greek imports, with U.K. second, and Roumania (wheat and oil), Yugoslavia, U.S.A., and Argentina high on the list. The major exports are classified as 'horticultural products', which include tobacco, currants, and other dried fruit, olives, and olive oil, wine and citrus fruit. Tobacco is by far the most important, representing about half the total value. Animal skins and minerals are other items. Germany again, in the 1930s, dominated the market, especially for tobacco, with U.S.A. (also tobacco), and U.K. (mainly currants and sultanas) next in order.

ALBANIA

Total Land Surface: 27,538 sq. km.

Population: 1,045,683 (1938) (of which 69 per cent Moslem, 20 per cent Orthodox, and 10 per cent Catholic). Density: 38 per sq. km.

Cultivated land forms 11 per cent of total, of which 6 per cent is under sown crops and 5 per cent under fruit-trees, including vineyards. Elbasan is the province with the highest percentage of cultivated land, which reaches 32 per cent; Shkodër and Kosovë, the northern provinces, have 2 per cent or less.

Pasture (alpine and lowland) covers 31 per cent; woodland and forest, 36 per cent; 11 per cent is potentially productive but uncultivated, and 11 per cent is barren and unproductive.

The principal crops (average 1935–9) were—maize, 225,000 acres; wheat, 101,000; olives, 44,000.

In 1938 the figures for live stock were as follows: goats, 932,000; sheep, 1,574,000; cattle, 391,000; asses, 55,000; horses, 54,000; pigs, 15,000; buffaloes, 21,000.

For 1938 the annual imports were valued at 22,398,000 gold francs, and the exports at 9,750,000 gold francs.

Italy supplied nearly 25 per cent of the imports, Yugoslavia, Roumania, and Japan following with much lesser amounts. Italy took considerably more than three-quarters of the exports, followed by Greece, and the U.S.A., again with greatly diminished quantities.

REFERENCES

Greek official map, 1/100,000. About 80 sheets published (1925–41), not quite complete.

Greek Air Ministry map, 1/400,000. 12 sheets (1932–5).

War Office (G.S.G.S.) maps: Series 4087, scale 1/100,000, 38 provisional sheets (1940); Series 4088, scale 1/250,000, 15 sheets (1940–41).

Karte von Albanien, 1/200,000. Based on H. Louis' Surveys (Vienna, 1928).

Geologische Karte von Albanien, 1/200,000. By E. Nowack (Berlin, 1928).

GREECE

GENERAL AND HUMAN GEOGRAPHY

Y. Châtaigneau and J. Sion, *Pays Balkaniques*, Tome 7, 2e partie, *Géographie Universelle* series. Theobald Fischer, *Die Südosteuropäische Halbinsel*, in Kirchhoff's *Länderkunde von Europa* III, 2 (Vienna, 1893). Otto Maull, *Griechisches Mittelmeergebiet* (Breslau, 1922), (Bibliography). Otto Maull, *Länderkunde von Südeuropa*, in *Enzyklopädie der Erdkunde* (Leipzig u. Wien, 1929), (Bibliography). For Statistics see *Annuaire Statistique de la Grèce* (p. 398), text in French and Greek. Jovan Cvijić, *La Péninsule Balkanique: Géographie Humaine* (Paris, 1918). Jacques Ancel, *Peuples et Nations des Balkans* (Paris, 1926, and later editions), (Bibliography, chiefly French books).

STRUCTURE

The classical article on the structure of Greece is A. Philippson, 'La Tectonique de l'Égéide, in *Annales de Géographie* (Paris, 1898). See also articles by the same author and Fr. Frech in *Petermann's Mitteilungen*, 1912, 2, and Otto Maull, 'Beiträge zur Morphologie des Peloponnesus u. des südlichen Mittelgriechenlands' in *Penck's Geogr. Abhandlungen*, Series 1, Vol. X, Pt. 3 (Leipzig, 1921).

TRAVELS AND SCENERY

J. G. Frazer, *Studies in Greek Scenery, Legend and History* (London, 1917). J. G. Frazer, *Graecia Antiqua: Maps and Plans to illustrate Pausanias's Description of Greece*, with explanatory text by A. W. Van Buren. New Edition (London, 1930). W. M. Leake, *Travels in the Morea*, 3 vols. (London, 1830). W. M. Leake, *Travels in Northern Greece*, 4 vols. (London, 1835). F. S. Burnell, *Wanderings in Greece* (London, 1931), (Bibliography).

POLITICAL AND SOCIAL

William Miller, *Greece* (London, 1928). E. G. Mears, *Greece To-day: The Aftermath of the Refugee Impact* (Stanford University and London, 1929). Henry Morgenthau, *An International Drama* (London, n.d.). C. B. Eddy, *Greece and the Greek Refugees* (London, 1931). A. W. Gomme, *Greece* (Oxford, 1945).

REGIONAL STUDIES

Thessaly and Epirus. Alfred Philippson, 'Thessalien u. Epirus', in *Zeitschrift d. Gesellschaft f. Erdkunde*, XXX–XXXII (Berlin, 1895–7). Leonidas Chalikipoulos, 'Wirtschaftsgeographische Skizze von Thessalien', in *Geog. Zeitschrift*, XI (Berlin, 1905). Friedrich Stählin, *Das Hellenische Thessalien* (Stuttgart, 1924).

Central Greece. W. J. Woodhouse, *Aetolia: Its Geography, Topography, and Antiquities* (Oxford, 1897).

Crete and the Islands. A. Trevor-Battye, *Camping in Crete: with Notes upon the Animal and Plant Life of the Island* (London, 1913). V. C. Scott O'Connor, *Isles of the Aegean* (London, 1929). C. D. Booth and I. B. Booth, *Italy's Aegean Possessions* (London, 1928).

Mt. Athos. Robert Byron, *The Station: Athos, Treasures and Men* (London, 1928).

ALBANIA

No. 17 of Handbooks of the Historical Section of the Foreign Office. *Handbook of Serbia, Montenegro, Albania, and the Adjacent Parts of Greece* (London, 1920). Roberto Almagia, *L'Albania* (Rome, 1930), (Bibliography). This is an excellent and concise summary, with useful maps and tables. C. A. Chekrezi, *Albania past and present* (New York, 1919), (Bibliography). Jacques Bourcart, *L'Albanie et les Albanais* (Paris, 1921). Herbert Louis, 'Albanien', *Penck's Geog. Abhandlungen*, II, 3 (Stuttgart, 1927), (Bibliography). J. Swire, *Albania: the Rise of a Kingdom* (London, 1929), (History and Politics), (Bibliography). H. A. Bernatzik, *Albanien* (2nd edition, Vienna, 1932).

INDEX

References to pages with some detailed description are in heavy type, those to a figure in italics. The pages after the names of authors are those where details are given of the book or paper referred to.

389